Dr & Mrs Richard S. Wiersema

4/25

PSALTER HYMNAL

Centennial Edition

Doctrinal Standards and Liturgy

of the

Christian Reformed Church

PUBLICATION COMMITTEE OF THE CHRISTIAN REFORMED CHURCH, Inc.

Publishers

GRAND RAPIDS 8, MICHIGAN

1959

PUBLISHED BY AUTHORITY OF THE SYNOD

Notice

Acknowledgment

Grateful acknowledgment is hereby made to all who granted use of texts or tunes or both for this edition of the *Psalter Hymnal*. Diligent efforts were made to trace all copyright material to the owners. If in some instances proper acknowledgment has not been made, the publishers will give due credit in future editions upon receipt of notice.

The Scripture text used is taken from the American Standard Edition of the Revised Bible, copyright 1929, by the International Council of Religious Education, and is used by permission.

PREFACE TO CENTENNIAL EDITION

The present edition of the *Psalter Hymnal* is dedicated to the praise of Almighty God. The psalms and hymns, together with doctrinal standards and liturgical forms, constitute an official book of praise and prayer, of profession and practice for the Christian Reformed Church.

From the days of prophets and apostles, the church has been called to enter God's presence with singing. During the reformation of the church in the sixteenth century, new emphasis was placed upon congregational song. Under the guidance of John Calvin, the church in Geneva adopted a collection of Psalm texts set to newly-prepared tunes. This heritage, by way of France, the Netherlands, and England, forms part of the Christian Reformed musical tradition. Some of the Psalm texts, in English translation from Dutch versions of the original French, and some tunes from the Genevan *Psalter* of 1562 itself, are included in this *Psalter Hymnal*.

The Christian Reformed Church, from its American beginnings in 1857, used the Dutch language in worship. The Synod of 1914 authorized the use of an English-language *Psalter* which was produced by a committee drawn largely from the United Presbyterian Church. Twenty years later, another Synod approved the first *Psalter Hymnal* (1934). The latter book contained a large number of hymns.

The Synod of 1951 approved a request that it appoint a committee "to set forth concretely the principles of good music for our churches, and in harmony therewith to revise and improve our *Psalter Hymnal*." The committee's statement of principle was approved by the Synod of 1953,[1] and its final recommendations for revision were adopted by the Synod of 1956. Features of the revision are metrical settings of all one hundred fifty Psalms in more concise form than before, a number of additional hymns, new texts and tunes submitted by members of the denomination, and amplification of the indices.[2] In keeping with plans to mark the denomination's one hundredth birthday in 1957, Synod declared that the revised *Psalter Hymnal* would be called the "Centennial Edition."

---

1. The principle for music in the church is printed immediately following the preface. It is worthy of repeated study by all members of the church.
2. A total of fifty-seven songs is covered by copyright of the Publication Committee of the Christian Reformed Church. These songs are listed in the copyright notice on page II.

The committee appointed in 1951 consisted of eleven members. Dr. Henry A. Bruinsma was named chairman. Also designated were Marvin Baas, James De Jonge, Adrian Hartog, Trena Haan, Johanna Oranje, Dr. William H. Rutgers, Seymour Swets (member of the committee which prepared the 1934 *Psalter Hymnal*), Dr. Dick L. Van Halsema (secretary of the committee), Rev. Dick H. Walters, and Dr. Henry Zylstra. Providentially, the committee was kept intact through the five years of main revision effort. Shortly afterwards, Dr. Zylstra was called from this life. The "Centennial Edition" incorporates many of his invaluable recommendations for improvement, including a new versification of Psalm 121. Rev. Henry J. Kuiper, also a member of the 1934 *Psalter Hymnal* committee, prepared the excellent *Index of Topics*.

Unto him that sitteth on the throne, and unto the Lamb, be the blessing, and the honor, and the glory, and the dominion, for ever and ever. —Revelation 5:13

COMMITTEE FOR THE IMPROVEMENT AND REVISION
OF THE PSALTER HYMNAL

STATEMENT OF PRINCIPLE FOR MUSIC IN THE CHURCH

The Statement of Principle itself was adopted by the Synod of 1953, while the Implications were recommended to the churches for study.

PRINCIPLE: THE MUSIC OF THE CHURCH SHOULD BE APPROPRIATE FOR WORSHIP

1. *The music of the church should be liturgical* — In spirit, form, and content it must be a positive expression of Scripturally religious thought and feeling. It should serve the ministry of the Word.

2. *The music of the church should be beautiful* — Its religious thought or spirit should be embodied appropriately in the poetry as poetry, in the music as music, and in the blending of these in song. It should satisfy the aesthetic laws of balance, unity, variety, harmony, design, rhythm, restraint, and fitness which are the conditions of all art.

IMPLICATIONS

1. The music of the church should represent the full range of the revelation of God.

2. The minister of the Word, on the one hand, and the organist and the choir director on the other, should cooperate constantly, so that the service of music will contribute to the service of the Word.

3. The poetry of the songs should be good poetry; it should not have to rely upon the music to carry it. The music of the songs should be artistically defensible as good music; it should not have to rely upon the words to carry it.

4. Whenever Psalms or other portions of Scripture are involved, the poetry of the songs should be true to the inspired Word. Such poetry should at the same time be vital—free from the defects of artificiality and sentimentality.

5. Whenever songs other than versifications of portions of Scripture are involved, the poetry should be genuinely expressive of religious experience, but should also be in harmony with the whole counsel of God.

6. The music of the church should be suitable to the liturgical text to which it has been adapted. It should be free from association with the currently secular or with anything that does violence to our Reformed conception of worship.

7. The music of the church should not be borrowed from that of the dance nor from concert or other music which suggests places and occasions other than the church and the worship service.

8. Such devices as extreme syncopation and extreme chromaticism (although on occasion these may be of value for special text settings) should generally be avoided.

9. Great care must be exercised by the organist and choir director in selecting organ music and anthems, lest a secular association with the music interfere with the worshiper's service.

10. The music of the church should be expressive of our Reformed tradition and, so far as possible, should make use of the Genevan Psalm tunes and other music of Calvinistic inspiration.

CONTENTS

INDEX OF FIRST LINES

INDEX OF SCRIPTURAL REFERENCES
IN HYMNS

INDEX OF TOPICS

Look for desired topic both in alphabetical listing and under following general headings:
CHURCH — FAITH — GOD — GRACE OF GOD — INNER LIFE — ISRAEL — JESUS CHRIST
LAST THINGS — LAW OF GOD — LOVE — MAN — MEANS OF GRACE — PRAISE — SIN

INDEX OF TOPICS

INDEX OF TOPICS

INDEX OF TOPICS

INDEX OF AUTHORS

Including Translators, Versifiers, and Sources of Words

INDEX OF COMPOSERS

(Including Arrangers and Sources of Tunes)

ALPHABETICAL INDEX OF TUNES

METRICAL INDEX OF TUNES

XLVIII

1   That Man Is Blest

PSALM 1

MEDITATION C. M.

John H. Gower, 1890

1 That man is blest who, fear - ing God, From
2 Yea, blest is he who makes God's law His
3 That man is nour - ished like a tree Set

sin re - strains his feet, Who will not stand with
por - tion and de - light, And med - i - tates up -
by the riv - er's side; Its leaf is green, its

wick - ed men, Who shuns the scorn - ers' seat.
on that law With glad - ness day and night.
fruit is sure, And thus his works a - bide.

4 The wicked like the driven chaff
   Are swept from off the land;
They shall not gather with the just,
   Nor in the judgment stand.

5 The Lord will guard the righteous well,
   Their way to Him is known;
The way of sinners, far from God,
   Shall surely be o'erthrown.

Blest Is He Who Loves God's Precepts

REDEEMER 8 7 8 7

Luther O. Emerson, 1863

1 Blest is he who loves God's pre - cepts, Who from
2 Blest is he who makes the stat - utes Of the
3 He is like a tree well plant - ed By the

sin re-strains his feet, He who will not stand with
Lord his chief de - light, In the law of God re -
flow - ing riv - er's side, Ev - er green of leaf and

sin - ners, He who shuns the scorn-ers' seat.
joic - ing, Med - i - tat - ing day and night.
fruit - ful— Thus shall all his works a - bide.

4 Like the driven chaff the wicked
  Shall be swept from off the land;
With the just they shall not gather,
  Nor shall in the judgment stand.

5 Well the Lord will guard the righteous,
  For their way to Him is known;
But the way of evildoers
  Shall by Him be overthrown.

3   Wherefore Do the Nations Rage

PSALM 2   MONSEY CHAPEL 7 7 7 7 D.

Dick L. Van Halsema, 1952

1 Where-fore do the na-tions rage, And the peo-ple vain - ly dream,
2 But the Lord will scorn them all, Calm He sits en-throned on high;

That in tri-umph they can wage War a-gainst the Lord su-preme?
Soon His wrath will on them fall, An-gered then He will re - ply:

His A-noin-ted they de - ride, And the ru-lers plot-ting say:
Yet ac-cord-ing to My will I have set My King to reign,

Their do-min-ion be de-fied, Let us cast their bonds a-way.
And on Zi-on's ho - ly hill Mine A-noint-ed I main-tain.

(Alternate tune: MENDELSSOHN, No. 339)

3 This the word declared to me,
    This Jehovah's firm decree:
Thou art My beloved Son,
    Yea, I have begotten Thee.
Ask and have Thy full demands,
    Thine shall all the heathen be,
Thine the utmost of the lands,
    They shall be possessed of Thee.

4 Dash them like a potter's urn,
    Thou shalt break them with a rod.
Therefore, kings and judges, learn
    Anxiously to serve your God.
Kiss the Son and worship Him,
    Lest ye perish in the way;
Blest are all who trust in Him,
    Yea, supremely blest are they.

4

O Lord, How Swiftly Grows

PSALM 3

MORNING PRAISE 6 6 7 6 6 7 D.

Louis Bourgeois, 1551
Harmonized by Henry Bruinsma, 1954

Forcefully; may be sung in unison

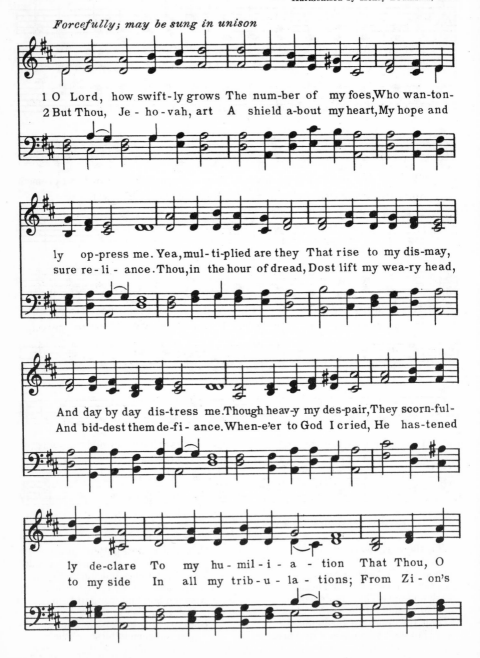

1 O Lord, how swift-ly grows The num-ber of my foes,Who wan-ton-
2 But Thou, Je - ho-vah, art A shield a-bout my heart,My hope and

ly op-press me. Yea,mul-ti-plied are they That rise to my dis-may,
sure re - li - ance.Thou,in the hour of dread, Dost lift my wea-ry head,

And day by day dis-tress me.Though heav-y my des-pair,They scorn-ful-
And bid-dest them de-fi - ance.When-e'er to God I cried, He has-tened

ly de-clare To my hu - mil-i - a - tion That Thou, O
to my side In all my trib-u - la - tions; From Zi - on's

O Lord, How Swiftly Grows

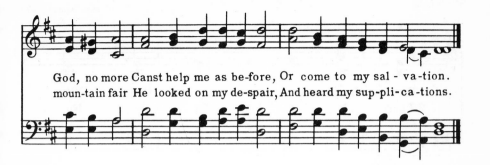

God, no more Canst help me as be-fore, Or come to my sal - va-tion.
moun-tain fair He looked on my de-spair, And heard my sup-pli-ca-tions.

3 I laid me down and slept;
   I waked, for I was kept
     In His divine protection;
   The Lord was at my side,
   My succor He supplied,
     Whatever my affliction.
   Defended by His hand,
   I shall undaunted stand,
     While thousands surge about me;
   Though furious foemen wage
   Their war with mighty rage,
     I know they shall not rout me.

4 Arise and save me, Lord,
   For Thou hast smitten hard
     The jaws of them that hate me;
   Yea, Thou didst fiercely break
   For me Thy servant's sake
     The teeth of the ungodly.
   I shall not suffer long,
   For my salvation strong
     Belongeth to Jehovah;
   Thou, Lord, wilt freely pour
   A blessing from Thy store
     Upon us; Hallelujah!

Dewey Westra, 1931

5   O Lord, How Many They Who Deeply Trouble Me

PSALM 3   SOUTHWELL S. M.

William Daman, 1579

1 O Lord, how man - y they Who deep - ly trou - ble me; How great - ly are they mul - ti - plied Who do me in - ju - ry.

2 There is no help for him, No help in God, they say; Thou art my shield and glo - ry, Lord, Thou art my cer - tain stay. A - men.

3 I called to God, He heard
   From out His holy hill.
I fell asleep, I woke in peace,
   For He sustained me still.

4 Arise and save, O Lord,
   For Thou didst smite my foe.
Salvation cometh from the Lord;
   His saints His blessings know.

6   O Hear Me, Thou Most Righteous God

PSALM 4   STANTON C.M.

Adrian Hartog, 1954

1 O hear me, Thou most right - eous God, When I ap - peal to Thee, Have mer - cy still, and an - swer Thou, For Thou didst set me free.

2 O sons of men, how long, how long, Will ye de - spise my name? How long will ye love van - i - ty, My glo - ry turn to shame?

3 Now learn that men of god - ly heart The Lord our God holds dear, That when they call up - on His name He grants a list - ening ear.

4 Then stand in awe and fear the Lord,
  Consider and be still.
  Present a righteous sacrifice
  And wait upon His will.

5 O who will show us any good?
  The anxious many say.
  Then lift on us, O gracious God,
  Thy loving face alway.

6 My joy in Thy good favor, Lord,
  Exceeds their harvest glee;
  I rest in confidence, for Thou
  Art my security.

7 On the Good and Faithful

PSALM 4

PENITENCE 6 5 6 5 D.

Spencer Lane, 1879

1 On the good and faith - ful God has set His love;
2 Lay up - on God's al - tar Good and lov - ing deeds,
3 In God's love a - bid - ing, I have joy and peace

When they call He sends them Bless - ings from a - bove.
And in all things trust Him To sup - ply your needs.
More than all the wick - ed, Though their wealth in - crease.

Stand in awe and sin not, Bid your heart be still;
Anx - ious and de - spair - ing, Man - y walk in night;
In His care con - fid - ing, I will sweet - ly sleep,

Through the si - lent watch - es, Think up - on His will.
But to those that fear Him, God will send His light.
For the Lord, my Sav - ior, Will in safe - ty keep.

O Jehovah, Hear My Words

PSALM 5 RILEY 7 7 7 7 D.

Martin Shaw, 1915

1 O Je-ho-vah, hear my words, To my thoughts at-ten-tive be;
2 Thou, Je-ho-vah, art a God Who de-light-est not in sin;
3 In the ful-ness of Thy grace To Thy house I will re-pair;

Hear my cry, my King, my God, I will make my prayer to Thee.
E-vil shall not dwell with Thee, Nor the proud Thy fa-vor win.
Bow-ing toward Thy ho-ly place, In Thy fear to wor-ship there.

With the morn-ing light, O Lord, Thou shalt hear my voice a-rise,
E-vil-do-ers Thou dost hate, Ly-ing tongues Thou wilt de-feat;
Lead me in Thy right-eous-ness, Let my foes as-sail in vain;

And ex-pec-tant I will bring Prayer as morn-ing sac-ri-fice.
God ab-hors the man who loves Vi-o-lence and base de-ceit.
Lest my feet be turned a-side, Make Thy way be-fore me plain.

4 False and faithless are my foes,
   Wicked are their inward parts,
Deadly are the words they speak,
   They employ the flatterer's arts.
Let transgressors be destroyed,
   For their sins by Thee expelled;
By their counsels let them fall,
   For against Thee they rebelled.

5 O let all that trust Thy care
   Ever glad and joyful be;
Let them joy who love Thy Name,
   Safely guarded, Lord, by Thee.
For a blessing from Thy store
   To the righteous Thou wilt yield;
Thou wilt compass him about
   With Thy favor as a shield.

Lord, Rebuke Me Not

PSALM 6   BATTY 8 7 8 7   Moravian Melody, 1745

1 Lord, re - buke me not in an - ger, Nor in wrath still
2 I am vexed; no long - er tar - ry, Nor the way of
3 Shall the dead Thy name re - mem - ber? Can they praise Thee

chas - ten me, Pi - ty now and show me mer - cy,
an - ger take. Lord, O Lord, my soul de - liv - er,
from the grave? Pi - ty, Lord, my sad con - di - tion,

Help Thou my in - fir - mi - ty.
Save me for Thy mer - cy's sake.
Lo, my bed with tears I lave. A - men.

4 I am worn and near exhausted,
    Wasted now mine eye appears;
   Part from me, ye adversaries,
    God hath marked my falling tears.

5 God hath heard my supplication,
    He will surely grant my plea.
   Let mine enemies be routed,
    Be defeated suddenly.

10   No Longer, Lord, Do Thou Despise Me

PSALM 6   PLEADING 9 7 6   7 7 6

Louis Bourgeois, 1549
Harmonized by Henry Bruinsma, 1954

Edward A. Collier, 1911

Quietly; may be sung in unison

1 No long-er, Lord, do Thou de-spise me,
2 To me, O Lord, to me re-turn-ing,
3 The Lord my God will ev-er hear me,

Nor in Thy wrath chas-tise me; Thy mer-cy I im-
Save Thou, with pit-y yearn-ing. Shall death Thy mem-ory
And when I pray be near me, To put my foes to

plore. How long Thine an-ger cher-ish? Con-sumed there-
keep? Or shall the grave con-fess Thee? Or I give
shame; Turned back, no more to grieve me, They sud-den-

by I per-ish; My soul is trou-bled sore.
thanks and bless Thee, While day and night I weep?
ly shall leave me. All glo-ry to His name!

11   Jehovah, My God, on Thy Help I Depend

PSALM 7   PAULINA 11 11 11 11

Arranged from G. Donizetti, 1797-1848

1 Je - ho - vah, my God, on Thy help I de - pend;
2 When wronged with-out cause I have kind - ness re - turned;

From all that pur - sue me O save and de - fend;
But if I my neigh-bor mal - treat - ed and spurned,

Lest they like a li - on should rend me at will,
My soul let the en - e - my seize for his prey,

While no one is near me their rag - ing to still.
My life and mine hon - or in dust let him lay.

Jehovah, My God, on Thy Help I Depend
PSALM 7

3 O Lord, in Thy wrath stay the rage of my foes;
Awake, and Thy judgment ordained interpose.
Let peoples surround Thee and wait at Thy feet,
While o'er them for judgment Thou takest Thy seat.

4 All nations of men shall be judged by the Lord;
To me, O Jehovah, just judgment accord,
As faithful and righteous in life I have been,
And ever integrity cherished within.

5 Establish the righteous, let evil depart,
For God, who is just, tries the thoughts of the heart.
In God for defense I have placed all my trust;
The upright He saves and He judges the just.

6 The Lord with the wicked is wroth every day,
And if they repent not is ready to slay;
By manifold ruin for others prepared
They surely at last shall themselves be ensnared.

7 Because He is righteous His praise I will sing,
Thanksgiving and honor to Him I will bring,
Will sing to the Lord on whose grace I rely,
Extolling the Name of Jehovah Most High.

O Lord, Our Lord, in All the Earth

PSALM 8

CLINTON C. M.

Joseph P. Holbrook, 1870

1 O   Lord, our Lord, in   all   the earth How ex - cel - lent Thy Name!
2 From lips of   chil-dren, Thou, O Lord, Hast might-y strength or-dained,
3 When I   re-gard the won-drous heavens, Thy hand-i - work   on   high,

Thy   glo - ry Thou hast spread a - far   In   all   the star - ry frame.
That ad - ver - sa - ries should be stilled And venge-ful foes re-strained.
The moon and stars or-dained by Thee, O   what is man, I   cry.

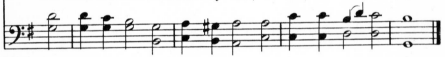

4 O what is man, in Thy regard
　　To hold so large a place,
　And what the son of man, that Thou
　　Dost visit him in grace?

5 For Thou hast made him little less
　　Than Thy blest angels be;
　With honor Thou hast crowned his head
　　And glorious dignity.

6 Thou hast subjected all to him,
　　And lord of all is he,
　Of flocks and herds, and beasts and birds,
　　And all within the sea.

7 Thy mighty works and wondrous grace
　　Thy glory, Lord, proclaim.
　O Lord, our Lord, in all the earth
　　How excellent Thy Name!

13   Lord, Our Lord, Thy Glorious Name

PSALM 8   EVENING PRAISE 7 7 7 7 4, with Refrain

William F. Sherwin, 1877

1 Lord, our Lord, Thy glo-rious Name All Thy won-drous works pro-claim;
2 In - fant lips Thou dost or - dain Wrath and ven-geance to re-strain;
3 Moon and stars in shin-ing height Night-ly tell their Mak-er's might;

In the heavens with ra-diant signs Ev - er-more Thy glo-ry shines.
Weak - est means ful - fil Thy will, Might-y en - e - mies to still.
When Thy won-drous heavens I scan, Then I know how weak is man.

REFRAIN

How great Thy Name! Lord, our Lord, in all the earth, How great Thy Name!

Thine the Name of match-less worth, Ex-cel-lent in all the earth; How great Thy Name!

4 What is man that he should be
Loved and visited by Thee,
Raised to an exalted height,
Crowned with honor in Thy sight!
How great Thy Name!

5 With dominion crowned he stands
O'er the creatures of Thy hands;
All to him subjection yield
In the sea and air and field.
How great Thy Name!

14 Whole-hearted Thanksgiving to Thee I Will Bring

PSALM 9

To God Be The Glory 11 11 11 11, with Refrain

William H. Doane, 1834-1915

1 Whole - heart - ed thanks-giv - ing to Thee I will bring,
2 Thou, Lord, art a ref - uge for all the op- pressed;
3 Give praise to Je - ho - vah, the might - y deeds tell

In praise of Thy mar - vel - ous deeds I will sing;
All trust Thee who know Thee, and trust - ing are blest;
Of Him who has chos - en in Zi - on to dwell,

In Thee I will joy and ex - ult - ing - ly cry,
For nev - er, O Lord, did Thy mer - cy for - sake
Of Him to whom jus - tice and ven-geance be - long,

Thy Name I will praise, O Je - ho - vah Most High.
The soul that has sought of Thy grace to par - take.
Who vis - its the low - ly and o - ver-throws wrong.

Whole-hearted Thanksgiving to Thee I Will Bring

(May be sung after last stanza only)

REFRAIN

Praise the Lord, praise the Lord, let the earth hear His voice!

Praise the Lord, praise the Lord, let the peo - ple re - joice!

O come to Je - ho - vah, de - clare ye His fame,

And give Him all hon - or, for just is His Name.

4 Behold my affliction, Thy mercy accord,
  And back from death's portals restore me, O Lord,
  That I in the gates of Thy Zion may raise
  My song of salvation and show forth Thy praise.

15   O Why So Far Removed, O Lord

PSALM 10   Sawley C. M.   James Walch, 1860

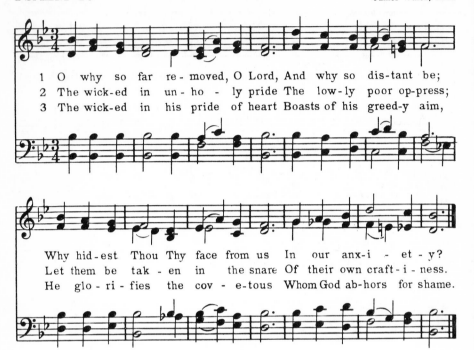

1 O why so far re-moved, O Lord, And why so dis-tant be;
2 The wick-ed in un-ho - ly pride The low-ly poor op-press;
3 The wick-ed in his pride of heart Boasts of his greed-y aim,

Why hid-est Thou Thy face from us In our anx-i - et-y?
Let them be tak - en in the snare Of their own craft-i - ness.
He glo-ri-fies the cov - e-tous Whom God ab-hors for shame.

4 The wicked in his arrogance
    Refuses God to fear,
Nor is it in his thoughts at all
    The sovereign God to hear.

5 His ways are grievous and Thy laws
    Too high for him to see;
He therefore his defiance bids,
    And taunts his enemy.

6 For he within his heart has said,
    I suffer no distress,
Adversity comes not to me,
    I still have had success.

7 In cursing and deceit and fraud
    His tongue is ever skilled;
With festering iniquity
    His mouth is ever filled.

O Why So Far Removed, O Lord

8 He lurks in village hiding-place,
   And in dark corners bent,
He watches for the humble poor,
   To seize the innocent.

9 In stealth he cowers covertly
   As lion in his lair,
That he may pounce upon the poor,
   And catch him in his snare.

10 He crouches low so that the poor
   To his strong friends may fall,
And tells himself that God forgets
   Or sees it not at all.

11 Arise, O Lord, and lift Thy hand,
   The poor in memory keep.
How can the wicked blaspheme God
   And say He is asleep?

12 For surely Thou dost see, O Lord,
   Dost see the sin and spite;
And when the helpless look to Thee
   Thou dost their wrong requite.

13 Break Thou the force of evil men,
   Befriend the fatherless,
Trace out the wicked everywhere,
   Uproot their wickedness.

14 The Lord our God is sovereign still,
   The heathen all are slain.
Thou, Lord, hast heard the suppliant's prayer
   And dost his heart sustain.

15 No more shall boasting arrogance
   Or taunting pride oppress;
The poor and orphaned Thou wilt hear
   And judge with righteousness.

16

In God Will I Trust

PSALM 11   PROTECTION 11 11 11 11

Anonymous

1 In God will I trust, though my coun - sel - ors say,
2 The Lord in His tem - ple shall ev - er a - bide,
3 The Lord is most right - eous, the Lord loves the right,

O flee as a bird to your moun - tain a - way;
His throne is e - ter - nal, what - ev - er be - tide;
The e - vil He hates and will sure - ly re - quite;

The wick - ed are strong and the right - eous are weak,
The chil - dren of men He be - holds from on high,
The wick - ed His an - ger will drive from their place,

Foun - da - tions are shak - en, yet God will I seek.
The wick - ed to pun - ish, the right - eous to try.
The up - right in rap - ture shall gaze on His face.

17 Help, Lord, for Those Who Love Thee Fail

PSALM 12 BROOKFIELD L. M.

Thomas B. Southgate, 1855

1 Help, Lord, for those who love Thee fail, Thy faith - ful
  ones fall from the ranks, And leave the li - ars
  to their tale, False grat - i - tude and treach - erous thanks.

2 Lord, may those flat - tering lips be lashed, The boast - ing
  mouths stripped of their pride, Those tongues that mur - mur
  un - a - bashed, Who is this God? We shall a - bide!

3 Be - cause the poor have been op-pressed, And in their
  pa - tience sigh a - lone, I will pro - tect them
  in My breast, The Lord has said, These are Mine own.

4 And what He saith is purified
   Like silver, sevenfold assayed.
  Though by this evil age defied,
   His word of truth shall be obeyed.

5 His promises shall stand secure,
   His saints are safe, though ill betide;
  He will protect His humble poor,
   Though rogues are honored far and wide.

Richard Church, *Alt.*

18   How Long Wilt Thou Forget Me

PSALM 13   FAR OFF LANDS 7 6 7 6 D.

Melody of the Bohemian Brethren
in *Hemmets Koral Bok*

Brightly, may be sung in unison

1 How long wilt Thou for - get me, O Lord, Thou God of
2 O Lord my God, be - hold me, And hear mine ear - nest
3 But I with ex - pec - ta - tion Have on Thy grace re -

grace? How long shall fears be - set me While dark-ness hides Thy
cries; Lest sleep of death en - fold me, En - light-en Thou mine
lied; My heart in Thy sal - va - tion Shall still with joy con -

face? How long shall griefs dis-tress me And turn my day to
eyes; Lest now my foe in - sult - ing Should boast of his suc -
fide; And I with voice of sing - ing Will praise the Lord a -

night? How long shall foes op-press me And tri - umph in their might?
cess, And en - e - mies ex - ult - ing Re - joice in my dis - tress.
bove, Who, rich-est boun-ties bring-ing, Has dealt with me in love.

22

19 The God Who Sits Enthroned on High

PSALM 14

EISENACH L. M.

Johann Hermann Schein, 1586-1630

1 The God who sits en-throned on high The fool-ish in their heart de-ny; Not one does good; cor-rupt in thought, Un-right-eous works their hands have wrought.

2 From heaven the Lord with search-ing eye Looked down the sons of men to try, To see if an-y un-der-stood And sought for God, the on-ly good.

3 From right-eous-ness they all de-part, Cor-rupt are all, and vile in heart; Yea, ev-ery man has e-vil done; Not one does good, not e-ven one.

4 Has knowledge with the wicked failed,
That they My people have assailed,
That they delight in works of shame,
And call not on Jehovah's Name?

5 Thy lowly servant they despise,
Because he on the Lord relies;
But they shall tremble yet in fear,
For to the righteous God is near.

6 O that from Zion, His abode,
Salvation were on us bestowed!
When God His exiles shall restore,
They shall in song His grace adore.

20   Who, O Lord, with Thee Abiding

PSALM 15   HELEN 8 7 8 7 D.

Silas J. Vail, 1818-1883

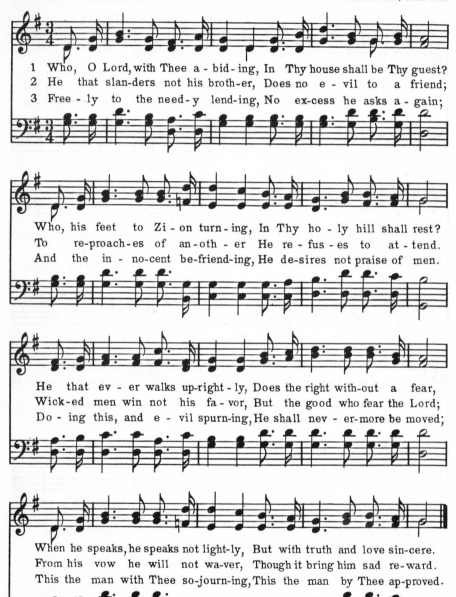

1 Who, O Lord, with Thee a-bid-ing, In Thy house shall be Thy guest?
2 He that slan-ders not his broth-er, Does no e-vil to a friend;
3 Free-ly to the need-y lend-ing, No ex-cess he asks a-gain;

Who, his feet to Zi-on turn-ing, In Thy ho-ly hill shall rest?
To re-proach-es of an-oth-er He re-fus-es to at-tend.
And the in-no-cent be-friend-ing, He de-sires not praise of men.

He that ev-er walks up-right-ly, Does the right with-out a fear,
Wick-ed men win not his fa-vor, But the good who fear the Lord;
Do-ing this, and e-vil spurn-ing, He shall nev-er-more be moved;

When he speaks, he speaks not light-ly, But with truth and love sin-cere.
From his vow he will not wa-ver, Though it bring him sad re-ward.
This the man with Thee so-journ-ing, This the man by Thee ap-proved.

21   O God, Preserve Me

PSALM 16   ANCHORAGE C. M.

Dick L. Van Halsema, 1953

(Alternate tune: ST. PETER, No. 384)

1 O God, pre - serve me, for in Thee A -
lone my trust has stood; My soul has said, Thou
art my Lord, My chief and on - ly good.

2 I love Thy saints, who fear Thy name And
walk as in Thy sight; They are the ex - cel -
lent of earth, In them is my de - light.

3 Their sor - rows shall be mul - ti - plied Who
wor - ship aught but Thee; I share not in their
of - fer - ings, Nor join their com - pa - ny.

4 The Lord is mine inheritance,
    The Lord alone remains
The fulness of my cup of bliss;
    The Lord my lot maintains.

5 The lines are fallen unto me
    In places large and fair;
A goodly heritage is mine,
    Marked out with gracious care.

When in the Night I Meditate

PSALM 16 MAITLAND C. M.

George N. Allen, 1850

1 When in the night I med - i - tate On
2 For - ev - er in my thought the Lord Be -
3 Mine in - most be - ing thrills with joy And

mer - cies mul - ti - plied, My grate - ful heart in -
fore my face shall stand; Se - cure, un - moved, I
glad - ness fills my breast; Be - cause on Him my

spires my tongue To bless the Lord, my Guide.
shall re - main, With Him at my right hand.
trust is stayed, My flesh in hope shall rest.

4 I know that I shall not be left
   Forgotten in the grave,
   That from corruption, Thou, O Lord,
   Thy Holy One wilt save.

5 The path of life Thou showest me;
   Of joy a boundless store
   Is ever found at Thy right hand,
   And pleasures evermore.

To Thee, O Lord, I Fly

PSALM 16

Mary S. M. D.

Henry A. Lewis

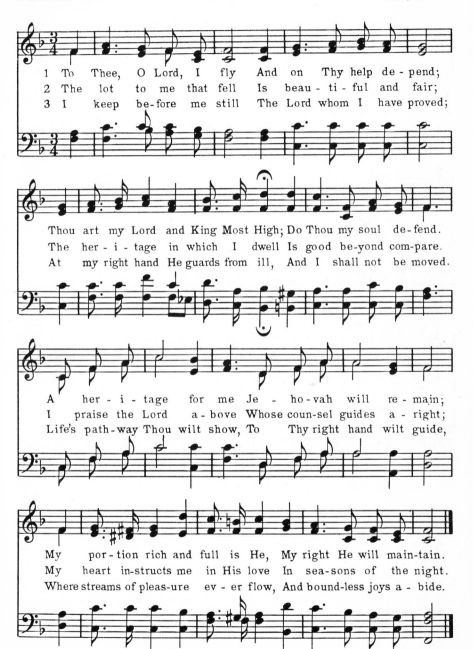

1 To Thee, O Lord, I fly And on Thy help de - pend;
2 The lot to me that fell Is beau - ti - ful and fair;
3 I keep be - fore me still The Lord whom I have proved;

Thou art my Lord and King Most High; Do Thou my soul de - fend.
The her - i - tage in which I dwell Is good be - yond com - pare.
At my right hand He guards from ill, And I shall not be moved.

A her - i - tage for me Je - ho - vah will re - main;
I praise the Lord a - bove Whose coun - sel guides a - right;
Life's path - way Thou wilt show, To Thy right hand wilt guide,

My por - tion rich and full is He, My right He will main - tain.
My heart in - structs me in His love In sea - sons of the night.
Where streams of pleas - ure ev - er flow, And bound - less joys a - bide.

24 Lord, Hear the Right

PSALM 17   LONGFELLOW 8 6 8 6 8 8   Frederic F. Bullard, 1864-1904

1 Lord, hear the right, re-gard my cry, My prayer from lips sin-cere;
2 With sted-fast cour-age I de-sign No wrong to speak or do;
3 O Thou that ev - er sav-est those Whose trust on Thee is stayed,

Send Thine ap-prov-al from on high, My right-eous-ness make clear.
Thy path of life I choose for mine And walk with pur-pose true.
Pre-serv-ing them from all their foes By Thine al-might-y aid,

Thou in the night my heart hast tried, Nor found it turned from Thee a-side.
For help, O God, I cry to Thee, As-sured that Thou wilt an-swer me.
Let me Thy lov-ing-kind-ness see, Thy won-drous mer-cy, full and free.

4 O guard me well as one would guard
  The apple of the eye;
While deadly foes are pressing hard,
  To Thee, to Thee I cry.
Do Thou my rest and refuge be,
O let Thy wings o'ershadow me.

5 Mine enemy, grown strong in pride,
  Would take my life away,
A lion lurking by my side,
  Most greedy for his prey.
Confront and cast him down, O Lord,
From evil save me by Thy sword.

6 Defend me from the men of pride,
  Whose portion is below,
Who, with life's treasures satisfied,
  No better portion know;
They, with earth's joys and wealth content,
Must leave them all when life is spent.

7 When I in righteousness at last
  Thy glorious face shall see,
When all the weary night is past,
  And I awake with Thee
To view the glories that abide,
Then, then I shall be satisfied.

25   I Love the Lord

PSALM 18   MENDON L. M.

German Melody
Arranged by S. Dyer, 1824

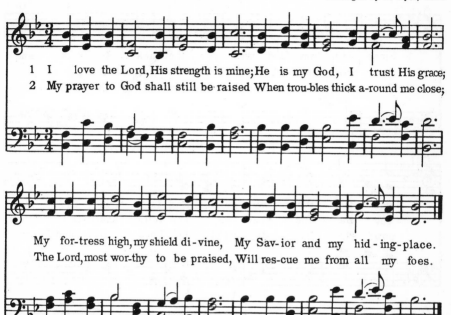

1 I love the Lord, His strength is mine; He is my God, I trust His grace;
2 My prayer to God shall still be raised When trou-bles thick a-round me close;

My for-tress high, my shield di-vine, My Sav-ior and my hid-ing-place.
The Lord, most wor-thy to be praised, Will res-cue me from all my foes.

3 When, floods of evil raging near,
  Down nigh to death my soul was
    brought,
  I cried to God in all my fear;
  He heard and great deliverance
    wrought.

4 He came: the earth's foundations quake,
  The hills are shaken from their
    place,
  Thick smoke and fire devouring break
  In anger dread before His face.

5 Descending through the bending skies,
  With gloom and darkness under Him,
  Forth through the storm Jehovah flies
  As on the wings of cherubim.

6 Thick darkness hides Him from the view,
  And swelling clouds His presence veil,
  Until His glorious light breaks through
  In lightning flash and glistening hail.

7 Jehovah's thunders fill the heaven,
  The dreadful voice of God Most
    High;
  With shafts of light the clouds are
    riven,
  His foes, dismayed, in terror fly.

8 The raging torrents overflow,
  And sweep the world's foundations
    bare,
  Because Thy blasts of anger blow,
  O Lord of earth and sea and air.

9 He took me from the whelming waves
  Of bitter hate and sore distress;
  The Lord, my Stay and Helper, saves,
  Though mighty foes around me press.

10 From direful straits He set me free,
  He saved the man of His delight;
  For good the Lord rewarded me,
  Because I kept His ways aright.

26   Since with My God with Perfect Heart

PSALM 18   ROCKINGHAM OLD L. M.

Arranged by Edward Miller, 1790

1 Since with my God with per - fect heart I walk and
2 The mer - ci - ful shall know Thy grace, The per - fect
3 To smite the proud and bring them low, To save the

make His Word my guide, And from in - iq - ui -
Thy per - fec - tion see, The pure shall see Thine
poor is Thy de - light. The Lord will cause my

ty de - part, The Lord His bless - ing will pro - vide.
own pure face, The fro - ward find a foe in Thee.
lamp to glow, My God will make my dark - ness light.

4 From God the victory I receive;
  Most perfect is His Holy way;
  His Word is tried, they who believe
  Will find the Lord their shield and stay.

5 For who is God, and strong to save,
  Beside the Lord, our God of might?
  'Tis He that makes me strong and brave,
  The Lord who guides my steps aright.

6 Thy free salvation is my shield,
  My sure defense in every strait;
  Thy hand upholds me, lest I yield;
  Thy gentleness has made me great.

27   As Thou, O Lord, Hast Made Me Strong

PSALM 18   MOZART L. M.

Arranged from Mozart, 1756-1791

1 As Thou, O Lord, hast made me strong To o - ver -
2 From strife Thou wilt de - liv - er me, And make the
3 Je - ho - vah lives, and blest is He, My rock, my

come my might - y foe, So now to fight a -
na - tions own my sway; Strange peo - ples, when my
ref - uge and de - fense, My Sav - ior who de -

gainst the wrong And con - quer in Thy Name I go.
power they see, Shall come with trem - bling and o - bey.
liv - ers me, And will the wick - ed rec - om - pense.

4 For grace and mercy ever near,
    For foes subdued and victories won,
All nations of the earth shall hear
    My praise for what the Lord has done.

5 To David, His anointed king,
    And to his sons upon his throne,
The Lord will great salvation bring
    And ever make His mercy known.

31

The Spacious Heavens Declare

PSALM 19 ARTHUR'S SEAT 6 6 6 6 8 8

Arranged from Sir John Goss
by Uzziah C. Burnap, 1874

1 The spa-cious heavens de-clare The glo-ry of our God,
2 A - loud they do not speak, They ut-ter forth no word,
3 The clouds of heaven are spread, A tent to hold the sun,

The fir-ma-ment dis-plays His hand-i-work a-broad;
Nor in-to lan-guage break, Their voice is nev-er heard;
And like a bride-groom fair Comes forth the might-y one,

Day un-to day pro-claims His might, And night His wis-dom tells to night.
Yet through the world the truth they bear And their Cre-a-tor's power de-clare.
Re - joic-ing in his strength and grace To run his won-drous dai-ly race.

4 His daily going forth
   Is from the end of heaven;
   The firmament to him
   Is for his circuit given;
   His journey reaches to its ends,
   And everywhere his heat extends.

5 Jehovah's perfect law
   Restores the soul again;
   His testimony sure
   Gives wisdom unto men;
   The precepts of the Lord are right,
   And fill the heart with great delight.

29

Jehovah's Perfect Law

PSALM 19

HADDAM 6 6 6 6 8 8

Arranged by Lowell Mason, 1822

1 Je - ho - vah's per - fect law Re - stores the soul a - gain; His
2 The Lord's com-mands are pure, They light and joy re - store; Je -
3 They are to be de - sired A - bove the fin - est gold; Than

tes - ti - mo - ny sure Gives wis-dom un - to men; The pre - cepts of the
ho - vah's fear is clean, En - dur - ing ev - er-more; His stat - utes, let the
hon - ey from the comb More sweet-ness far they hold; With warn-ings they Thy

Lord are right, And fill the heart with great de - light.
world con - fess, Are whol - ly truth and right - eous - ness.
ser - vant guard, In keep - ing them is great re - ward.

4 His errors who can know?
    Cleanse me from hidden stain;
Keep me from wilful sins,
    Nor let them o'er me reign;
And then I upright shall appear
And be from great transgressions clear.

5 When Thou dost search my life,
    May all my thoughts within
And all the words I speak
    Thy full approval win.
O Lord, Thou art a rock to me,
And my Redeemer Thou shalt be.

The Spacious Heavens Laud

PSALM 19

REVELATION 6 6 6 D. 6 6 7 D.

Louis Bourgeois, 1549
Harmonized by Seymour Swets, 1954

Smoothly, joyfully; may be sung in unison

1 The spa-cious heav-ens laud The glo-ry of our God With
2 The fear of God is clean, A foun-tain of se-rene And

full, ma-jes-tic praise; The o-pen fir-ma-ment, Un-
ev-er-last-ing bliss; The judg-ments of the Lord, Which

meas-ured in ex-tent, His hand-i-work dis-plays. Day
pur-est light af-ford, Are truth and right-eous-ness. More

will to day pro-claim His sov-ereign-ty and fame With
to be sought are they Than gold and sil-ver, yea, More

The Spacious Heavens Laud

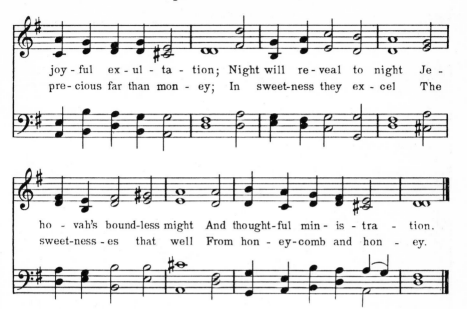

joy - ful ex - ul - ta - tion; Night will re - veal to night Je -
pre - cious far than mon - ey; In sweet-ness they ex - cel The

ho - vah's bound-less might And thought-ful min - is - tra - tion.
sweet-ness - es that well From hon - ey-comb and hon - ey.

3 God's law, a perfect whole,
Is saving to the soul,
    And every secret tries.
His testimony sure,
Which ever shall endure,
    Will make the simple wise.
His statutes, right and true,
Rejoice the heart anew
    And show the Lord's salvation;
His pure commands have lent
Mine eyes enlightenment
    In all my meditation.

4 Moreover, they forewarn
Thy servant that he scorn
    All evil ways, O Lord.
He that in faith on Thee
Observes them piously
    Shall reap a great reward.
But, Lord, where is the man
Who with precision can
    Discern his every error?
Thou Fount of joy divine,
O clear this heart of mine
    From secret faults forever!

Dewey Westra, 1931

31   The Heavens Declare Thy Glory

PSALM 19   FAITHFUL 7 6 7 6 D.

Johann Sebastian Bach, 1685-1750
from *My Heart Ever Faithful*

May be sung in unison

1 The heavens de-clare Thy glo - ry, The fir - ma-ment Thy power;
2 The sun with roy - al splen-dor Goes forth to chant Thy praise,
3 All heaven on high re - joic-es To do its Mak - er's will;

Day un - to day the sto - ry Re - peats from hour to hour;
And moon-beams soft and ten - der Their gen - tler an - them raise;
The stars with sol-emn voic - es Re - sound Thy prais - es still;

Night un - to night re - ply - ing, Pro - claims in ev - ery land,
O'er ev - ery tribe and na - tion The mu - sic strange is poured,
So let my whole be - hav-ior, Thoughts, words and ac - tions, be,

O Lord, with voice un - dy - ing, The won - ders of Thy hand.
The song of all cre - a - tion To Thee, cre - a - tion's Lord.
O Lord, my strength, my Sav - ior, One cease - less song to Thee.

Thomas R. Birks, 1874

32 Jehovah Hear Thee in Thy Grief

PSALM 20   TALLIS' CANON L.M.   Thomas Tallis, 1520-1585

1 Je - ho - vah hear thee in thy grief, Our
2 Thy sac - ri - fice may He re - gard, And
3 In thy sal - va - tion we re - joice, And

fa - ther's God de - fend thee still, Send from His ho - ly
all thine of - ferings bear in mind; Thy heart's de - sire to
in God's Name our ban - ners raise; Je - ho - vah heark - en

place re - lief, And strength-en thee from Zi - on's hill.
thee ac-cord, Ful - fil - ling all thou hast de-signed.
to thy voice, Ful - fil thy prayers through all thy days. A - men.

4 Salvation will the Lord command,
   And His anointed will defend;
Yea, with the strength of His right hand
   From heaven He will an answer send.

5 In chariots some have confidence,
   On horses others will rely,
But we acknowledge our defense
   Is God, Jehovah, Lord Most High.

6 Now we arise and upright stand,
   While they, subdued and helpless, fall;
Jehovah, save us by Thy hand;
   The King give answer when we call. Amen.

33 Now the King in Thy Strength Shall Be Joyful

PSALM 21 LATAKIA 12 9 12 9

E. G. Taylor

1 Now the King in Thy strength shall be joy-ful, O Lord, Thy sal-
va-tion shall make Him re-joice; For the wish of His heart Thou didst
free-ly ac-cord, The re-quest of His sup-pli-ant voice.

2 All the bless-ings of good-ness Thou free-ly didst give; With the
pur-est of gold He is crowned; When He asked of Thee life, Thou hast
made Him to live While the a-ges shall cir-cle a-round.

3 Through sal-va-tion from Thee has His fame spread a-broad, Thou didst
glo-ry and hon-or im-part; Thou hast made Him most bless-ed for-
ev-er, O God, And Thy pres-ence has glad-dened His heart.

4 For the King in the strength of Je-ho-vah Most High Did un-
wav-er-ing con-fi-dence place; On the Name of Je-ho-vah He
still will re-ly, And shall stand ev-er-more in His grace.

5 By the hand of Thy might and the dread of Thy name
    All Thy foes Thou wilt burn in Thy fire;
  Thou wilt swallow them up in the vengeance of flame,
    And their race shall succumb to Thine ire.

6 Though they plotted their schemes against Thee and Thy might,
    In their purpose they cannot succeed;
  Thou wilt certainly make them turn backward in flight,
    For Thine arrows are ready to speed.

7 Be Thou then high exalted, Jehovah our God,
    And arise in the weight of Thy might;
  We shall sing of Thy strength and omnipotent rod;
    In Thy praises shall be our delight.

38

34   My God, My God, I Cry to Thee

PSALM 22   HEBRON L.M.   Lowell Mason, 1830

1 My God, My God, I cry to Thee; O why hast Thou for-sak-en Me?
2 But Thou art ho - ly in Thy ways, En-throned up-on Thy peo-ple's praise;
3 They cried, and, trust-ing in Thy Name, Were saved, and were not put to shame;

A - far from Me, Thou dost not heed, Though day and night for help I plead.
Our fa-thers put their trust in Thee, Be - lieved, and Thou didst set them free.
But in the dust Mine hon-or lies, While all re-proach and all de-spise.

4 My words a cause for scorn they make,
The lip they curl, the head they shake,
And, mocking, bid Me trust the Lord
Till He salvation shall afford.

5 My trust on Thee I learned to rest
When I was on My mother's breast;
From birth Thou art My God alone,
Thy care My life has ever known.

6 O let Thy strength and presence cheer,
For trouble and distress are near;
Be Thou not far away from Me,
I have no source of help but Thee.

7 Unnumbered foes would do Me wrong,
They press about Me, fierce and strong,
Like beasts of prey their rage they vent,
My courage fails, My strength is spent.

8 Down unto death Thou leadest Me,
Consumed by thirst and agony;
With cruel hate and anger fierce
My helpless hands and feet they pierce.

9 While on My wasted form they stare,
The garments torn from Me they share,
My shame and sorrow heeding not,
And for My robe they cast the lot.

10 O Lord, afar no longer stay;
O Thou My Helper, haste, I pray;
From death and evil set Me free;
I live, for Thou didst answer Me.

11 I live and will declare Thy fame
Where brethren gather in Thy Name;
Where all Thy faithful people meet,
I will Thy worthy praise repeat.

35　　All Ye That Fear Jehovah's Name

PSALM 22　　PARK STREET L.M.

Arranged from Frederick M. A.
Venua about 1810

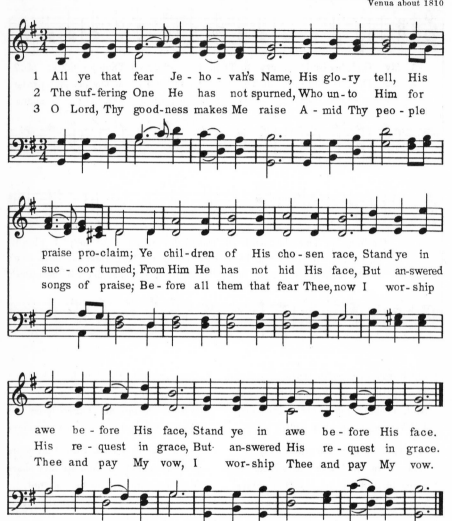

1 All ye that fear Je - ho - vah's Name, His glo-ry tell, His
2 The suf-fering One He has not spurned, Who un-to Him for
3 O Lord, Thy good-ness makes Me raise A - mid Thy peo - ple

praise pro-claim; Ye chil-dren of His cho - sen race, Stand ye in
suc - cor turned; From Him He has not hid His face, But an-swered
songs of praise; Be - fore all them that fear Thee, now I wor-ship

awe be - fore His face, Stand ye in awe be - fore His face.
His re - quest in grace, But an-swered His re - quest in grace.
Thee and pay My vow, I wor-ship Thee and pay My vow.

4 For all the meek Thou wilt provide,
  They shall be fed and satisfied;
  All they that seek the Lord shall live
  And never-ending praises give.

The Ends of All the Earth Shall Hear

PSALM 22   Vision L.M., with Refrain

William H. Doane, 1834-1915

1 The ends of all the earth shall hear And turn un-to the
2 For His the king-dom, His of right, He rules the na-tions

Lord in fear; All kin-dreds of the earth shall own
by His might; All earth to Him her hom-age brings,

REFRAIN

And wor-ship Him as God a-lone.   All earth to Him
The Lord of lords, the King of kings.

her hom-age brings, The Lord of lords, the King of kings.

3 Both rich and poor, both bond and free
Shall worship Him on bended knee,
And children's children shall proclaim
The glorious honor of His Name.

4 The Lord's unfailing righteousness
All generations shall confess,
From age to age shall men be taught
What wondrous works the Lord has
wrought.

Amid the Thronging Worshippers

BOVINA C.M.D.

Laura A. Tate

1 A - mid the throng-ing wor- ship-pers Je - ho - vah will I bless;
2 The bur - den of the sor - row- ful The Lord will not de- spise;
3 He feeds with good the hum- ble soul And sat - is- fies the meek,

Be- fore my breth - ren, gath- ered there, His Name will I con - fess.
He has not turned from those that mourn, He heark- ens to their cries.
And they shall live and praise the Lord Who for His mer- cy seek.

Come, praise Him, ye that fear the Lord, Ye chil- dren of His grace;
His good-ness makes me join the throng Where saints His praise pro-claim,
The ends of all the earth take thought, The na - tions seek the Lord;

With rev- erence sound His glo - ries forth And bow be - fore His face.
And there will I ful - fil my vows 'Mid those who fear His Name.
They wor - ship Him, the King of kings, In earth and heaven a- dored.

The Lord's My Shepherd

38

PSALM 23

Evan C.M.

William H. Havergal, 1846

1 The Lord's my Shep - herd, I'll not want; He
2 My soul He doth re - store a - gain, And
3 Yea, though I walk through death's dark vale, Yet

makes me down to lie In pas - tures green; He
me to walk doth make With - in the paths of
will I fear no ill, For Thou art with me,

lead - eth me The qui - et wa - ters by.
right - eous - ness, E'en for His own Name's sake.
and Thy rod And staff me com - fort still.

4 A table Thou hast furnished me
    In presence of my foes;
  My head Thou dost with oil anoint,
    And my cup overflows.

5 Goodness and mercy all my life
    Shall surely follow me,
  And in God's house forevermore
    My dwelling-place shall be.

39 My Shepherd Is the Lord

PSALM 23

TALLIS' ORDINAL C.M.

Thomas Tallis, c. 1567

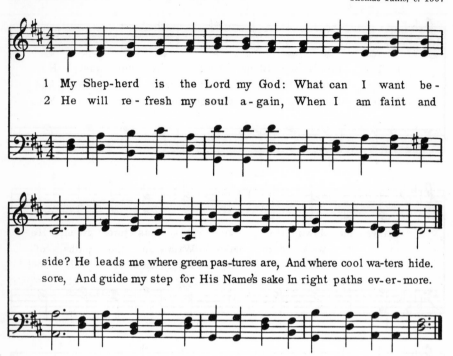

1 My Shep-herd is the Lord my God: What can I want be-
side? He leads me where green pas-tures are, And where cool wa-ters hide.

2 He will re-fresh my soul a-gain, When I am faint and
sore, And guide my step for His Name's sake In right paths ev-er-more.

3 Though I should walk the vale of death,
  I should not know a fear.
Thy rod and staff they comfort me:
  Thou, Lord, art ever near.

4 A table Thou hast spread for me
  In presence of my foes;
Thou dost anoint my head with oil,
  My cup, Lord, overflows.

5 Thy goodness and Thy mercy, Lord,
  Will surely follow me,
And in Thy house forevermore
  My dwelling-place shall be.

40 The Lord My Shepherd Holds Me

PSALM 23   PASTORALE 7 6 7 6 D.

Adrian Hartog, 1954

Gently

1 The Lord my Shep-herd holds me With-in His ten-der care,
2 What-ev-er ill be-tides me, He will re-store and bless;
3 My food Thou dost ap-point me, Sup-plied be-fore my foes;

And with His flock He folds me, No want shall find me there.
For His Name's sake He guides me In paths of right-eous-ness.
With oil Thou dost a-noint me, My cup of bliss o'er-flows.

In pas-tures green He feeds me, With plen-ty I am blest;
Thy rod and staff shall cheer me In death's dark vale and shade,
Thy good-ness, Lord, shall guide me, Thy mer-cy cheer my way;

By qui-et streams He leads me And makes me safe-ly rest.
For Thou wilt then be near me; I shall not be a-fraid.
A home Thou wilt pro-vide me With-in Thy house for aye.

(Alternate tune: EWING, No. 471)

45

41 The Earth and the Fulness with Which It Is Stored

PSALM 24

MALDWYN 11 11 11 11

Welsh Melody, c. 1600

1 The earth and the ful-ness with which it is stored,
2 What man shall the hill of Je-ho-vah as-cend,
3 That man ev-er blest of Je-ho-vah shall live,

The world and its dwell-ers be-long to the Lord;
And who in the place of His pres-ence at-tend?
The God of sal-va-tion shall right-eous-ness give;

For He on the seas its foun-da-tions has laid,
The man of pure heart and of hands with-out stain,
For this is the peo-ple, yea, this is the race,

And firm on the wa-ters its pil-lars has stayed.
Who swears not to false-hood nor loves what is vain.
The Is-ra-el true that are seek-ing His face. A-men.

46

42   Ye Gates, Lift Your Heads

PSALM 24   LANSING 11 11 11 11   Charles H. Gabriel, 1856-1932

1 Ye gates, lift your heads, the glad sum-mons o - bey,
2 What King of all glo - ry is this that ye sing?
3 The King of all glo - ry high hon - ors a - wait,

Ye doors ev - er - last - ing, wide o - pen the way.
The Lord, strong and might - y, the con - quer - ing King.
The King of all glo - ry shall en - ter in state.

The King of all glo - ry high hon - ors a - wait,
Ye gates, lift your heads, and His sum-mons o - bey,
What King of all glo - ry is this that ye sing?

The King of all glo - ry shall en - ter in state.
Ye doors ev - er - last - ing, wide o - pen the way.
Je - ho - vah of Hosts, He of glo - ry is King.

43

Unto Thee, O Lord Jehovah

PATHWAY 8 7 8 7 7 8 7 8

Louis Bourgeois, 1551
Harmony from De Vries *Koraalboek*
Adapted by Henry Bruinsma, 1946

1 Un - to Thee, O Lord Je - ho - vah, Do I lift my wait - ing soul.
2 Un - to me, O Lord Je - ho - vah, Show Thy ways and teach Thou me;

O my God, in Thee I trust - ed; Let no shame now o'er me roll.
So that, by Thy Spir - it guid - ed, Clear - ly I Thy paths may see.

On my en - e - my be shame, Oft with - out a cause trans - gress - ing;
In Thy truth wilt Thou me guide, Teach me, God of my sal - va - tion;

But all those who trust Thy Name Hon - or with a - bun - dant bless - ing.
All the day for Thee I bide, Lord, with ea - ger ex - pec - ta - tion.

Unto Thee, O Lord Jehovah

3 Call to mind, O Lord Jehovah,
  Tender mercies manifold,
And Thy store of lovingkindness
  Which has ever been of old.
Sins of youth remember not,
  Nor recall my hid' transgression;
For Thy goodness' sake, O God,
  Think of me in Thy compassion.

4 Good and upright is Jehovah
  In His dealings evermore.
Sinners are by Him instructed
  In the way untrod before.
He will ever guide the meek
  In His judgments true and holy;
Teach His ways to those who seek
  With a contrite heart and lowly.

5 All the pathways of Jehovah
  Speak of truth and mercies pure
Unto such as keep His covenant
  And His testimony sure.
For the glory of Thy Name,
  Pardon, Lord, my evil-doing;
Grievous though my sin and shame,
  Hear my cry, Thy love renewing.

6 Who is he that fears Jehovah,
  Walking with Him day by day?
God will lead him safely onward,
  Guide him in the chosen way.
Then at ease his soul shall rest,
  In Jehovah still confiding;
E'en his children shall be blest,
  Safely in the land abiding.

7 Yea, the secret of Jehovah
  Is with those who fear His Name;
With His friends in tender mercy
  He His covenant will maintain.
With a confidence complete,   [ing;
  Toward the Lord mine eyes are turn-
From the net He'll pluck my feet;
  He will not despise my yearning.

8 Turn Thou unto me in mercy;
  Have compassion on my soul.
I am sore distressed and lonely;
  Waves of trouble o'er me roll.
Myriad woes beset my heart,
  Myriad doubts and bitternesses;
Thou who my Deliverer art,
  Bring me out of my distresses.

9 O consider mine affliction,
  All my travail, Lord, behold;
Grant me full and free remission
  Of my trespasses untold.
See mine enemies; for great
  Is the number that upbraid me;
Who, in their consuming hate,   [me.
  With their cruel scorn have flayed

10 Keep my soul, O gracious Savior;
  Come, I pray, deliver me,
Lest my head with shame be covered,
  For my refuge is in Thee.
Trusting in Thy power supreme,
  Lord, I wait for Thy salvation;
Come, Jehovah, and redeem
  Israel from tribulation.

Samuel G. Brondsema, 1931

Lord, I Lift My Soul to Thee

SPANISH HYMN 7 7 7 7 D.

Arranged by Benjamin Carr, 1824

1 Lord, I lift my soul to Thee, O my God, I trust Thy might;
2 Lord, to me Thy ways make known, Guide in truth and teach Thou me;
3 Sins of youth re-mem-ber not, Nor my tres-pass-es re-cord;

Let not foes ex - ult o'er me, Shame me not be - fore their sight.
Thou my Sav-ior art a - lone, All the day I wait for Thee.
Let not mer - cy be for - got, For Thy good-ness' sake, O Lord.

Yea, may none be put to shame, None who wait for Thee to bless;
Lord, re-mem - ber in Thy love All Thy mer-cies man - i - fold,
Just and good the Lord a-bides, He His way will sin-ners show,

But dis-hon-ored be their name Who with-out a cause trans-gress.
Ten - der mer-cies from a-bove, Change-less from the days of old.
He the meek in jus-tice guides, Mak - ing them His way to know.

45   Grace and Truth Shall Mark the Way

PSALM 25   Evening Prayer 7 7 7 7

Alberto Randegger

1 Grace and truth shall mark the way   Where the Lord His own will lead,
2 For Thy Name's sake hear Thou me,   For Thy mer-cy, Lord, I wait;
3 He who walks in god-ly fear   In the path of truth shall go;

If His Word they still o-bey   And His tes-ti-mo-nies heed.
Par-don mine in-iq-ui-ty,   For my sin is ver-y great.
Peace shall be his por-tion here,   And his sons all good shall know.

4 They that fear and love the Lord
   Shall Jehovah's friendship know;
He will grace to them accord,
   And His faithful covenant show.

5 Ever are my longing eyes
   On the Lord, whose watchful care,
When my foes their plots devise,
   Keeps my feet from every snare.

6 Turn to me, Thy grace impart,
   I am desolate indeed;
Great the troubles of my heart;
   Save Thou me, O Lord, I plead.

7 Look on mine afflicted state,
   Freely all my sins forgive;
Mark my foes, their cruel hate;
   Keep my soul and let me live.

8 Shame me not; I hide in Thee;
   Truth and right preserve me still;
Mark Thy people, Lord my God,
   Save Thou them from every ill.

46 Lord, to Me Thy Ways Make Known

PSALM 25

SEYMOUR 7 7 7 7

Arranged from Carl M. von Weber, 1826

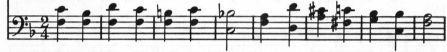

1 Lord, to me Thy ways make known, Guide in truth and teach Thou me;
2 Lord, re-mem-ber in Thy love All Thy mer-cies man-i-fold,
3 Sins of youth re-mem-ber not, Nor my tres-pass-es re-cord;

Thou my Sav-ior art a-lone, All the day I wait for Thee.
Ten-der mer-cies from a-bove, Change-less from the days of old.
Let not mer-cy be for-got, For Thy good-ness' sake, O Lord.

4 Just and good the Lord abides,
   He His way will sinners show,
   He the meek in justice guides,
   Making them His way to know.

5 Grace and truth shall mark the way
   Where the Lord His own will lead,
   If His Word they still obey
   And His testimonies heed.

47   Be Thou My Judge

PSALM 26   BELIEF C.M.

English Melody

1 Be Thou my Judge, O right-eous Lord, Try Thou mine in - most heart;
2 O search me, Lord, and prove me now; Thy mer-cy I a - dore;
3 My hands I wash in in - no-cence And seek Thine al - tar, Lord,

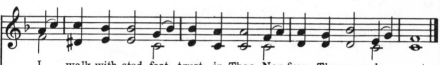

I walk with sted-fast trust in Thee, Nor from Thy ways de - part.
I choose Thy truth to be my guide, And sin - ful ways ab - hor.
That there I may with thank-ful voice Thy won-drous works re - cord.

4 The habitation of Thy house
    Is ever my delight;
    The place where dwells Thy glory, Lord,
    Is lovely in my sight.

5 Let not the judgment fall on me
    For evil men decreed,
    For cruel men and violent,
    Inspired by bribes and greed.

6 But I in mine integrity
    Will humbly walk with Thee;
    O my Redeemer and my Lord,
    Be merciful to me.

7 Redeemed by Thee, I stand secure
    In peace and happiness;
    And in the Church, among Thy saints,
    Jehovah I will bless.

48 Jehovah Is My Light

PSALM 27

MILLENNIUM 6 6 6 6 8 8

English, 1826

1 Je - ho - vah is my light, And my sal - va - tion near;
Who shall my soul af - fright, Or cause my heart to fear?
While God my strength, my life sus - tains,
Se - cure from fear my soul re - mains.

2 When e - vil - do - ers came To make my life their prey,
They stum - bled in their shame And fell in sore dis - may;
Though hosts make war on ev - ery side,
Still fear - less I in God con - fide.

3 My one re - quest has been, And still this prayer I raise,
That I may dwell with - in God's house through all my days,
Je - ho - vah's beau - ty to ad - mire,
And in His tem - ple to in - quire.

4 When troubles round me swell,
  When fears and dangers throng,
Securely I will dwell
  In His pavilion strong;
Within the covert of His tent
He hides me till the storm is spent.

5 Uplifted on a rock
  Above my foes around,
Amid the battle shock
  My song shall still resound;
Then joyful offerings I will bring,
Jehovah's praise my heart shall sing.

49   O Lord, Regard Me When I Cry

PSALM 27   ST. MARGARET 8 8 8 8 6   Albert L. Peace, 1885

1 O Lord, re - gard me when I cry, In mer - cy
2 Hide not Thy face a - far from me, For Thou a -
3 Though earth - ly friends no pit - y take, Yet Thy com -

hear me when I speak; Thou bidst me seek Thy face, and I,
lone canst help af - ford; O cast me not a - way from Thee
pas - sion knows no end; E'en though my fa - ther shall for - sake,

O Lord, with will-ing heart re - ply, Thy face, Lord, will I seek.
Nor let my soul for-sak - en be, My Sav - ior and my Lord.
E'en though my moth-er's love shall break, The Lord will be my Friend.

4 Jehovah, guide me in Thy way,
   And lead me in the path of right;
Give me not up unto my foes,
That rise to multiply my woes
   With false and cruel might.

5 My heart had failed in fear and woe
   Unless in God I had believed,
Assured that He would mercy show
And that my life His grace should
    know;
   Nor was my hope deceived.

6 Fear not, though succor be delayed,
   Still wait for God, and He will hear;
Be strong, nor be thy heart dismayed,
Wait, and the Lord shall bring thee aid,
   Yea, trust and never fear.

50

O Lord, to Thee I Cry

PSALM 28

OWEN S.M.

Adrian Hartog, 1954

Plaintively

1 O Lord, to Thee I cry; Thou art my rock and trust; O
2 O hear me when in prayer Thy fa-vor I en-treat; Hear,

be not si-lent, lest I die And slum-ber in the dust; O
while I lift im-plor-ing hands Be-fore Thy mer-cy-seat; Hear

be not si-lent, lest I die And slum-ber in the dust.
while I lift im-plor-ing hands Be-fore Thy mer-cy-seat.

3 O draw me not away
  With those of evil will;
With them who speak of peace indeed,
  But still are plotting ill.

4 Requite them for their wrong,
  Their evil deeds, O Lord;
O give them then their just desert,
  And to their deeds reward.

5 Thy deeds they disregard,
  Thy handiwork despise;
And therefore Thou wilt cast them
  And never let them rise. [down,

6 But blessed be the Lord
  Who hearkens when I cry;
The Lord, my strength, my help, my
  On Him will I rely. [shield,

7 His help makes glad my heart,
  And songs of praise I sing;
Jehovah is His people's strength,
  The stronghold of their king.

8 Bless Thine inheritance,
  Our Savior be, I pray;
Supply Thou all Thy people's need,
  And be their constant stay.

56

51 Now unto Jehovah, Ye Sons of the Mighty

PSALM 29 ARLES 12 11 12 11

Charles H. Gabriel, 1856-1932

1 Now un-to Je-ho-vah, ye sons of the might-y,
2 The voice of Je-ho-vah, the God of all glo-ry,

All glo-ry and strength and do-min-ion ac-cord;
Rolls o-ver the wa-ters, the thun-ders a-wake;

As-cribe to Him glo-ry, and ren-der Him hon-or,
The voice of Je-ho-vah, ma-jes-tic and might-y,

In beau-ty of ho-li-ness wor-ship the Lord.
Is heard, and the ce-dars of Leb-a-non break.

3 His voice makes the mountains and deserts to tremble,
   Wild beasts are affrighted, the forests laid bare,
And through all creation, His wonderful temple,
   All things He has fashioned His glory declare.

4 The Lord ruled in might at the flood of great waters,
   A King whose dominion is never to cease;
The Lord will give blessing and strength to His people,
   The Lord all His people will comfort with peace.

52   O Lord, by Thee Delivered

PSALM 30

GREENLAND 7 6 7 6 D.

Arranged from J. M. Haydn
in B. Jacob's *National Psalmody*, 1819

Not too slow

1 O   Lord, by Thee de-liv-ered, I   Thee with songs ex - tol;
2 His   ho - ly Name re-mem-ber, Ye saints, Je - ho-vah praise;
3 In   pros-perous days I boast-ed, Un-moved   I   shall re-main;

My   foes Thou hast not suf-fered To   glo-ry o'er   my   fall.
His   an-ger lasts a   mo-ment, His   fa-vor   all   our days;
For, Lord, by Thy good fa-vor   My cause Thou didst main-tain;

O   Lord, my God, I sought Thee, And Thou didst heal and   save;
For   sor-row, like a   pil-grim, May tar-ry for   a   night,
I   soon was sore-ly trou-bled, For Thou didst hide Thy face;

Thou, Lord, from death didst ran-som And keep me from the grave.
But   joy the heart will glad-den When dawns the morn-ing light.
I   cried to Thee, Je - ho-vah, I   sought Je - ho-vah's grace.

4 What profit if I perish,
    If life Thou dost not spare?
Shall dust repeat Thy praises,
    Shall it Thy truth declare?
O Lord, on me have mercy,
    And my petition hear;
That Thou mayst be my Helper,
    In mercy, Lord, appear.

5 My grief is turned to gladness,
    To Thee my thanks I raise,
Who hast removed my sorrow
    And girded me with praise;
And now, no longer silent,
    My heart Thy praise will sing;
O Lord, my God, forever
    My thanks to Thee I bring.

53　　In Thee, O Lord, I Put My Trust

PSALM 31　　　　NAOMI C.M.

Arranged from Hans G. Nägeli
by Lowell Mason, 1836

1 In　　Thee, O Lord, I　put my trust, I　call up - on Thy Name;
2 Bow down Thine ear to　my re-quest, And swift de - liv-erance send;
3 Since Thou my rock and　for-tress art, My Lead - er be, and Guide;

O　save me in　Thy right-eous-ness, Nor let me suf - fer shame.
Be Thou to me　a　rock of strength, A　for-tress to　de - fend.
From all temp-ta - tion res - cue me, Thou dost my strength a - bide.

4 To Thee my spirit I commend;
　Redemption is with Thee,
　O Thou Jehovah, God of truth,
　Who hast delivered me.

5 I hate all those that love the false,
　My trust is in the Lord;
　I will be glad, and joyfully
　Thy mercy will record.

6 For mine affliction Thou hast seen,
　And known my many woes;
　Thou hast not let me be enslaved,
　But freed me from my foes.

7 Show mercy, Lord, to me distressed,
　And send my soul relief;
　My life is spent with bitterness,
　My strength consumed with grief.

8 My life has agéd grown with woe,
　With sighs my years decay;
　Mine eye is worn for very grief:
　I pine and waste away.

9 My foes have made me a reproach,
　My state my neighbors see;
　My friends, appalled at mine approach,
　Turn them about and flee.

10 For I have heard defaming tongues,
　And marked the terror rife,
　When all in league deliberate
　To take away my life.

11 But, Lord, in Thee is all my trust,
　Thou art my God, I cried;
　My life, my times are in Thy hand,
　I in Thy strength confide.

54 How Great the Goodness Kept in Store

PSALM 31

ARIEL 8 8 6 D.

Arranged from Mozart
by Lowell Mason, 1836

1 How great the good - ness kept in store For
2 Se - cured by Thine un - fail - ing grace, In

those who fear Thee and a - dore   In   meek hu - mil - i - ty.
Thee they find a hid-ing-place   When foes their plots de - vise;

How great the deeds with mer-cy fraught Which o - pen - ly   Thy
A   sure re-treat Thou wilt pre-pare,   And keep them safe - ly

hand has wrought For those who trust in Thee, For those who trust in Thee.
shel-tered there, When strife of tongues shall rise, When strife of tongues shall rise.

3 Blest be the Lord, for He has showed,
While giving me a safe abode,
His love beyond compare;
Although His face He seemed to hide,
He ever heard me when I cried,
And made my wants His care.

4 Ye saints, Jehovah love and serve,
For He the faithful will preserve,
And shield from men of pride;
Be strong, and let your hearts be brave,
All ye that wait for Him to save,
In God the Lord confide.

How Blest Is He Whose Trespass

RUTHERFORD 7 6 7 6 D.

Arranged from Chrétien Urhan
by E. F. Rimbault, 1867

1 How blest is he whose tres-pass Has free-ly been for-given,
2 While I kept guilt-y si-lence My strength was spent with grief,
3 So let the god-ly seek Thee In times when Thou art near;

Whose sin is whol-ly cov-ered Be-fore the sight of heaven.
Thy hand was heav-y on me, My soul found no re-lief;
No whelm-ing floods shall reach them, Nor cause their hearts to fear.

Blest he to whom Je-ho-vah Will not im-pute his sin,
But when I owned my tres-pass, My sin hid not from Thee,
In Thee, O Lord, I hide me, Thou sav-est me from ill,

Who has a guile-less spir-it, Whose heart is true with-in.
When I con-fessed trans-gres-sion, Then Thou for-gav-est me.
And songs of Thy sal-va-tion My heart with rap-ture thrill.

4 I graciously will teach thee
    The way that thou shalt go,
And with Mine eye upon thee
    My counsel make thee know.
But be ye not unruly,
    Or slow to understand,
Be not perverse, but willing
    To heed My wise command.

5 The sorrows of the wicked
    In number shall abound,
But those that trust Jehovah,
    His mercy shall surround.
Then in the Lord be joyful,
    In song lift up your voice;
Be glad in God, ye righteous,
    Rejoice, ye saints, rejoice.

Jehovah from His Throne on High

GREITER 8 8 6   8 8 6 D.

Matthaeus Greiter, 1526
Harmonized by H. W. Wooldridge, c. 1899.

1 Je-ho-vah from His throne on high Looks down with clear and search-ing eye On

all that dwell be-low; . . . And He that fash-ioned heart and mind Looks

ev - er down on all man-kind, The works of men to know . . . . Not

hu-man strength or might-y hosts, Not charg-ing steeds or war-like boasts Can

Jehovah from His Throne on High

PSALM 33

save from o-ver-throw; . . . . But God will save from death and shame All

those who fear and trust His Name, And they no want shall know. . . .

2 His eye is on all those who fear;
To those who hope, the Lord is near
According to His word.
Death cannot touch those in His hand,
Nor famine conquer in the land;
We wait upon the Lord.
Our hope is on Jehovah stayed,
In Him our hearts are joyful made,
Our help and shield is He.
Our trust is in His holy Name,
Thy mercy, Lord, in faith we claim,
As we have hoped in Thee.

Text adapted by Marie Post

Ye Righteous, in the Lord Rejoice

PSALM 33　　FRANCES 8 8 6 D.

James McGranahan, 1840-1907

1 Ye right-eous, in the Lord re-joice; 'Tis come-ly that with joy-ful voice
2 For up-right is Je-ho-vah's word, And all the do-ings of the Lord
3 Je-ho-vah speaks, the heavens ap-pear; He breathes, and, lo, each shin-ing sphere

God's saints His Name should praise. With harp and hymn of glad-ness sing,
In jus-tice have their birth. In judg-ment and in deeds of right
In splen-dor stands ar-rayed. He rolls the wat-ers heap on heap,

Your gift of sweet-est mu-sic bring, To Him a new song raise.
The Lord for-ev-er takes de-light, His good-ness fills the earth.
He stores a-way the might-y deep In gar-ners for it made.

4 Let all the earth Jehovah fear,
　Let all that dwell both far and near
　　In awe before Him stand;
　For, lo, He spake and it was done,
　And all, with sovereign power begun,
　　Stood fast at His command.

5 He makes the nations' counsels vain,
　The plans the peoples would maintain
　　Are thwarted by His hand.
　Jehovah's counsel stands secure,
　His purposes of heart endure,
　　Forevermore they stand.

6 O truly is the nation blest
　　Whose God, before the world confessed,
　　　Jehovah is alone;
　　And blest the people is whom He
　　Has made His heritage to be,
　　　And chosen for His own.

The Lord I Will at All Times Bless

PSALM 34

EUPHEMIA C.M.D.

Benjamin C. Unseld

1 The Lord I will at all times bless, In praise my mouth em-ploy;
2 We looked to Him and light re-ceived, A-shamed we shall not be;
3 O taste and see that God is good To all that seek His face;

My soul shall in Je - ho - vah boast, The meek shall hear with joy.
Our hum - ble cry Je - ho - vah heard, From trou - ble set us free.
Yea, blest the man that trusts in Him, Con - fid - ing in His grace.

O mag - ni - fy the Lord with me, Let us ex - alt His Name;
The an - gel of the Lord en-camps A - round a-bout His own,
O fear the Lord, all ye His saints; No want shall bring dis-tress;

When in dis-tress on Him I called, He to my res-cue came.
De - liv-ers them from all their foes, Lest they be o - ver - thrown.
The li-ons young may pine for food, The saints all good pos-sess.

59   Ye Children, Come, Give Ear to Me

PSALM 34   MANOAH C.M.

Henry W. Greatorex's *Collection*, 1851

1 Ye chil - dren, come, give ear to me And learn Je - ho - vah's fear, He who would long and hap - py live, Let him my coun - sel hear.

2 Re - strain thy lips from speak - ing guile, From wick - ed speech de - part, From e - vil turn and do the good, Seek peace with all thy heart.

Ye Children, Come, Give Ear to Me

PSALM 34

3 Jehovah's eyes are on the just,
    He hearkens to their cry;
  Against the wicked sets His face;
    Their very name shall die.

4 He hears the righteous when they cry,
    From trouble sets them free;
  He saves the broken-hearted ones
    And those who contrite be.

5 The Lord may suffer many griefs
    Upon the just to fall,
  But He will bring them safely through,
    Delivering them from all.

6 By evil are the evil slain,
    And they that hate the just;
  But all His servants God redeems,
    And safe in Him they trust.

60   Be Thou My Helper in the Strife

PSALM 35

He Leadeth Me   L.M.D.

William B. Bradbury, 1864

1 Be Thou my Help-er in the strife, O Lord, my strong De -
2 A-shamed, con-found-ed let them be Who seek my ru - in

fend - er be; Thy might - y shield pro - tect my life,
and dis - grace; O let Thine an - gel fight for me,

Thy spear con - front the en - e-my. A - mid the con - flict,
And drive my foes be - fore his face. With-out a cause my

O my Lord, Thy pre-cious prom-ise let me hear, The faith-ful,
life they sought, With-out a cause their plots they laid; Them-selves with-

Be Thou My Helper in the Strife

PSALM 35

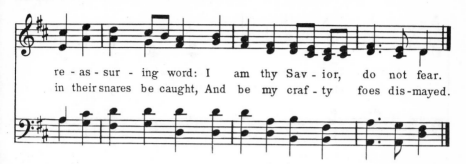

re - as - sur - ing word: I am thy Sav - ior, do not fear.
in their snares be caught, And be my craf - ty foes dis - mayed.

3 My soul is joyful in the Lord,
  In His salvation I rejoice;
To Him my heart will praise accord
  And bless His name with thank-
    ful voice.
For who, O Lord, is like to Thee,
  Defender of the poor and meek?
The needy Thy salvation see
  When mighty foes their ruin seek.

4 Unrighteous witnesses have stood
  And told of crimes beyond belief;
Returning evil for my good,
  They overwhelm my soul with
    grief.
When in affliction they were sad,
  I wept and made their grief my
    own;
But in my trouble they are glad
  And strive that I may be o'er-
    thrown.

5 O Lord, how long wilt Thou delay?
  My soul for Thy salvation waits;
My thankfulness I will display
  Amid the crowds that throng Thy
    gates.
Let not my enemies rejoice
  And wrongfully exult o'er me;
They speak not peace, but lift their
    voice
  To trouble those that peaceful be.

6 My foes with joy my woes survey,
  But Thou, O Lord, hast seen it
O be no longer far away,   [all;
  Nor silent when on Thee I call.
O haste to my deliverance now,
  O Lord, my righteous cause main-
    tain;
My Lord and God alone art Thou;
  Awake, and make Thy justice
    plain.

7 O Lord my God, I look to Thee,
  Be Thou my righteous Judge, I
    pray;
Let not my foes exult o'er me
  And laugh with joy at my dismay.
With shame and trouble those
    requite
  Who would my righteous cause
    destroy;
But those who in the good delight,
  Let them be glad and shout for
    joy.

8 Yea, let the Lord be magnified,
  Because Thy servants Thou dost
    bless;
And I, from morn till eventide,
  Will daily praise Thy righteous-
    ness.
My soul is joyful in the Lord,
  In His salvation I rejoice;
To Him my heart will praise accord
  And bless His Name with thank-
    ful voice.

The Trespass of the Wicked Man

LAMBETH C.M.

William Schulthes, 1871

1 The tres - pass of the wick - ed man
2 He cher - ish - es the emp - ty hope,

Most plain - ly tes - ti - fies That fear of God's
Al - though his sin be great, It nev - er shall

most ho - ly Name Is not be - fore his eyes.
be brought to light And viewed with right - eous hate.

3 The words he utters with his mouth
  Are wickedness and lies;
  He keeps himself from doing good,
  And ceases to be wise.

4 While on his bed his thought he gives
  To planning wickedness;
  He sets himself in evil ways,
  He shuns not to transgress.

62   Thy Mercy and Thy Truth, O Lord

PSALM 36   CADDO C.M.   William B. Bradbury, 1816-1868

1 Thy mer - cy and Thy truth, O Lord, Tran-
2 Lord, Thou pre - serv - est man and beast. Since
3 With the a - bun - dance of Thy house We

scend the loft - y sky; Thy judg-ments are a
Thou art ev - er kind, Be - neath the shad - ow
shall be sat - is - fied; From riv - ers of un-

might - y deep, And as the moun-tains high.
of Thy wings We may a ref - uge find.
fail - ing joy Our thirst shall be sup - plied.

4 The fountain of eternal life
   Is found alone with Thee,
  And in the brightness of Thy light
   We clearly light shall see.

5 From those that know Thee may Thy love
   And mercy ne'er depart,
  And may Thy justice still protect
   And bless the upright heart.

6 The workers of iniquity
   Are fallen utterly;
  They shall not triumph in their pride,
   Or drive my soul from Thee.

63   Fret Not Thyself

PSALM 37

JOSEPHINE 8 8 6 D.

Ernest R. Kroeger

1 Fret not thy-self, nor en-vious be, When wick-ed work-ers thou shalt see,
2 Trust in the Lord and still do well, With-in the land se-cure-ly dwell,
3 Yea, to the Lord thy way is known; Con-fide in Him who on the throne

Who pros-per in their way; For like the grass they per-ish soon,
Feed on His faith-ful-ness; De-light thee al - so in the Lord,
A - bides in power di - vine; Thy right-eous-ness He shall dis-play;

And, like the herb cut down at noon, They with-er in a day.
And to thy heart He will ac-cord The good it would pos-sess.
Re - splend-ent as the light of day, It shall un-cloud-ed shine.

4 Rest in the Lord and be thou still,
  With patience wait His holy will,
    Enduring to the end.
  Fret not though sinners' gains increase;
  Forsake thy wrath, from anger cease;
    It will to evil tend.

5 The evil-doer soon shall die,
  But those that on the Lord rely
    Shall all the land obtain.
  A little while and thou shalt see
  That wicked men cut off shall be,
    They shall be sought in vain.

6 Yea, thou shalt soon consider well
  The place where they were wont to
    And it shall not be found;   [dwell,
  But saints shall all the land possess,
  And find delight and happiness
    Where fruits of peace abound.

7 The vile may plot against the just
  Who in the Lord Jehovah trust,
    But God will scorn them all;
  The Lord their coming day shall see,
  When broken all their power shall be,
    And ruin on them fall.

A Little That the Righteous Hold

RAMOTH 8 8 6 D.

English Melody

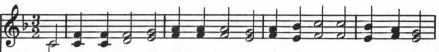

1 A lit - tle that the right-eous hold Is bet-ter than the wealth un-told
2 He knows the days the per-fect live, To them a her- i - tage will give
3 Al- though the wick-ed pros-pered seem, At last they van-ish like a dream

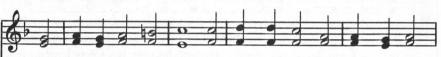

Of man-y wick - ed men; De-stroyed shall be their arm of pride,
Which ev- er shall a - bide; In e - vil times no shame they know,
And per-ish in a day; Je - ho - vah's foes shall soon ap-pear

But they who in the Lord con-fide Shall be up-hold - en then..
And in the days of fam - ine's woe They shall be sat - is - fied.
Like fields once fair, now brown and sere; Like smoke they fade a - way.

4 They borrow oft and pay not back;
But righteous men do nothing lack,
And give with gracious hand;
Those cursed by Him shall be destroyed,
But such as have His grace enjoyed,
They shall possess the land.

65   The Good Man's Steps Are Led Aright

PSALM 37   PRESSLY 8 8 6 D.

Charles H. Gabriel, 1856-1932

1 The good man's steps are led a-right, His way is pleas-ing in God's sight,
2 Though I am old who young have been, No saint have I for-sak-en seen,
3 De - part from e - vil, do thou well, And ev - er-more se-cure - ly dwell;

Es - tab-lished it shall stand; He shall not per-ish though he fall,
Nor yet his home in need; He ev - er lends in gra-cious ways,
Je - ho - vah loves the right. His faith-ful-ness His saints have proved,

The might - y Lord, who rules o'er all, Up-holds him with His hand.
His life true char - i - ty dis-plays, His sons are blest in - deed.
For - ev - er they shall stand un-moved, But sin-ners God will smite.

4 The righteous, through His favoring
  Shall yet inherit all the land   [hand,
    And dwell therein for aye;
  He talks of wisdom and of right,
  In God's pure law is his delight,
    His steps go not astray.

5 The wicked, watching for their prey,
  Desire the righteous man to slay,
    But God is on his side;
  He will not leave him in their hands,
  Nor count him guilty when he stands
    In judgment to be tried.

6 Wait on the Lord and keep His way;
  He will exalt thee, nor delay
    To give the land to thee;
  And when the wicked are cut off,
  The wicked who against thee scoff,
    Their judgment thou shalt see.

7 The wicked in great power are seen,
  Like spreading tree with foliage green
    That grows in native ground.
  I looked again, they were no more;
  I sought the men so proud before,
    But they could not be found.

8 Mark thou the upright day by day,
  Behold the perfect in his way,
    His journey ends in peace.
  Destroyed at once shall rebels be;
  Cut off from all posterity,
    Their very name shall cease.

9 Salvation is from God alone,   [known
  Whom as their covert saints have
    When by sore troubles tried;
  The Lord, who helped in troubles past,
  Will save them to the very last,
    For they in Him confide.

66   In Thy Wrath and Hot Displeasure

PSALM 38   St. Sylvester 8 7 8 7

John B. Dykes, 1862

1 In   Thy wrath and hot dis - pleas-ure,   Chas-ten not Thy ser-vant, Lord;
2 Heav-y   is   my trib-u - la - tion,   Sore my pun-ish-ment has been;
3 With my bur-den of trans-gres-sion   Heav-y   la-den, o - ver-borne,

Let   Thy mer-cy, with-out meas-ure,   Help and peace to me af - ford.
Bro - ken by Thine in - dig-na - tion,   I   am trou-bled by my   sin.
Hum-bled low I make con - fes - sion,   For   my   fol - ly now I   mourn.

4 Weak and wounded, I implore Thee:
    Lord, to me Thy mercy show;
  All my prayer is now before Thee,
    All my trouble Thou dost know.

5 Darkness gathers, foes assail me,
    But I answer not a word;
  All my friends desert and fail me,
    Only Thou my cry hast heard.

6 Lord, in Thee am I confiding;
    Thou wilt answer when I call,
  Lest my foes, the good deriding,
    Triumph in Thy servant's fall.

7 I am prone to halt and stumble,
    Grief and sorrow dwell within,
  Shame and guilt my spirit humble,
    I am sorry for my sin.

8 Foes about my soul are closing,
    Full of hatred, false, and strong;
  Choosing good, I find opposing
    All who love and do the wrong.

9 Lord, my God, do not forsake me,
    Let me know that Thou art near,
  Under Thy protection take me,
    As my Savior now appear.

67 Lord, in Thy Wrath Rebuke Me Not

PSALM 38

HARMINE L.M.

Hanna Datema Van Houten, 1954

1 Lord, in Thy wrath re - buke me not, For Thy sharp
2 Thine an - ger wears my flesh a - way, And in my
3 Such are my wounds, they will not heal, Cor - rupt - ed

ar - rows wound me sore; Thy just dis-pleas - ure wax - eth
bones I feel my sin. Yea, mine in - iq - ui - ties to -
by my fool - ish - ness; Bowed down up - on the earth I

hot, And my sad heart can bear no more.
day De - prive my soul of strength with - in.
feel The pangs of my com - plete dis - tress.

4 In every limb lurks foul disease,
    Loathsome my flesh in every part;
And I do groan because of these
    Disquietnesses in my heart.

5 I know, O Lord, that my desire,
    My griefs and groans are known to Thee;
My heart has lost its strength and fire;
    My eyes are blind: I cannot see.

Lord, in Thy Wrath Rebuke Me Not

PSALM 38

6 My kinsman shuns me, and my friend,
    Acquaintances stand off afar;
  And they who seek my life to end
    Lay snares of words in slanderous war.

7 But I am as a man whose ear
    Is deaf, whose mouth continues dumb;
  And what they say, I cannot hear,
    Nor from my lips reproaches come.

8 In Thee alone I hope, O Lord,
    And Thou, O Lord, wilt hear my cry,
  No triumph to my foes afford,
    Who would rejoice if I should die.

9 For they do magnify my fault,
    And my defeat is all their care;
  But my own sorrow bids me halt,
    My sin and guilt I now declare.

10 Yet these my foes are strong in fight,
    And they who hate me grow apace;
  Evil for good they would requite,
    While I pursue the way of grace.

11 Forsake me not, O Lord, my God,
    Be not, O Lord, far off from me,
  O haste to my deliverance,
    And let me Thy salvation see.

Richard Church, Alt.

Teach Me the Measure of My Days

PSALM 39

NORTHSIDE C.M.

Dick L. Van Halsema, 1954

1 Teach me the meas-ure of my days, Thou Ma-ker of my frame;
2 A span is all that we can boast; How short, how fleet our time!
3 See the vain race of mor-tals move Like shad-ows on the plain:

I would sur-vey life's nar-row space, And learn how frail I am.
Man is but van - i - ty and dust, In all his flower and prime.
They rage and strive, de-sire and love, But all their noise is vain.

4 Some walk in honor's gaudy show,
    Some dig for golden ore:
 They toil for heirs they know not who,
    And straight are seen no more.

5 What should I wish or wait for then,
    From creatures, earth, or dust?
 They make our expectations vain,
    And disappoint our trust.

6 Now I forbid my carnal hope,
    My fond desires recall;
 My mortal interest I give up,
    And make my God my all.

69   With Firm Resolve I Held My Peace

PSALM 39   BERA L.M.   John E. Gould, 1849

1 With firm re-solve I held my peace And spake not ei-ther bad or good,
2 While I was dumb my grief was stirred, My heart grew hot with thought sup-pressed;
3 Make me, O Lord, to know my end, Teach me the meas-ure of my days,

Lest I should ut-ter sin-ful thoughts While wick-ed men be-fore me stood.
The while I mused the fire in-creased, Then to the Lord I made re-quest.
That I may know how frail I am And turn from pride and sin-ful ways.

4 My time is nothing in Thy sight,
  Behold, my days are but a span;
Yea, truly, at his best estate,
  A breath, a fleeting breath, is man.

5 Man's life is passed in vain desire
  If troubled years be spent for gain;
He knows not whose his wealth shall be,
  And all his toil is but in vain.

6 And now, O Lord, what wait I for?
  I have no hope except in Thee;
Let not ungodly men reproach,
  From all transgression set me free.

7 Because Thou didst it I was dumb,
  I spoke no word of rash complaint;
Remove Thy stroke away from me,
  Beneath Thy chastisement I faint.

8 When Thou for his iniquity
  Rebukest and correctest man,
His beauty is consumed away; [plan.
  How weak his strength, how vain his

9 Lord, hear my prayer, regard my cry;
  I weep; be Thou my Comforter.
I am a stranger here below,
  A pilgrim as my fathers were.

10 O spare me, Lord, avert Thy wrath,
  Deal gently with me, I implore,
That I may yet recover strength
  Ere I go hence and be no more.

Thy Tender Mercies, O My Lord

RUTH C.M.D.

W. Irving Hartshorn

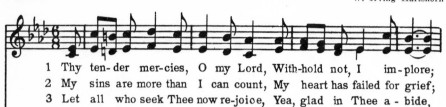

1 Thy ten-der mer-cies, O my Lord, With-hold not, I im-plore;
2 My sins are more than I can count, My heart has failed for grief;
3 Let all who seek Thee now re-joice, Yea, glad in Thee a - bide,

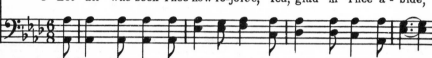

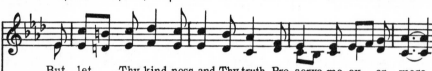

But let Thy kind-ness and Thy truth Pre-serve me ev - er - more.
Be pleased, O Lord, to res-cue me, O haste to my re - lief.
And, lov - ing Thy sal-va-tion, say, The Lord be mag-ni - fied.

For count-less ills have com-passed me, My sin - ful deeds a - rise;
Be those who seek to hurt my soul Dis-mayed and put to flight,
My low - ly state and bit - ter need The Lord has not for-got;

Yea, they have o - ver-tak-en me; I dare not raise my eyes.
And they them-selves be put to shame Who in my woe de - light.
Thou art my Sav - ior and my help, Come, Lord, and tar-ry not.

71   I Waited for the Lord Most High

PSALM 40

DUNSTAN 8 8 8 6 8 6

Joseph Barnby, 1838-1896

1 I wait-ed for the Lord Most High, And He in-clined to hear my cry;
2 A new and joy-ful song of praise He taught my thank-ful heart to raise;
3 O Lord my God, how man-i - fold Thy won-drous works which I be-hold,

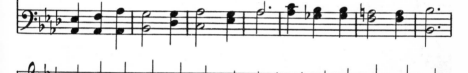

He took me from de-struc-tion's pit And from the mir - y clay;
And man-y, see - ing me re-stored, Shall fear the Lord and trust;
And all Thy lov - ing, gra-cious thought Thou hast be-stowed on man;

Up - on a rock He set my feet, And sted-fast made my way.
And blest are they that trust the Lord, The hum-ble and the just.
To count Thy mer-cies I have sought, But bound-less is their span.

4 Not sacrifice delights the Lord,
    But he who hears and keeps His Word;
      Thou gavest me to hear Thy will,
      Thy law is in my heart;
      I come the Scripture to fulfill,
      Glad tidings to impart.

72

Before Thy People I Confess

FLEMMING 8 8 8 6 8 6

Arranged from F. F. Flemming, 1811

1 Be - fore Thy peo - ple I con - fess
2 With-hold not Thou Thy grace from me,

The won - ders of Thy right - eous - ness;
O Lord, Thy mer - cy let me see,

Thou know - est, Lord, that I have made
To me Thy lov - ing - kind - ness show,

Thy great sal - va - tion known, Thy truth and faith - ful -
Thy truth be still my stay; Let them pre - serve me

Before Thy People I Confess

PSALM 40

ness   dis - played,   Thy   lov - ing - kind - ness   shown.
where   I   go,   And   keep   me   ev - ery   day.

3 Let all who seek to see Thy face
    Be glad and joyful in Thy grace;
        Let those who Thy salvation love
            Forevermore proclaim:
        O praise the Lord who dwells above,
            And magnify His Name.

4 Although I poor and needy be,
    The Lord in love takes thought for me;
        Thou art my help in time of need,
            My Savior, Lord, art Thou;
        Then, O my God, I pray, I plead:
            Stay not, but save me now.

5 A new and joyful song of praise
    He taught my thankful heart to raise;
        And many, seeing me restored,
            Shall fear the Lord and trust;
        And blest are they that trust the Lord,
            The humble and the just.

73

How Blest the Man Who Thoughtfully

DEDEKAM C.M.D.

Sophie Dedekam

1 How blest the man who thought-ful-ly The poor and weak be-friends;
2 Up - on the bed of suf - fer-ing Je - ho-vah will sus-tain,

De - liv-erance in the e-vil day To him Je - ho - vah sends.
And in his sick-ness God will soothe The wea - ri - ness and pain.

The Lord will keep him, guard his life, On earth he shall be blest;
O Lord, to Thee my cry as-cends, Let me Thy mer-cy see;

The Lord will not sur-ren-der him By foes to be dis - tressed.
Heal Thou my soul, for I have sinned, I have of-fend - ed Thee.

How Blest the Man Who Thoughtfully

PSALM 41

3 My enemies against me speak,
  And they my life have scorned;
 They wish my name to pass away,
  Unhonored and unmourned.
 My foe, deceitful, visits me,
  By seeming kindness led,
 His heart intent on gathering
  Some hurtful news to spread.

4 My foes, together whispering,
  Their evil plans devise;
 Disease, they say, cleaves fast to him,
  Laid low, he shall not rise.
 Yea, he who was my chosen friend,
  In whom I put my trust,
 Who ate my bread, now turns in wrath
  To crush me in the dust.

5 Do Thou, Jehovah, show me grace,
  And raise me up again,
 That I with justice may requite
  These base and wicked men.
 By this I know assuredly
  That I am loved by Thee,
 Because my foe does not exult
  In triumph over me.

6 And as for me, in uprightness
  Thou dost uphold me well,
 And settest me before Thy face
  Forevermore to dwell.
 Blest be Jehovah, Israel's God
  Forevermore. Amen.
 Let age to age eternally
  Repeat His praise. Amen.

As the Hart, About to Falter

THIRSTING 8 7 8 7 7 7 8 8

Louis Bourgeois, 1551
Harmony from De Vries *Koraalboek*
Adapted by Henry Bruinsma, 1946

1 As the hart, a-bout to fal-ter, In its trem-bling ag-o-ny,
2 Bit-ter tears of lam-en-ta-tion Are my food by night and day;
3 O my soul, why art thou griev-ing, Why dis-qui-et-ed in me?

Pant-eth for the brooks of wa-ter, So my soul doth pant for Thee.
In my deep hu-mil-i-a-tion, Where is now thy God? they say.
Hope in God, thy faith re-triev-ing; Let Him still thy ref-uge be.

Yea, a-thirst for Thee I cry; God of life, O when shall I
Yea, my soul doth melt in me, When I bring to mem-o-ry
I shall yet ex-tol His grace For the com-fort of His face;

Come a-gain to stand be-fore Thee In Thy tem-ple, and a-dore Thee?
How of yore I did as-sem-ble With the joy-ful in Thy tem-ple.
He has ev-er turned my sor-row In-to glad-ness on the mor-row.

As the Hart, About to Falter

4 From the land beyond the Jordan
    I bewail my misery;
From the foothills of Mount Hermon,
    O my God, I think of Thee.
As the waters plunge and leap,
Deep re-echoes unto deep;
All Thy waves and billows roaring
O'er my troubled soul are pouring.

5 But the Lord will send salvation,
    And by day His love provide;
He shall be mine exultation,
    And my song at eventide.
On His praise e'en in the night
I will ponder with delight,
And in prayer, transcending distance,
Seek the God of my existence.

6 I will say to God, my fortress:
    Why hast Thou forsaken me?
Why go I about in sadness
    For my foes' dread tyranny?
Their rebukes and scoffing words
Pierce my bones as pointed swords,
As they say with proud defiance:
Where is God, thy soul's reliance?

7 O my soul, why art thou grieving;
    Why disquieted in me?
Hope in God, thy faith retrieving;
    He will still thy refuge be.
I shall yet through all my days
Give to Him my thankful praise;
God, who will from shame deliver,
Is my God, my rock, forever.

Dewey Westra, 1931

75   As Thirsts the Hart for Water Brooks

PSALM 42   Baca L.M., 5 Lines

William B. Bradbury, 1816-1868

1 As thirsts the hart for wa - ter brooks, So thirsts my
2 Far from the courts of God, my tears Have been my
3 With grief I think of days gone by, When oft I

soul, O God, for Thee; It seeks for God, and ev - er looks And longs the
food by night and day, While con-stant-ly with bit-ter sneers, Where is thy
trod the hal-lowed way To Zi - on, prais-ing God on high With throngs who

liv - ing God to see, And longs the liv - ing God to see.
God? the scoff-ers say, Where is thy God? the scoff-ers say.
kept the ho - ly day, With throngs who kept the ho - ly day.

4 O why art thou cast down, my soul,

And why so troubled shouldst thou be?

Hope thou in God, and Him extol,

Who gives His saving help to me.

76 As Pants the Hart for Streams

PSALM 42 FELIX (RAYNOLDS) 11 10 11 10

Arranged from
Felix Mendelssohn, 1809-1847

1 As pants the hart for streams of liv-ing wa-ter, So longs my
2 O Lord my God, o'er-whelmed in deep af-flic-tion, Far from Thy
3 Thou wilt com-mand Thy ser-vant's con-so-la-tion, Thy lov-ing-

soul, O liv-ing God, for Thee; I thirst for Thee, for Thee my
rest, to Thee I lift my soul; Deep calls to deep and storms of
kind-ness yet shall cheer my day, And in the night Thy song shall

heart is yearn-ing; When shall I come Thy gra-cious face to see?
trou-ble thun-der, While o'er my head the waves and bil-lows roll.
be my com-fort; God of my life, to Thee I still will pray.

4 Why, O my soul, art thou cast down within me,

Why art thou troubled and oppressed with grief?

Hope thou in God, the God of thy salvation,

Hope, and thy God will surely send relief.

Send Forth, O Lord of My Salvation

PSALM 43

HOLY HILL 9 8 9 9 8 6

Louis Bourgeois, 1543
Harmony from De Vries *Koraalboek*
Adapted by Henry Bruinsma, 1946

1 Send forth, O Lord of my sal - va - tion,
2 Then at Thy sa - cred al - tar bend - ing,

Thy light and truth to be my guide;
My heart to God in prayer I'll raise.

O let their rays, in my pri - va - tion,
With harp and voice, in wor - ship blend - ing,

Lead me un - to Thy hab - i - ta - tion,
Thy courts re - sound; while psalms, as - cend - ing

Send Forth, O Lord of My Salvation

PSALM 43

Where 'neath Thy wing I'll be sup - plied
To God, my high - est joy, bring praise

With grace Thou wilt pro - vide.
For all His won - drous ways.

3 My soul, why art thou sad and grieving?
  Why so oppressed with anxious care?
  Hope thou in God! His Word believing,
  Thou shalt behold His face, receiving
    The blessings of His countenance fair—
    What bliss beyond compare!

William Kuipers, 1931

78 Judge Me, God of My Salvation

PSALM 43   AMARA 8 7 8 7, with Refrain

William O. Perkins

1 Judge me, God of my sal-va-tion, Plead my cause, for Thee I trust;
2 On Thy strength a-lone re-ly-ing, Why am I cast off by Thee,

Hear my ear-nest sup-pli-ca-tion, Save me from my foes un-just.
In my help-less sor-row sigh-ing, While the foe op-press-es me?

REFRAIN

O my soul, why art thou griev-ing? What dis-qui-ets and dis-mays?

Hope in God; His help re-ceiv-ing, I shall yet my Sav-ior praise.

3 Light and truth, my way attending,
　Send Thou forth to be my guide,
Till Thy holy mount ascending,
　I within Thy house abide.

4 At Thy sacred altar bending,
　God, my God, my boundless joy,
Harp and voice, in worship blending,
　For Thy praise will I employ.

79 Send Out Thy Light and Thy Truth

PSALM 43

Lux Fiat 11 10 11 10 10 10

Charles F. Gounod, 1818-1893

1 Send out Thy light and Thy truth, let them lead me;   O let them
2 Lead me, O Lord, in the way ev - er - last-ing;   O lead and

bring me to Thy ho - ly hill. Send out Thy light and Thy truth, let them
guide me to Thy ho - ly hill. Lead me, O Lord, in the way ev - er -

lead me;   O let them bring me to Thy ho - ly hill.   O   let them
last - ing;   O lead and guide me to Thy ho - ly hill.   O   do Thou

lead me, O let them lead me, O let them bring me to Thy ho - ly hill.
lead me, O do Thou guide me, O lead and guide me to Thy ho - ly hill.

80

O God, We Have Heard

PSALM 44

RESIGNATION 11 11 11 11

Anonymous

(Alternate tune: SANKEY, No. 136)

1 O God, we have heard and our fa - thers have told
2 They gained not the land by the edge of the sword,
3 Com - mand, and Thy word shall de - liv - er - ance bring,

What won - ders Thou didst in the great days of old;
Their own arm to them could no safe - ty af - ford,
O God, to Thy cho - sen, for Thou art our King;

The na - tions were crushed and ex - pelled by Thy hand,
But Thy right hand saved, and the light of Thy face,
Through Thee we will sure - ly de - feat all our foes,

Cast out that Thy peo - ple might dwell in their land.
Be - cause of Thy fa - vor and won - der - ful grace.
Through Thy Name will tri - umph o'er those that op - pose.

O God, We Have Heard

PSALM 44

4 No trust will I place in my strength to defend,
   Nor yet on my sword as a safeguard depend;
   In Thee, who hast saved us and put them to shame,
   We boast all the day, ever praising Thy Name.

5 Thou, Lord, hast forsaken, to shame brought our boasts;
   No more to the field dost Thou go with our hosts;
   Thou turnest us back from the foe in dismay,
   And spoilers who hate us have made us their prey.

6 Like sheep to the slaughter Thy people are given,
   Dispersed through the nations, afar we are driven;
   Thou sellest Thy people to strangers for naught,
   Their price to Thy treasure no increase has brought.

7 Thou makest our neighbors reproach us in pride,
   And those that are near us to scoff and deride;
   A byword the nations have made of our name,
   With scorn and derision they put us to shame.

8 Yea, all the day long I behold my disgrace,
   And covered am I with confusion of face;
   The voice of blasphemers and scoffers I hear,
   The foe and avenger against me appear.

9 All this have we suffered, and never forgot
   To serve Thee, Jehovah, nor falsely have wrought;
   Our heart is not turned and our steps have not strayed,
   Though crushed amid ruins and under death's shade.

God, Who Omniscient Art

PSALM 44

CUTTING 6 6 4 6 6 6 4

William F. Sherwin, 1826-1888

1 God, who om-nis-cient art, Could we from
2 Sore-ly op-pressed are we, Naught but af-
3 Hum-bled un-to the dust, In Thee a-

Thee de-part, Hide aught from Thee, Thou, Lord, wouldst
flic-tion see, O Lord, a-wake! Lord, from Thy
lone we trust; Thy love we plead. Ref-uge in

search it out, Know all our sin and doubt,
sleep a-rise, No long-er close Thine eyes;
Thee to take, Lord, for Thy mer-cy's sake,

Search-ing with-in, with-out, Our se-crets see.
See how we are de-spised, All for Thy sake.
Our hum-ble plea we make: Thy help we need.

Mrs. John Folkerts

82 · A Goodly Theme Is Mine

PSALM 45

FAIRFIELD S.M.D.

Peter La Trobe, 1795-1863

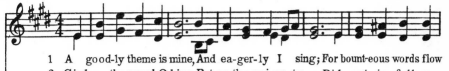

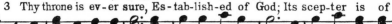

1 A good-ly theme is mine, And ea-ger-ly I sing; For bount-eous words flow
2 Gird on thy sword, O king, Put on thy maj-es-ty; Ride out in full re-
3 Thy throne is ev-er sure, Es-tab-lish-ed of God; Its scep-ter is of

from my lips As I sa-lute the king. Su-preme-ly fair he is, In
ga - li - a, And rich-est pan-o - ply. Tri-umph in ve - ry truth, In
right-eous-ness, Of eq-ui - ty its rod. Thou lov-est per-fect right, Hat-

beau-ty peer-less he; For him the fa-vor of the Lord Doth grace e-ter-nal-ly.
meek-ness and in right, Let fly the ar-rows of re-venge, And van-quish in thy might.
est in-iq-ui-ty; There-fore with oil of fes-tive joy The Lord a-noint-ed thee.

4 Thy garments breathe of myrrh,
    Of spices rich and rare;
Glad strains of joyous music ring
    Throughout thy palace fair.
Amid thy glorious train
    King's daughters waiting stand,
And on thy right the queen adorned
    In gold from Ophir land.

5 O royal bride, give heed,
    This king is now thy lord;
Forsake thy former loyalties,
    Full fealty accord.
Thy beauty and thy grace
    Will then delight the king;
And they to thee, since thou art his,
    Their precious gifts will bring.

6 Enthroned in royal state
    All glorious thou shalt dwell, [gold.
With garments fair, inwrought with
    His bride he loveth well.
And they who honor thee
    Shall in thy train attend,
And to the palace of the king
    Shall joyfully ascend.

7 Then in thy father's place,
    The sons of royal birth
Thou wilt endow with regal gifts
    As princes of the earth.
Thy name shall be proclaimed
    Through all succeeding days,
And all the peoples everywhere
    Shall give thee endless praise.

O Royal Bride, Give Heed

PSALM 45

GERAR S.M.

Lowell Mason, 1792-1872

1 O roy - al bride, give heed, And to my words at - tend; For Christ the King for - sake the world And ev - ery for - mer friend.

2 Thy beau - ty and thy grace Shall then de - light the King; He on - ly is thy right - ful Lord, To Him thy wor - ship bring.

3 To thee, since thou art His, Great hon - or shall be shown; The rich shall bring their gifts to thee, Thy glo - ry they shall own.

4 Enthroned in royal state,
    All glorious thou shalt dwell,
With garments fair, inwrought
    with gold;
The Church He loveth well.

5 And they that honor thee
    Shall in thy train attend,
And to the palace of the King
    Shall joyfully ascend.

6 O King of royal race,
    Thy sons of heavenly birth
Thou wilt endow with kingly gifts
    As princes in the earth.

7 Thy Name shall be proclaimed
    Through all succeeding days,
And all the nations of the earth
    Shall give Thee endless praise.

God Is Our Refuge and Our Strength

PSALM 46

GERARD C.M.D.

Arranged by Arthur S. Sullivan, 1871

1 God is our ref - uge and our strength, Our ev - er pres - ent aid,
2 A riv-er flows whose streams make glad The cit - y of our God,
3 The na-tions raged, the king-doms moved, But when His voice was heard

And, there-fore, though the earth re-move, We will not be a - fraid;
The ho - ly place where-in the Lord Most High has His a - bode;
The trou-bled earth was stilled to peace Be - fore His might-y word.

Though hills a-midst the seas be cast, Though foam-ing wa - ters roar,
Since God is in the midst of her, Un - moved her walls shall stand,
The Lord of hosts is on our side, Our safe - ty to se - cure;

Yea, though the might-y bil-lows shake The moun-tains on the shore.
For God will be her ear - ly help, When trou-ble is at hand.
The God of Ja - cob is for us A ref - uge strong and sure.

4 O come, behold what wondrous works
  Jehovah's hand has wrought;
Come, see what desolation great
  He on the earth has brought.
To utmost ends of all the earth
  He causes war to cease;
The weapons of the strong destroyed,
  He makes abiding peace.

5 Be still and know that I am God,
  O'er all exalted high;
The subject nations of the earth
  My Name shall magnify.
The Lord of hosts is on our side,
  Our safety to secure;
The God of Jacob is for us
  A refuge strong and sure.

85   God Is Our Refuge and Our Strength

PSALM 46

Ein' Feste Burg 8 7 8 7   6 6 6 6 7

Martin Luther, 1483-1546

1 God   is   our   ref-uge   and   our strength, A Help-er   ev-er   near us;
2 God's cit-y   is   for-ev-er   blest With liv-ing wa-ters well-ing;
3 Be-hold what God has   done on earth; His wrath brings des-o-la-tion,

We   will not fear though earth be moved, For God   is nigh to   cheer us.
Since God is there she stands un-moved 'Mid tu-mults round her swell-ing;
His grace, com-mand-ing   wars to   cease, Brings peace to ev-ery na-tion;

Al-though the moun-tains quake And earth's foun-da-tions shake, Though an-gry
God speaks and all   is peace, From war the   na-tions cease; The Lord of
Be   still, for He   is Lord, By   all the earth a-dored; The Lord of

bil-lows roar And break a-gainst the shore, Our might-y God will   hear us.
hosts is   nigh, Our fa-thers' God Most High Is our   e-ter-nal dwell-ing.
hosts is   nigh, Our fa-thers' God Most High Is our strong hab-i-ta-tion.

86

PSALM 47

Praise the Lord, Ye Lands

ASCENDING KING 5 5 5 5 5 5 D.

Louis Bourgeois, 1551
Harmony from De Vries *Koraalboek*
Adapted by Henry Bruinsma, 1946

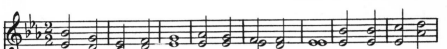

1 Praise the Lord, ye lands; Na-tions, clap your hands; Shout a - loud to
2 God has gone on high With a joy - ful cry; Hosts with trum-pet-
3 Praise His maj - es - ty Un - der-stand-ing - ly; God is King a -

God, Spread His fame a-broad; Praise Him loud and long With a tri-umph song;
sound Make His praise a-bound; Sing ye praise to God, Tell His fame a-broad,
lone On His ho-ly throne, Is-sues His com-mands To all hea-then lands.

Bow as ye draw nigh, For the Lord Most High, Ter - ri - ble is He
Take a psalm and shout, Let His praise ring out, Lift your voice and sing
Lo, the princ-es all Gath-er at His call; His the shields of earth,

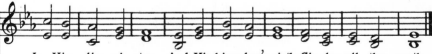

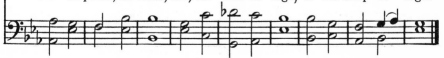

In His dig - ni - ty; And His king-dom's girth Cir-cles all the earth.
Glo-ry to our King; He is Lord of earth, Mag-ni - fy His worth.
His the power, the worth; He, the God on high, Is our Help - er nigh.

Dewey Westra, 1931

All Nations, Clap Your Hands

SILVER STREET S.M.

Isaac Smith, 1770

1 All na - tions, clap your hands, Let
2 A - bove our might - y foes He
3 With shouts as - cends our King, With

shouts of tri - umph ring, For might - y o - ver
gave us pow-er to stand, And as our her - i -
trum - pet's stir - ring call; Praise God, praise God, His

all the lands The Lord Most High is King.
tage He chose The good - ly prom - ised land.
prais - es sing, For God is Lord of all.

4 O sing in joyful strains,
    And make His glory known;
God over all the nations reigns,
    And holy is His throne.

5 Our fathers' God to own
    The kings of earth draw nigh,
For none can save but God alone,
    He is the Lord Most High.

88 The Lord Is Great

PSALM 48

ST. JOHN'S HIGHLANDS L.M.

Anonymous

1 The Lord is great; with wor - thy praise Pro - claim His power, His Name con - fess, With - in the cit - y of our God, Up - on His mount of ho - li - ness.

2 Mount Zi - on, glo - ri - ous and fair, Gives joy to peo - ple in all lands; The cit - y of the might - y King In maj - es - ty se - cure - ly stands.

3 With - in her dwell - ings for de - fense Our God has made His pres - ence known, And hos - tile kings, in sud - den fear, Have fled as ships by temp - ests blown.

4 With our own eyes we have beheld
What oft our fathers told before,
That God who in His Zion dwells
Will keep her safely evermore.

89

Within Thy Temple, Lord

PSALM 48

DIADEMATA S.M.D.

George J. Elvey, 1868

1 With - in Thy tem - ple, Lord, In that most ho - ly place,
2 Let Zi - on now re - joice, And all her chil - dren sing;
3 Ob - serve her pal - a - ces, Mark her de - fen - ses well,

We on Thy lov - ing - kind - ness dwell, The won - ders of Thy grace.
Let them with thank - ful - ness pro - claim The judg - ments of their King.
That to the sons that fol - low you Her glo - ries you may tell;

Men sing Thy praise, O God, Wher - e'er Thy Name is known;
Mount Zi - on's walls be - hold, A - bout her ram - parts go,
For God as our own God For - ev - er will a - bide,

By ev - ery deed Thy hand has wrought Thy right - eous - ness is shown.
And num - ber ye the loft - y towers That guard her from the foe.
And till life's jour - ney close in death Will be our faith - ful Guide.

Hear This, All Ye People, Hear

PSALM 49　　　　FISK 7 7 7 7

Calvin S. Harrington, 1826-1886

1 Hear this, all ye peo-ple, hear, Earth's in-hab-it-ants, give ear; All of high and low de-gree, Rich and poor, give heed to me.

2 Truth with all my heart I seek, And my mouth shall wis-dom speak; Heark-en while in lyr-ic strain I make hid-den wis-dom plain.

3 Why should I to fear give way When I see the e-vil day, When with wick-ed-ness my foes Shall sur-round me and op-pose?

4 They that trust in treasured gold,
　Though they boast of wealth untold,
　None can bid his brother live,
　None to God a ransom give.

5 If from death one would be free
　And corruption never see,
　Costly is life's ransom price,
　Far beyond all sacrifice.

Dust to Dust, the Mortal Dies

PSALM 49

WATCHMAN 7 7 7 7 D.

Lowell Mason, 1830

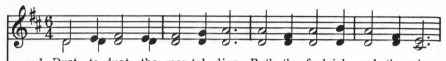

1 Dust to dust, the mor-tal dies, Both the fool-ish and the wise;
2 To their lands they give their name In the hope of last - ing fame;

None for - ev - er can re-main, Each must leave his hoard-ed gain.
But man's hon-or quick-ly flies, Like the low - ly beast he dies.

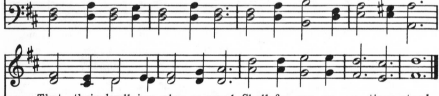

Yet with-in their heart they say That their hous - es are for aye,
Though such fol - ly mark their way, Men ap-prove of what they say;

That their dwell-ing-plac-es grand Shall for gen-er - a - tions stand.
Death their shep-herd, they the sheep, He with-in his fold will keep.

3 O'er them soon shall rule the just,
  All their beauty turn to dust;
  God my waiting soul shall save,
  He will raise me from the grave.
  Let no fear disturb your peace
  Though one's house and wealth increase;
  Death shall end his fleeting day,
  He shall carry naught away.

4 Though in life he wealth attained,
  Though the praise of men he gained,
  He shall join those gone before,
  Where the light shall shine no more.
  Crowned with honor though he be,
  Highly gifted, strong and free,
  If he be not truly wise,
  Man is like the beast that dies.

92 The Mighty God, Jehovah, Speaks

PSALM 50

ST. PETERSBURG L.M., 6 lines

Arranged from
Dimitri Bortniansky, 1752-1828

1 The might-y God, Je-ho-vah, speaks And calls the earth from sea to sea;
2 He calls a-loud to heaven and earth That He may just-ly judge His own:

From beau-teous Zi-on God shines forth, He comes and will not si-lent be;
My cho-sen saints to-geth-er bring Who sac-ri-fice to Me a-lone;

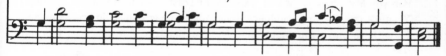

De-vour-ing flame be-fore Him goes, And dark the tem-pest round Him grows.
The heavens His right-eous-ness de-clare, For God Him-self as Judge is there.

3 Hear, O my people, I will speak,
   Against thee I will testify;
Give ear to Me, O Israel,
   For God, thy covenant God, am I;
     I do not spurn thy sacrifice,
     Thy offerings are before My eyes.

4 I will receive from out thy fold
   No offering for My holy shrine;
The cattle on a thousand hills
   And all the forest beasts are Mine;
     Each mountain bird to Me is known,
     Whatever roams the field I own.

5 Behold, if I should hungry grow,
   I would not tell My need to thee,
For all the world itself is Mine,
   And all its wealth belongs to Me;
     Why should I aught of thee receive,
     My thirst or hunger to relieve?

6 Bring thou to God the gift of thanks,
   And pay thy vows to God Most High;
Call ye upon my holy Name
   In days when sore distress is nigh;
     Deliverance I will send to thee,
     And praises thou shalt give to Me.

93   Thus Speaks the Lord to Wicked Men

PSALM 50   St. Chrysostom (Ellerton) L.M., 6 Lines

Joseph Barnby, 1838-1896

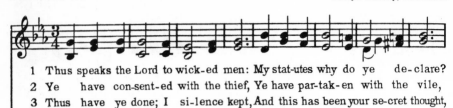

1 Thus speaks the Lord to wick-ed men: My stat-utes why do ye de-clare?
2 Ye have con-sent-ed with the thief, Ye have par-tak-en with the vile,
3 Thus have ye done; I si-lence kept, And this has been your se-cret thought,

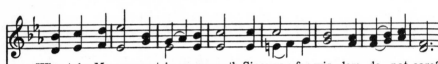

Why take My cove-nant in your mouth, Since ye for wis-dom do not care?
Your mouths to e-vil words ye give, Your tongues pro-claim de-ceit and guile,
That I was whol-ly as your-selves, To take your e-vil deeds as nought;

For ye My ho-ly words pro-fane And cast them from you in dis-dain.
Ye glo-ry in your broth-er's shame, Your moth-er's son do ye de-fame.
I will re-prove you and ar-ray Your deeds be-fore your eyes this day.

4 Consider this, who God forget,

Lest I destroy with none to free;

Who offers sacrifice of thanks,

He glorifies and honors Me;

To him who orders well his way

Salvation free I will display.

94 God, Be Merciful to Me

PSALM 51   AJALON (GETHSEMANE) 7 7 7 7 7 7   Richard Redhead, 1853

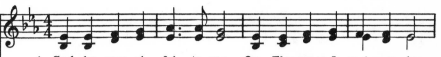

1 God, be mer - ci - ful to me, On Thy grace I rest my plea;
2 My trans-gres-sions I con-fess, Grief and guilt my soul op-press;
3 I am e - vil, born in sin; Thou de - sir - est truth with-in.

Plen-teous in com-pas-sion Thou, Blot out my trans-gres-sions now;
I have sinned a-gainst Thy grace And pro-voked Thee to Thy face;
Thou a - lone my Sav-ior art, Teach Thy wis-dom to my heart;

Wash me, make me pure with-in, Cleanse, O cleanse me from my sin.
I con-fess Thy judg-ment just, Speech-less, I Thy mer-cy trust.
Make me pure, Thy grace be-stow, Wash me whit-er than the snow.

4 Broken, humbled to the dust
  By Thy wrath and judgment just,
  Let my contrite heart rejoice
  And in gladness hear Thy voice;
  From my sins O hide Thy face,
  Blot them out in boundless grace.

95 Gracious God, My Heart Renew

PSALM 51

GETHSEMANE 7 7 7 7 7 7

John B. Dykes, 1823-1876

1 Gra-cious God, my heart re - new, Make my spir- it right and true;
2 Sin-ners then shall learn from me And re-turn, O God, to Thee;
3 Not the for-mal sac - ri-fice Has ac-cept-ance in Thine eyes;

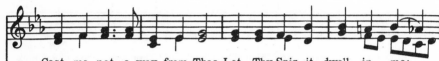

Cast me not a-way from Thee, Let Thy Spir-it dwell in me;
Sav - ior, all my guilt re-move, And my tongue shall sing Thy love;
Bro-ken hearts are in Thy sight More than sac - ri - fi - cial rite;

Thy sal-va-tion's joy im-part, Sted-fast make my will - ing heart.
Touch my si-lent lips, O .Lord, And my mouth shall praise ac - cord.
Con - trite spir-it, plead-ing cries, Thou, O God, wilt not de-spise.

4 Prosper Zion in Thy grace
  And her broken walls replace;
  Then our righteous sacrifice
  Shall delight Thy holy eyes;
  Free-will offerings, gladly made,
  On Thine altar shall be laid.

O God, the God That Saveth Me

PSALM 51

SERENITY C.M.

Arranged from William V. Wallace

1 O God, the God that sav-eth me, Re-move my guilt-y stains, And I will sing Thy right-eous-ness In grate-ful, joy-ous strains.

2 O Lord, now o-pen Thou my lips, Long closed by sin and shame; My mouth shall show be-fore the world The glo-ry of Thy Name.

3 No sac-ri-fice dost Thou de-sire, Else would I give it Thee; Nor with ap-point-ed of-fer-ings Wilt Thou de-light-ed be.

4 A broken spirit is to God
 A pleasing sacrifice;
 A broken and a contrite heart
 Thou, Lord, wilt not despise.

5 Do good to Zion in Thy grace,
 Her ruined walls restore;
 Then sacrifice of righteousness
 Shall please Thee as of yore.

6 Thy people then, with willing hands
 And hearts that Thou hast blessed,
 Shall bring in thankful sacrifice
 Their choicest gifts and best.

O Mighty Man, Why Wilt Thou Boast

PSALM 52

WALTHAM L.M.

J. Baptiste Calkin, 1872

1 O might - y man, why wilt thou boast Thy-self in
2 Thy tongue de - vis - eth wick - ed - ness, A weap - on
3 Since, O thou false, de - ceit - ful tongue, In dead - ly

hate - ful cru - el - ty, When God Al - might - y
treach - er - ous and keen; Thou lov - est e - vil
words thou find - est joy, The Lord shall pluck thee

is most kind, And ev - er mer - ci - ful is He?
more than good, And false-hood in thy sight is clean.
from thy place And all thy wick - ed - ness de - stroy.

4 The good, confirmed in godly fear,
　The pride and folly shall confess
Of those who make not God their
　　strength,
　But trust in wealth and wickedness.

5 But as for me, my strength is like
　A verdant temple olive tree;
My trust is in God's tender love,
　Which shall endure eternally.

6 With endless thanks, O Lord, to Thee,
　Thy wondrous works will I proclaim,
And in the presence of Thy saints
　Will ever hope in Thy good Name.

98   Fools in Their Heart Have Said

PSALM 53

Badea S.M.

German Melody

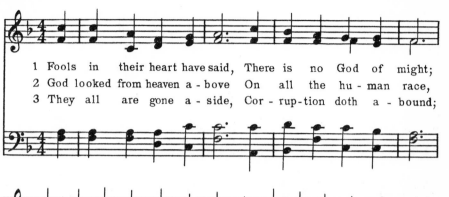

1 Fools in their heart have said, There is no God of might;
2 God looked from heaven a - bove On all the hu - man race,
3 They all are gone a - side, Cor - rup-tion doth a - bound;

Cor - rupt are they and base their deeds, In e - vil they de - light.
To see if an - y un - der-stood, If an - y sought His face.
There is not one that do - eth good, Not e - ven one is found.

4 These men of evil deeds,
    Will they no knowledge gain,
  Who feed upon my people's woes,
    And prayer to God disdain?

5 The day is drawing nigh
    When they shall fear and quail,
  For God shall scatter and destroy
    Those who His saints assail.

6 Yea, God will put to shame
    And make them flee away,
  For He will cast them off in wrath
    And fill them with dismay.

7 O would that Israel's help
    Were out of Zion come!
  O would that God might early bring
    His captive people home!

8 When God from distant lands
    His exiled ones shall bring,
  His people shall exultant be,
    And gladly they shall sing.

99

O Save Me by Thy Name

PSALM 54

BOYLSTON S.M.

Lowell Mason, 1832

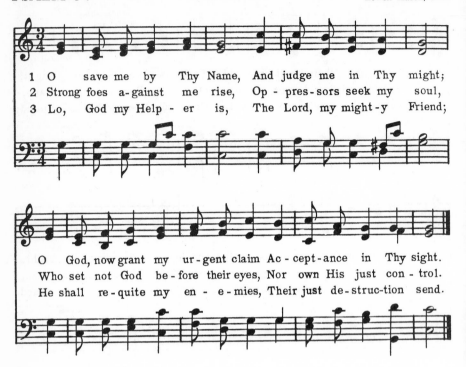

1 O save me by Thy Name, And judge me in Thy might;
2 Strong foes a-gainst me rise, Op - pres-sors seek my soul,
3 Lo, God my Help - er is, The Lord, my might - y Friend;

O God, now grant my ur-gent claim Ac-cept-ance in Thy sight.
Who set not God be-fore their eyes, Nor own His just con-trol.
He shall re-quite my en - e-mies, Their just de-struc-tion send.

4 My sacrifice of praise

To Thee I freely bring;

My thanks, O Lord, to Thee I raise

And of Thy goodness sing.

5 From troubles and from woes

Thou hast delivered me,

The overthrow of all my foes

Hast given me to see.

100

Jehovah, to My Prayer Give Ear

PSALM 55

Vox Dilecti C.M.D.

John B. Dykes, 1868

1 Je - ho - vah, to my prayer give ear, Nor hide Thee from my cry;
2 Sore pained in heart I find no ease, Death's ter-rors fill my soul,

At - tend my sad com-plaint, and hear My rest-less moan and sigh.
Great fear and trem-bling on me seize, And hor-rors o'er me roll.

My en - e-mies lift up their voice, The vi - o - lent op - press;
O had I wings, I sigh and say, Like some swift dove to roam,

To do me wrong my foes re-joice, And love my soul's dis-tress.
Then I would hast - en far a - way And find a peace - ful home.

3 Lo, wandering far, my rest should be
  In some lone desert waste;
I from the stormy wind would flee,
  And to a shelter haste.
O Lord, their malice recompense,
  Their wicked tongues confound,
For in the city violence
  And bitter strife abound.

4 They walk her walls both night and day,
  Within all vices meet;
Oppression, fraud and crime hold sway,
  Nor leave the crowded street.
No foreign foe provokes alarm,
  But enemies within;
May God destroy their power to harm
  And recompense their sin.

101

On God Alone My Soul Relies

PSALM 55 ASCRIPTION C. M.

Luther O. Emerson, 1866

1 On God a-lone my soul re-lies, And He will soon re-lieve;
2 He has re-deemed my soul in peace, From con-flict set me free;
3 The liv-ing God in right-eous-ness Will rec-om-pense with shame

The Lord will hear my plain-tive cries At morn-ing, noon, and eve.
My man-y foes are made to cease, And strive no more with me.
The men who, hard-ened by suc-cess, For-get to fear His Name.

4 All treacherous friends who overreach
   And break their plighted troth,
Who hide their hate with honeyed speech,
   With such the Lord is wroth.

5 Upon the Lord thy burden cast,
   To Him bring all thy care;
He will sustain and hold thee fast,
   And give thee strength to bear.

6 God will not let His saints be moved;
   Protected, they shall see
Their foes cut off and sin reproved;
   O God, I trust in Thee.

O God, Give Thou Ear to My Plea

PSALM 55   Assiut L. M.

George C. Stebbins, 1846-1945

1 O God, give Thou ear to my plea,
And hide not Thyself from my cry;
O heark-en and an-swer Thou me,
As rest-less and wea-ry I sigh.

2 O that I had wings like a dove,
For then I would fly far a-way
And seek for the rest that I love,
Where trou-ble no more could dis-may.

3 Nay, soul, call on God all the day;
   The Lord for thy help will appear;
At eve, morn, and noon humbly pray,
   And He thy petition will hear.

4 Thy burden now cast on the Lord,
   And He shall thy weakness sustain;
The righteous who trust in His word
   Unmoved shall forever remain.

103   O God, Be Merciful

PSALM 56

INVITATION 6 6 6 6 D.

Frederick C. Maker, 1881

1 O God, be mer-ci-ful, Be mer-ci-ful to me,
2 What time I am a-fraid I put my trust in Thee;

For man, with con-stant hate, Would fain my ru-in see.
In God I rest, and praise His word, so rich and free.

My man-y en-e-mies A-gainst me proud-ly fight;
In God I put my trust, I nei-ther doubt nor fear,

To o-ver-whelm my soul They watch from morn to night.
For man can nev-er harm, With God my Help-er near.

3 All day they wrest my words,
   Their thoughts are full of hate;
They meet, they lurk, they watch,
   As for my soul they wait.
Shall they by wickedness
   Escape Thy judgment right?
O God of righteousness,
   Destroy them in Thy might.

4 Thou knowest all my woes,
   O treasure Thou my tears;
Are they not in Thy book,
   Where all my life appears?
My foes shall backward turn
   When I appeal to Thee,
For this I surely know,
   That God is still for me.

What Time I Am Afraid

PSALM 56   Holy Guide 6 6 6 6

Uzziah C. Burnap, 1895

1 What time I am a-fraid I put my trust in Thee;
2 In God I put my trust, I nei-ther doubt nor fear,
3 In God, the Lord, I rest, His word of grace I praise,

In God I rest, and praise His word, so rich and free.
For man can nev-er harm With God my Help-er near.
His prom-ise stands se-cure, Nor fear nor foe dis-mays.

4 Upon me are Thy vows,
   O God, in whom I live;
The sacrifice of praise
   To Thee I now will give.

5 For Thou hast saved from death,
   From falling kept me free,
That in the light of life
   My walk may be with Thee.

105

O God, Be Merciful to Me

SWEET HOUR OF PRAYER L. M. D.

William B. Bradbury, 1859

PSALM 57

1 O God, be mer - ci - ful to me, My soul for ref-uge comes to Thee;
2 Great foes and fierce my soul a - larm, In-flamed with rage and strong to harm,

Be-neath Thy wings I safe will stay Un-til these trou-bles pass a-way.
But God, from heaven His dwell-ing-place, Will res-cue me with truth and grace.

To God Most High shall rise my prayer, To God who makes my wants His care;
Be thou, O God, ex - alt - ed high, Yea, far a - bove the star-ry sky,

From heaven He will sal-va-tion send, And me from ev - ery foe de-fend.
And let Thy glo-ry be dis-played O'er all the earth Thy hands have made.

3 My soul is grieved because my foes
With treacherous plans my way inclose;
But from the snares that they devise
Their own undoing shall arise.
My heart is stedfast, O my King,
My heart is tuned Thy praise to sing;
Awake, my soul, and swell the song,
Let vibrant harp the notes prolong.

4 Yea, I will early wake and sing,
A thankful hymn to Thee will bring,
For unto heaven Thy mercies rise,
Thy truth is lofty as the skies.
Be Thou, O God, exalted high,
Yea, far above the starry sky,
And let Thy glory be displayed
O'er all the earth Thy hands have made.

106   Do Ye, O Men, Speak Righteousness

PSALM 58

SWANWICK C. M.

James Lucas

1 Do ye, O men, speak right-eous-ness And up - right
2 The wick - ed, from their ear - liest days, In sin are
3 The God of ven - geance will de - stroy The wick - ed

judg-ment mete? Nay, in your hearts is wick - ed - ness,
gone a - stray, With fro - ward heart, in fool - ish pride,
from His sight; The Lord will bring to nought their power

And in your hands de - ceit, And in your hands de - ceit.
From wis - dom turned a - way, From wis - dom turned a - way.
And scat - ter all their might, And scat - ter all their might.

4 The good shall triumph and rejoice,
And this shall be confessed:
On earth the God of justice reigns,
And righteousness is blessed.

107   Protect and Save Me, O My God

PSALM 59

KATHRINE C. M.

Charles H. Gabriel, 1856-1932

Slowly

1 Pro - tect and save me, O my God, From
2 The work - ers of in - iq - ui - ty A -
3 Be - hold their wick - ed - ness, O Lord, To

foes that seek my life, And set me high, se -
gainst me lie in wait; Though I am in - no -
help me, O a - wake; Lord God of hosts, Thou,

cure, a - bove The ris - ing tide of strife.
cent, O Lord, They gath - er in their hate.
Is - rael's God, A - rise, and ven - geance take.

4 My enemies with deadly rage
　　Renew their fierce attack;
　　They think the Lord will not regard,
　　But Thou wilt turn them back.

5 O God, my strength, on Thee I wait,
    To Thee for refuge flee;
My God with mercy will defend,
    Triumphant I shall be.

6 O God, our shield, let wickedness
    And pride be put to shame,
Till all shall know that Thou dost rule
    And all shall fear Thy Name.

7 Let wickedness that raged in power
    Now rage in impotence;
But I will glory in Thy strength,
    My refuge and defense.

8 When all the night of woe is past
    And morning dawns at length,
Then I shall praise Thy grace, O God,
    My refuge and my strength.

9 To Thee, O God most merciful,
    My thankful song I raise;
My might, my strong, secure abode,
    I will proclaim Thy praise.

108 O God, Thou Hast Rejected Us

PSALM 60

DUNFERMLINE C. M.

Scottish Psalter, 1615

1 O God, Thou hast re-ject-ed us, And hast af-flict-ed sore;
2 Lo, Thou hast torn and rent our land, Thy judg-ments dread ap-pall;
3 Thro' ways of tri-al and dis-tress Thy peo-ple Thou hast led,

Thou hast been an-gry, but in grace O once a-gain re-store.
O heal her shat-tered strength be-fore She tot-ter to her fall.
A bit-ter cup Thou giv-est us Of mis-er-y and dread.

(Alternate Tune: CLINTON, No. 12)

4 A glorious banner Thou has given
　　To those who fear Thy Name,
　A banner to display abroad,
　　And thus the truth proclaim.

5 That Thy beloved may be saved
　　And from their foes set free,
　Help with the might of Thy right hand,
　　In mercy answer me.

6 God in His holiness has said:
　　I will triumphant be,
　All heathen lands I claim as Mine,
　　And they shall bow to Me.

7 Now, therefore, who will lead us on
　　Sin's strongholds to possess?
　No longer cast us off, O God,
　　But give our hosts success.

8 Give Thou Thy help against the foe,
　　For help of man is vain;
　Through God we shall do valiantly,
　　The victory He shall gain.

109 O God, Regard My Humble Plea

PSALM 61

MERIBAH 8 8 6 D.

Lowell Mason, 1839

1 O   God, re-gard my hum-ble plea; I   can-not be so far from Thee
2 In   Thee my soul has shel-ter found, And Thou hast been from foes a-round
3 For Thou, O God, my vows hast heard, On me   the her- it-age con-ferred

But Thou wilt hear my   cry; When I   by trou-ble am dis-tressed,
The tower to which I   flee. With-in Thy house will I   a - bide;
Of those that fear Thy Name; A blest a - noint-ing Thou dost give,

Then lead me on the rock to rest That high-er   is   than   I.
My   ref-uge sure, what-e'er be-tide, Thy shel-tering wings shall be.
And Thou wilt make me ev - er live Thy prais-es   to   pro - claim.

4 Before Thy face shall I abide;

O God, Thy truth and grace provide

To guard me in the way;

So I will make Thy praises known,

And, humbly bending at Thy throne,

My vows will daily pay.

110 My Soul in Silence Waits for God

PSALM 62

SERAPH C. M. D.

Gottfried Wilhelm Fink, 1842

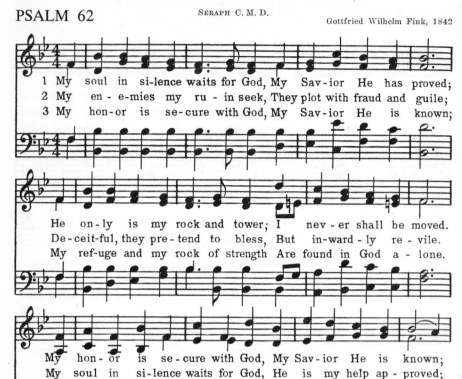

1 My soul in si-lence waits for God, My Sav-ior He has proved;
2 My en-e-mies my ru-in seek, They plot with fraud and guile;
3 My hon-or is se-cure with God, My Sav-ior He is known;

He on-ly is my rock and tower; I nev-er shall be moved.
De-ceit-ful, they pre-tend to bless, But in-ward-ly re-vile.
My ref-uge and my rock of strength Are found in God a-lone.

My hon-or is se-cure with God, My Sav-ior He is known;
My soul in si-lence waits for God, He is my help ap-proved;
On Him, ye peo-ple, ev-er-more Re-ly with con-fi-dence;

My ref-uge and my rock of strength Are found in God a-lone.
He on-ly is my rock and tower, And I shall not be moved.
Be-fore Him pour ye out your heart, For God is our de-fense.

4 For surely men are helpers vain,
    The high and the abased;
  Yea, lighter than a breath are they
    When in the balance placed.
  Trust not in harsh oppression's power
    Nor in unrighteous gain;
  If wealth increase, yet on your gold
    Ye set your hearts in vain.

5 For God has spoken o'er and o'er,
    And unto me has shown,
  That saving power and lasting strength
    Belong to Him alone.
  Yea, lovingkindness evermore
    Belongs to Thee, O Lord;
  And Thou according to his work
    Dost every man reward.

111

O Lord, My God, Most Earnestly

PSALM 63

THE GREEN HILL C. M. D. George C. Stebbins, 1878

1 O Lord, my God, most ear-nest-ly My heart would seek Thy face,
2 The lov-ing-kind-ness of my God Is more than life to me;
3 My Sav-ior, 'neath Thy shel-tering wings My soul de-lights to dwell;

With-in Thy ho-ly house once more To see Thy glo-rious grace.
So I will bless Thee while I live And lift my prayer to Thee.
Still clos-er to Thy side I press, For near Thee all is well.

A-part from Thee I long and thirst, And nought can sat-is-fy;
In Thee my soul is sat-is-fied, My dark-ness turns to light,
My soul shall con-quer ev-ery foe, Up-hold-en by Thy hand;

I wan-der in a des-ert land Where all the streams are dry.
And joy-ful med-i-ta-tions fill The watch-es of the night.
Thy peo-ple shall re-joice in God, Thy saints in glo-ry stand.

112 Thou Art My God, O God of Grace

PSALM 63

AMERICUS 8 8 6 D.

Charles H. Gabriel, 1856-1932

1 Thou art my God, O God of grace, And ear-nest-
ly I seek Thy face, My heart cries out for Thee; My spir-it
thirsts Thy grace to taste, An ex-ile in this des-ert waste
In which no wa-ters be, In which no wa-ters be.

2 I long as in the times of old Thy power and
glo-ry to be-hold With-in Thy ho-ly place; Be-cause Thy
ten-der love I see, More pre-cious far than life to me,
My lips shall praise Thy grace, My lips shall praise Thy grace.

3 Thus will I bless Thee while I live,
And with uplifted hands will give
   Praise to Thy Holy Name;
When by Thy bounty well supplied,
Then shall my soul be satisfied,
   My mouth shall praise proclaim.

4 My lips shall in Thy praise delight
When on my bed I rest at night
   And meditate on Thee;
Because Thy hand assistance brings,
Beneath the shadow of Thy wings
   My heart shall joyful be.

113   Hear, Lord, the Voice of My Complaint

PSALM 64   Monora C. M. D.

William B. Bradbury, 1863

1 Hear, Lord, the voice of my com-plaint, Pre-serve my life from fear,
2 The   wick-ed in their base de-signs Grow ar - ro-gant and bold;
3 The   wick-ed, by their sins o'er-come, Shall soon be brought to shame;

Hide me from plot-ting en - e-mies And e - vil, crowd-ing near.
Con - spir - ing se - cret - ly, they think That God will not be - hold;
The hand of God shall yet ap-pear, And all shall fear His Name.

The   work - ers of in - iq - ui - ty,   Their dead - ly shafts pre - pare;
They search out more in - iq - ui - ty,   Their thoughts and plans are deep,
The   just shall tri-umph in the Lord, Their trust shall be   se - cure,

They aim at me their treach-erous words; O save me from their snare.
But God will smite, for He   is near His saints to guard and keep.
And end-less glo - ry then shall crown The up-right and the pure.

Praise Waits for Thee in Zion

PSALM 65

MENDEBRAS 7 6 7 6 D.

German Melody
Arranged by Lowell Mason, 1839

1 Praise waits for Thee in Zi-on; All men shall wor-ship there
2 How blest the man Thou call-est And bring-est near to Thee,
3 O God of our sal-va-tion, Since Thou dost love the right,

And pay their vows be-fore Thee, O God who hear-est prayer.
That in Thy courts for-ev-er His dwell-ing-place may be;
Thou wilt an an-swer send us In won-drous deeds of might.

Our sins rise up a-gainst us, Pre-vail-ing day by day,
He shall with-in Thy tem-ple Be sat-is-fied with grace,
In all earth's hab-i-ta-tions, On all the bound-less sea,

But Thou wilt show us mer-cy And take their guilt a-way.
And filled with all the good-ness Of Thy most ho-ly place.
Man finds no sure re-li-ance, No peace, a-part from Thee.

115 Thy Might Sets Fast the Mountains

PSALM 65   Webb 7 6 7 6 D.

George J. Webb, 1837

1 Thy might sets fast the moun-tains; Strength girds Thee ev-er-more
2 To bless the earth Thou send-est From Thine a-bun-dant store
3 The year with good Thou crown-est, The earth Thy mer-cy fills,

To calm the rag-ing peo-ples And still the o-cean's roar.
The wa-ters of the spring-time, En-rich-ing it once more.
The wil-der-ness is fruit-ful, And joy-ful are the hills;

Thy maj-es-ty and great-ness Are through all lands con-fessed,
The seed by Thee pro-vid-ed Is sown o'er hill and plain,
With corn the vales are cov-ered, The flocks in pas-tures graze;

And joy on earth Thou send-est A - far, from east to west.
And Thou with gen - tle show-ers Dost bless the spring-ing grain.
All na - ture joins in sing-ing A joy-ful song of praise.

116

Forth from Thy Courts

PSALM 65

ZION'S PRAISE 9 6 9 6 D.

Louis Bourgeois, 1543
Harmonized by Henry Bruinsma, 1954

1 Forth from Thy courts, Thy sa-cred dwell-ing, In ju - bi-lant ac-cord,
2 A might - y stream of foul trans-gres-sion Pre-vails from day to day;

We hear sweet strains of prais-es swell-ing, O Is-rael's might-y Lord!
But Thou, O God, in great com-pas-sion, Wilt purge my guilt a-way.

To God, who hears our im-plo - ra - tion, We come to pay our vow;
Blest is the man whom Thou hast cho-sen, And bring-est nigh to Thee,

Soon men from ev - ery tribe and na - tion Be-fore our God shall bow.
That in Thy courts, in Thee re-pos - ing, His dwell-ing-place may be.

William Kuipers, 1931

132

Forth from Thy Courts

PSALM 65

3 There, in Thy holy habitation,
  Thou wilt Thy saints provide
With every blessing of salvation,
  Till all are satisfied.
By awful deeds, so just and mighty,
  God saves us from our foe;
To all who walk with Him uprightly
  He will salvation show.

4 From stores on high Thy streams flow over
  The hard and arid land;
The fields are sown with corn and clover,
  Provided by Thy hand;
The furrows, softened by Thy showers,
  Are blest with springing grain.
How great, O God, Thy love and power
  Throughout Thy vast domain!

5 The year is crowned, O Fount of blessing,
  With gifts to cheer the land;
Thy goodness fills the earth, expressing
  The wonders of Thy hand.
The hills rejoice; the pastures, teeming
  With flocks that skip and spring,
The golden grain, in valleys gleaming—
  All sing to God the King.

117

Before Thee, Lord, a People Waits

PSALM 65

MALONE 8 8 6 D.

Luther O. Emerson, 1869

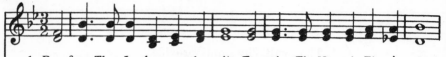

1 Be - fore Thee, Lord, a peo-ple waits To praise Thy Name in Zi-on's gates,
2 How great my tres-pass-es ap-pear; But Thou from guilt my soul wilt clear,
3 The good-ness of Thy house, O Lord, The joys Thy ho-ly courts af-ford,

To Thee shall vows be paid; Thou Hear-er of the sup-pliant's prayer,
And my trans-gres-sions hide. How blest Thy cho-sen, who by grace
Our souls shall sat - is - fy; By deeds of might, in jus-tice wrought,

To Thee in need shall all re-pair To seek Thy gra-cious aid.
Are brought with-in Thy dwell-ing-place That they may there a - bide.
The Lord will grant us what we sought, Our Sav-ior, God Most High.

4 On Thy sustaining arm depend,
  To earth and sea's remotest end,
    All men in every age;
Thy strength establishes the hills,
Thy word the roaring billows stills,
    And calms the peoples' rage.

5 The tribes of earth's remotest lands
  Behold the tokens of Thy hands
    And bow in godly fear;
          [light,
The east, where beams the morning
The west, in evening glories bright,
    Rejoice, for Thou art near.

118 All Lands, to God in Joyful Sounds

PSALM 66

MILES' LANE C. M.

Adapted from William Shrubsole, 1785

1 All lands, to God in joy - ful sounds A - loft your
2 Say ye to God, How ter - ri - ble In all Thy
3 Yea, all the earth shall wor-ship Thee, And un - to

voic - es raise; Sing forth the hon - or of His Name,
works art Thou! To Thee Thy foes by Thy great power
Thee shall sing; To Thy great Name shall songs of joy

And glo-rious make His praise, And glo-rious make His praise.
Shall be con-strained to bow, Shall be con-strained to bow.
With loud ho - san - nas ring, With loud ho - san - nas ring.

4 O come, behold the works of God,
   His mighty doings see;
In dealing with the sons of men
   Most wonderful is He.

5 He led in safety through the flood
   The people of His choice,
He turned the sea to solid ground;
   In Him let us rejoice.

6 He rules forever by His might,
   His eyes the nations try;
Let not the proud, rebellious ones
   Exalt themselves on high.

119   O All Ye Peoples, Bless Our God

PSALM 66   ANCYRA C. M. D.   Benjamin C. Unseld

1 O all ye peo - ples, bless our God, A -
2 Through pain and trou - ble Thou hast led, And

loud pro - claim His praise, Who safe - ly holds our
hum - bled all our pride; But, in the end, to

souls in life, And sted - fast makes our ways.
lib - er - ty And wealth Thy hand did guide.

Thou, Lord, hast proved and test - ed us As
Here in Thy house I give to Thee The

O All Ye Peoples, Bless Our God

PSALM 66

sil - ver tried by fire; Thy hand has made our
life that Thou dost bless, And pay the sol - emn

bur - den great And thwart - ed our de - sire.
vows I made When I was in dis - tress.

3 Come, ye that fear the Lord, and hear
    What He has done for me;
My cry for help is turned to praise,
    For He has set me free.
If in my heart I sin regard,
    My prayer He will not hear;
But truly God has heard my voice,
    My prayer has reached His ear.

4 O let the Lord, our gracious God,
    Forever blessed be,
Who has not turned my prayer from Him,
    Nor yet His grace from me.
O all ye peoples, bless our God,
    Aloud proclaim His praise,
Who safely holds our soul in life,
    And stedfast makes our ways.

120   Come, All Ye People, Bless Our God

PSALM 66   Adowa 8 8 6 D.

Charles H. Gabriel, 1856-1932

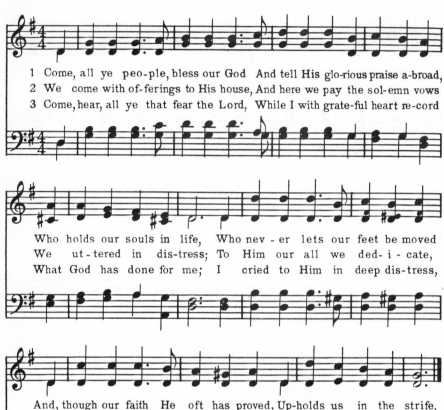

1 Come, all ye peo-ple, bless our God And tell His glo-rious praise a-broad,
2 We come with of-ferings to His house, And here we pay the sol-emn vows
3 Come, hear, all ye that fear the Lord, While I with grate-ful heart re-cord

Who holds our souls in life, Who nev-er lets our feet be moved
We ut-tered in dis-tress; To Him our all we ded-i-cate,
What God has done for me; I cried to Him in deep dis-tress,

And, though our faith He oft has proved, Up-holds us in the strife.
To Him we whol-ly con-se-crate The lives His mer-cies bless.
And now His won-drous grace I bless, For He has set me free.

4 The Lord, who turns away the plea

Of those who love iniquity,

Has answered my request;

He has not turned away my prayer,

His grace and love He makes me share;

His Name be ever blest.

121   O God, to Us Show Mercy

PSALM 67   AURELIA 7 6 7 6 D.   Samuel S. Wesley's setting of *Jerusalem the Golden*, 1864

1 O God, to us show mer - cy And bless us in Thy grace;
2 O God, let all men praise Thee, Let all the na - tions sing;
3 O God, let peo - ple praise Thee, Let all the na - tions sing,

Cause Thou to shine up - on us The bright-ness of Thy face;
In ev - ery land let prais - es And songs of glad-ness ring;
For earth in rich a - bun-dance To us her fruit shall bring.

That so Thy way· most ho - ly On earth may soon be known,
For Thou shalt judge the peo-ple In truth and right-eous - ness,
The Lord our God shall bless us, Our God shall bless - ing send,

And un - to ev - ery peo-ple Thy sav-ing grace be shown.
And through the earth the na - tions Shall Thy just rule con - fess.
And all the earth shall fear Him To its re - mot - est end.

122 Let God Arise, and by His Might

PSALM 68

TRURO L. M.

Charles Burney, 1726-1814

1 Let God a-rise, and by His might Let all His
foes be put to flight; But O ye right-eous,
glad-ly sing, Ex-ult be-fore your God and King.

2 Je-ho-vah's prais-es sound a-broad, Re-joice before the liv-ing God; Pre-pare the way that
He may come And make the des-ert plac-es bloom.

3 A Fa-ther of the fa-ther-less, A Judge of
wid-ows in dis-tress Is God, the God of
bound-less grace, Who dwells with-in His ho-ly place.

4 God frees the captive and He sends
The blessedness of home and friends,
And only those in darkness stay
Who will not trust Him and obey.

5 O Zion, 'tis thy God's command
That thou in strength securely stand;
O God, confirm and strengthen still,
Thy purposes in us fulfill.

6 O Thou, whose glorious temple stands
In Zion, famed through heathen lands,
Kings shall Thy power and glory see,
And bring their presents unto Thee.

7 Thou wilt rebuke the fierce and strong
Who hate the right and choose the wrong,
And scatter those who peace abhor,
The nations that delight in war.

8 The heathen princes yet shall flee
From idols and return to Thee;
Earth's sinful and benighted lands
To God shall soon stretch out their hands.

123   God Saved His People from Distress

PSALM 68

VANDER WERP L. M. D.

Henry Vander Werp, 1911

1 God saved His peo - ple from dis-tress And led them through the
2 With glo - rious pomp our King and God Has en-tered in - to

wil - der-ness; Then moun-tains trem-bled in their place,
His a - bode With sa - cred min-strel - sy and song,

The heavens were bowed be-fore His face. With co-pious showers Thou
While maid - ens with their tim-brels throng. As-sem - ble ye be-

didst as-suage The thirst-ing of Thy her - i - tage; Thy con - gre-
fore His face, All ye that spring from Is - rael's race; Ye cho - sen

ga - tion dwelt se-cure; Thou, God, art gra-cious to the poor.
tribes, with one ac - cord Come ye, and bless your God, the Lord.

124   God Shall Arise and by His Might

PSALM 68

GREITER 8 8 7   8 8 7 D.

Matthaeus Greiter, 1526
Harmonized by H. W. Wooldridge, c. 1899

Majestically; may be sung in unison

1 God shall a-rise and by His might Put all His en - e-mies to flight With
2 But let the right-eous, blessed of yore, Joy in their God as ne'er be-fore, Faith's
3 Sing praise, thou cho-sen Is - ra - el, Who with the folds of sheep dost dwell; Thou

shame and con-ster-na - tion. His hat-ers, haught-y though they be, Shall
vic - to - ry a - chiev-ing. Their joy shall then un-bound-ed be Who
art God's joy and treas - ure. Like doves on gold - en-feath-ered wing, In

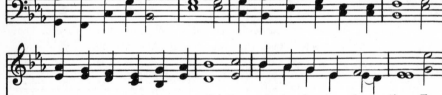

at His au-gust pres-ence flee In ut - ter des - o - la - tion; For.
see God's face e - ter - nal - ly, Their heart's de-sire re-ceiv - ing. Ex-
ho - ly beau-ty thou shalt bring Thy praise to God with pleas - ure. Je -

when Je-ho-vah shall ap-pear, He shall con-sume, a - far and near, All
alt, ex-alt the Name of God; Sing ye His roy-al fame a-broad With
ho-vah scat-tered kings and foes, Re-deem-ing thee from griev-ous woes; Praise

God Shall Arise and by His Might

PSALM 68

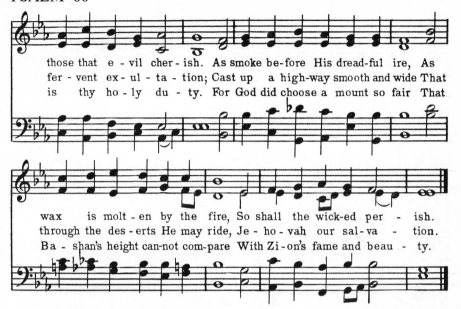

those that e - vil cher - ish. As smoke be-fore His dread-ful ire, As
wax is molt - en by the fire, So shall the wick-ed per - ish.

fer - vent ex - ul - ta - tion; Cast up a high-way smooth and wide That
through the des - erts He may ride, Je - ho - vah our sal - va - tion.

is thy ho - ly du - ty. For God did choose a mount so fair That
Ba - shan's height can-not com-pare With Zi - on's fame and beau - ty.

4 The Lord is great, His might untold,
His chariots thousand thousand fold,
His armies ne'er confounded.
Among them God with joy displays
The glory that in Moses' days
Mount Sinai surrounded.
When Thou, O Lord, in glory bright,
Ascendedst in the heavenly height
Our captive-bonds to sever,
Rich gifts from those who did rebel
Thou didst receive, that men might
With Thee, O Lord, forever. [dwell

5 Let God be praised with reverence deep;
He daily comes our lives to steep
In bounties freely given.
God cares for us, our God is He;
Who would not fear His majesty
In earth as well as heaven?
Our God upholds us in the strife;
To us He grants eternal life,
And saves from desolation.
He hears the needy when they cry,
He saves their souls when death draws
This God is our salvation. [nigh,

6 Ye kings and kingdoms of the earth,
Extol Jehovah's matchless worth
With psalms of adoration.
Praise Him whose glory rides on high,
Whose thunders roll through clouded sky
With mighty intonation.
Ascribe ye strength to God alone,
Whose worth in Israel is known,
For whom the heavens tremble.
O Lord, our strength, to Thee we bow,
For great and terrible art Thou
Out of Thy holy temple.

Benjamin Essenburg, 1931

125   O Lord, Thou Hast Ascended

PSALM 68   MISSIONARY HYMN 7 6 7 6 D.

Lowell Mason, 1828

1 O Lord, Thou hast as-cend-ed On high in might to reign;
2 Blest be the Lord who dai-ly Our heav-y bur-den bears,

Cap-tiv-i-ty Thou lead-est A cap-tive in Thy train.
The God of our sal-va-tion, Who for His peo-ple cares.

Rich gifts to Thee are of-fered By men who did re-bel,
Our God is near to help us, Our God is strong to save;

Who pray that now Je-ho-vah Their God with them may dwell.
The Lord a-lone is a-ble To ran-som from the grave.

3 Sing unto God, ye nations,
   Ye kingdoms of the earth;
Sing unto God, all people,
   And praise His matchless worth.
He rides in royal triumph
   Upon the heavens abroad;
He speaks, the mountains tremble
   Before the voice of God.

4 All glory, might, and honor
   Ascribe to God on high;
His arm protects His people
   Who on His power rely.
Forth from Thy holy dwelling
   Thine awful glories shine;
Thou strengthenest Thy people;
   Unending praise be Thine.

126
Save Me, O God

PSALM 69

GRÄFENBERG C. M.

Johann Crüger
Praxis Pietatis Melica, 1653

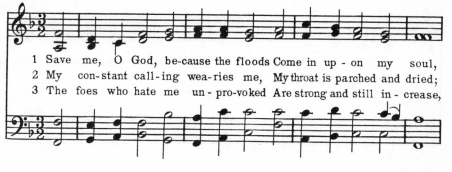

1 Save me, O God, be-cause the floods Come in up - on my soul,
2 My con-stant call-ing wea-ries me, My throat is parched and dried;
3 The foes who hate me un - pro-voked Are strong and still in - crease,

I sink in depths where none can stand, Deep wa-ters o'er me roll.
My eyes grow dim while for my God Still wait-ing I a - bide.
Though to dis-arm their en - mi - ty My right I yield for peace.

4 O God, my folly and my sin
   Thy holy eye can see;
  Yet save from shame, Lord God of hosts,
   Thy saints that wait on Thee.

5 Forbid, O God, our covenant God,
   That those who seek Thy face
  Should see Thy servant put to shame
   And share in my disgrace.

6 It is for Thee I am reproached,
   For Thee I suffer shame,
  Until my brethren know me not,
   And hated is my name.

7 It is my zeal for Thine abode
   That has consumed my life;
  Reproached by those reproaching Thee,
   I suffer in the strife.

8 I wept, with fasting bowed my soul,
   Yet that was made my shame;
  When I in sackcloth clothed myself,
   Their byword I became.

9 The men who sit within the gate
   With slander do me wrong,
  And they who linger at their cups
   Make me their jest and song.

127　In Full Assurance of Thy Grace

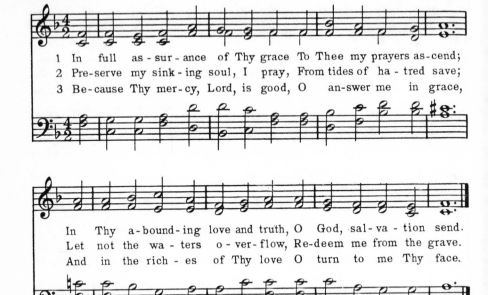

PSALM 69

St. Flavian C.M.

Day's *Psalter*, 1562

1 In full as-sur-ance of Thy grace To Thee my prayers as-cend;
2 Pre-serve my sink-ing soul, I pray, From tides of ha-tred save;
3 Be-cause Thy mer-cy, Lord, is good, O an-swer me in grace,

In Thy a-bound-ing love and truth, O God, sal-va-tion send.
Let not the wa-ters o-ver-flow, Re-deem me from the grave.
And in the rich-es of Thy love O turn to me Thy face.

4 Hide not Thy face from my distress,
　A speedy answer send;
　Draw near to me, my soul redeem,
　From all my foes defend.

5 Well known to Thee is my reproach,
　My shame and my disgrace;
　The adversaries of my soul
　Are all before Thy face.

6 My heart is broken by reproach,
　My soul is full of grief;
　I looked in vain for comforters,
　For pity and relief.

7 They gave Me bitter gall for food,
　And taunting words they spake;
　They gave Me vinegar to drink,
　My burning thirst to slake.

8 Their peace and plenty be their snare,
　In blindness let them grope;
　Thine indignation on them pour,
　And desolate their hope.

9 Because they proudly persecute
　Those whom Thou, Lord, dost smite,
　Let them be blotted from Thy book
　And banished from Thy sight.

128   Though I Am Poor and Sorrowful

PSALM 69   BALERMA C.M.   Arranged by Robert Simpson, 1833

1 Though I am poor and sor-row-ful, Hear Thou, O God, my cry;
2 Then will I praise my God with song, To Him my thanks shall rise,
3 The meek shall see it and re-joice; Ye saints, no more be sad;

Let Thy sal-va-tion come to me And lift me up on high.
And this shall please Je-ho-vah more Than of-fered sac-ri-fice.
For lo, Je-ho-vah hears the poor And makes His pris-oners glad.

4 Let heaven and earth and seas rejoice,
    Let all therein give praise,
    For Zion God will surely save,
    Her broken walls will raise.

5 In Zion they that love His Name
    Shall dwell from age to age;
    Yea, there shall be their lasting rest,
    Their children's heritage.

129 Thy Lovingkindness, Lord, Is Good and Free

PSALM 69

EVENTIDE 10 10 10 10

William H. Monk, 1861

1 Thy lov-ing-kind-ness, Lord, is good and free, In ten-der
2 Need-y and sor-row-ful, to Thee I cry; Let Thy sal-
3 With joy the meek shall see my soul re-stored; Your heart shall

mer-cy turn Thou un-to me; Hide not Thy face from
va-tion set my soul on high; Then I will sing and
live, ye saints that seek the Lord; He helps the need-y

me in my dis-tress, In mer-cy hear my prayer, Thy ser-vant bless.
praise Thy ho-ly Name, My thank-ful song Thy mer-cy shall pro-claim.
and re-gards their cries, Those in dis-tress the Lord will not de-spise.

4 Let heaven above His grace and glory tell,
   Let earth and sea and all that in them dwell;
   Salvation to His people God will give,
   And they that love His Name with Him shall live.

130   Make Haste, O My God, to Deliver

PSALM 70   DELPHINE 11 8 11 8

Hart P. Danks

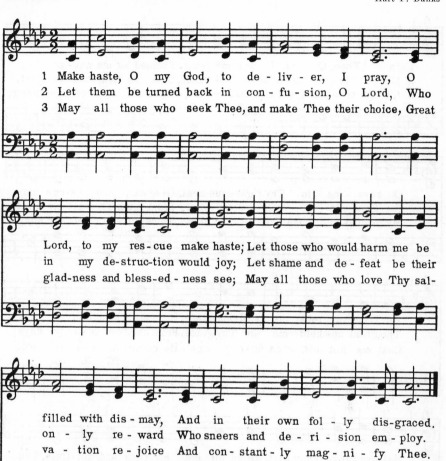

1 Make haste, O my God, to de - liv - er, I pray, O
Lord, to my res - cue make haste; Let those who would harm me be
filled with dis - may, And in their own fol - ly dis - graced.

2 Let them be turned back in con - fu - sion, O Lord, Who
in my de - struc - tion would joy; Let shame and de - feat be their
on - ly re - ward Who sneers and de - ri - sion em - ploy.

3 May all those who seek Thee, and make Thee their choice, Great
glad - ness and bless - ed - ness see; May all those who love Thy sal -
va - tion re - joice And con - stant - ly mag - ni - fy Thee.

4 I cry in deep need and Thy help I implore;
    Make haste to the rescue, I pray;
    My Savior Thou art, and my strength evermore,
    No longer Thy coming delay.

131 In Thee, O Lord, I Put My Trust

PSALM 71   I See Thee Standing, Lamb of God C. M. D.

Anonymous

1 In Thee, O Lord, I put my trust; Shamed let me nev-er be;
2 De - liv-er me from wick-ed hands, Save me from men un-just,
3 Though trou-bles great o'er-shad-ow me, Thou art my ref-uge strong;

O save me in Thy right-eous-ness, Give ear, and res-cue me.
For Thou, Je - ho - vah, art my hope, From youth Thou art my trust.
My mouth shall praise Thee all the day, Thine hon - or be my song.

Be Thou my rock, my dwell-ing-place, For - ev - er mine, as now;
Thou hast up-held me in Thy grace, From child-hood's ear-ly days;
Cast me not off when hoar-y age Be-comes my wea-ry lot,

Sal - va - tion Thou hast willed for me, My rock and for-tress, Thou.
To Thee from whom I life re-ceived Will I give con-stant praise.
And in the days of fail-ing strength Do Thou for-sake me not.

4 My foes are strong and confident,
    For I to them appear
  As one forsaken by his God,
    With none to help me near.
  My God, be Thou not far from me,
    Make haste to hear my call;
  Ashamed, consumed be all my foes,
    Dishonored let them fall.

5 But I will ever hope in Thee,
    My ceaseless praise is Thine;
  I will declare Thy countless deeds
    Of truth and grace divine.
  Yea, I will tell the mighty acts
    Performed by God the Lord;
  Thy righteousness, and Thine alone,
    With praise I will record.

132 From Days of Early Youth, O God

PSALM 71 AVON (MARTYRDOM) C. M.

Hugh Wilson, 1766-1824

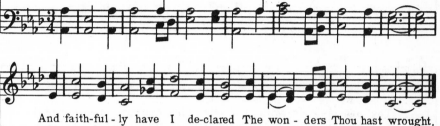

1 From days of ear-ly youth, O God, By Thee have I been taught,
2 O gra-cious God, for-sake me not When I am old and gray,
3 Thy per-fect right-eous-ness, O God, The height of heaven ex-ceeds;

And faith-ful-ly have I de-clared The won-ders Thou hast wrought.
That un-to those that fol-low me I may Thy might dis-play.
O who is like to Thee, who hast Per-formed such might-y deeds?

4 Thou who hast sent me many griefs
　Wilt yet my soul restore,
And out of sorrow's lowest depths
　Wilt bring me forth once more.

5 O turn again and comfort me,
　My waning strength increase,
And for Thy faithfulness, O God,
　My praise shall never cease.

6 Thou Holy One of Israel,
　To Thee sweet songs I raise;
The soul Thou hast redeemed from death
　Shall give Thee joyful praise.

7 My enemies that seek my hurt
　Thy help has put to shame;
My thankful tongue will ceaselessly
　Thy righteousness proclaim.

133　　O God, to Thine Anointed King

PSALM 72　　　　ISHPEMING C. M. D.

Gerhard Th. Alexis, 1924

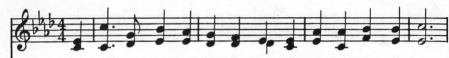

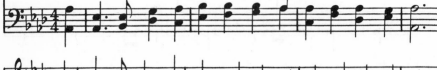

1　O　God, to Thine a-noint-ed King　Give truth and right-eous-ness;
2　The poor man's cause He will main-tain, The need-y　He　will　bless,
3　Like rain　up - on the new-mown grass, That falls re-fresh-ing - ly,

Thy peo-ple He will just - ly judge And give　the poor re-dress.
And　He will break the strength of those Who would the poor op-press.
Like gen-tle showers that cheer the earth, So　shall His com-ing　be.

Then　ev - ery fruit-ful moun-tain-side　Shall yield its rich　in-crease,
So　men shall fear Thee while the sun　In　dai - ly splen-dor glows,
The right-eous　in His glo-rious day　Shall flour-ish and in-crease;

And　right-eous-ness in all　the land Shall bear the fruit of peace.
And through all　a-ges, while the moon On　earth its light be-stows.
The earth, un-til　the moon shall fade, Shall have a-bun-dant peace.

134   His Wide Dominion Shall Extend

PSALM 72

HOLY CROSS C. M.

Adapted from Thomas Hastings, 1831

1 His wide do - min - ion shall ex - tend From sea to ut - most sea,
2 The tribes that in the des - ert dwell Shall bow be - fore His throne;
3 The kings shall come from dis - tant lands And is - lands of the sea;

And un - to earth's re - mot - est bounds His peace - ful rule shall be.
His en - e - mies shall be sub - dued, And He shall rule a - lone.
Ob - la - tions they shall bring to Him And wait on bend - ed knee.

4 Yea, all the kings shall bow to Him,
   His rule all nations hail;
  He will regard the poor man's cry
   When other helpers fail.

5 The poor and needy He shall spare,
   And save their souls from fear;
  He shall redeem them from all wrong,
   Their life to Him is dear.

6 So they shall live, and bring to Him
   Their gifts of finest gold;
  For Him shall constant prayer be made,
   His praise each day be told.

135   Christ Shall Have Dominion

PSALM 72   St. Gertrude 6 5 6 5 D., with Refrain

Arthur S. Sullivan, 1871

1 Christ shall have do - min - ion O - ver land and sea;
2 When the need - y seek Him, He will mer - cy show;

Earth's re - mot - est re - gions Shall His em - pire be;
Yea, the weak and help - less Shall His pit - y know.

They that wilds in - hab - it Shall their wor - ship bring;
He will sure - ly save them From op - pres - sion's might,

Kings shall ren - der trib - ute, Na - tions serve our King.
For their lives are pre - cious In His ho - ly sight.

Christ Shall Have Dominion

PSALM 72

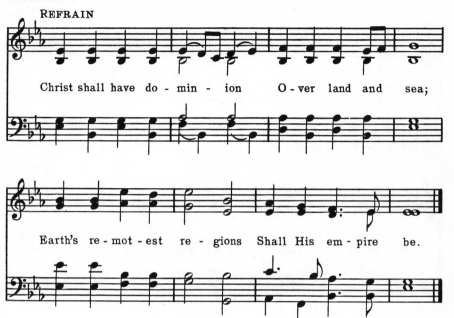

Christ shall have do - min - ion O - ver land and sea;

Earth's re - mot - est re - gions Shall His em - pire be.

3 Ever and forever
   Shall His Name endure;
Long as suns continue
   It shall stand secure;
And in Him forever
   All men shall be blest,
And all nations hail Him
   King of kings confessed.

4 Unto God Almighty
   Joyful Zion sings;
He alone is glorious,
   Doing wondrous things.
Evermore, ye people,
   Bless His glorious Name,
His eternal glory
   Through the earth proclaim.

God Loveth the Righteous

SANKEY 11 11 11 11

Ira D. Sankey, 1840-1908

1 God lov - eth the right - eous, His good - ness is sure,
2 The wick - ed are pros - pered and firm in their strength,

He nev - er for - sak - eth the good and the pure;
No pangs do they suf - fer, though death come at length;

Yet once my faith fal - tered, I en - vied the proud,
They are not in trou - ble as oth - er men are,

ritard.

In doubt and dis - qui - et my spir - it was bowed.
The plagues of their fel - lows they view from a - far.

God Loveth the Righteous

PSALM 73

3 In garments of boasting and violence decked,
   With wealth more abundant than heart could expect,
   They scoff, and the helpless they proudly oppress,
   The heavens and the earth they assume to possess.

4 Despising God's people, they cause them to drain
   The cup of oppression, injustice, and pain;
   They question God's knowledge and boldly defy
   The might and the justice of God the Most High.

5 The wicked, grown wealthy, have comfort and peace,
   While I, daily chastened, see troubles increase,
   And, wronging God's children, I cried in my pain,
   That clean hands are worthless and pure hearts are vain.

6 I went to God's temple: my doubts were dispelled,
   The end of life's journey I clearly beheld;
   I saw in what peril ungodly men stand,
   With sudden destruction and ruin at hand.

7 As when one awaking forgetteth his dream,
   So God will despise them, though great they may seem;
   My envy was senseless, my grief was for nought,
   Because I was faithless, and foolish my thought.

137 In Doubt and Temptation

PSALM 73   CARTER 11 11 11 11, with Refrain   E. Grace Updegraff

1 In doubt and temp-ta - tion I rest, Lord, in Thee; My hand is in
2 In glo - ry Thou on - ly my por - tion shalt be, On earth for none
3 All they that for-sake Thee must per-ish and die, But near to my

Thy hand, Thou car-est for me; My soul with Thy coun-sel through life
oth - er I long but for Thee; My flesh and heart fal-ter but God
Sav - ior most bless-ed am I; I make Thee my ref - uge, my Lord

Thou wilt guide, And af - ter-ward make me in glo - ry a - bide.
is my stay, The strength of my spir - it, my por-tion for aye.
and my God; Thy grace and Thy glo - ry I pub-lish a - broad.

REFRAIN

My God, I will ex - tol Thee And ev - er bless Thy Name;

Each day will I give thanks to Thee And all Thy praise pro - claim.

138   In Sweet Communion, Lord, with Thee

PSALM 73

PRAYER C. M.

William U. Butcher, 1860

1 In sweet com - mun - ion, Lord, with Thee I
2 Thy coun - sel through my earth - ly way Shall
3 Whom have I, Lord, in heaven but Thee, To

con - stant - ly a - bide; My hand Thou hold - est
guide me and con - trol, And then to glo - ry
whom my thoughts as - pire? And, hav - ing Thee, on

in Thine own To keep me near Thy side.
af - ter - ward Thou wilt re - ceive my soul.
earth is nought That I can yet de - sire.

4 Though flesh and heart should faint and fail,
 The Lord will ever be
The strength and portion of my heart,
 My God eternally.

5 To live apart from God is death,
 'Tis good His face to seek;
My refuge is the living God,
 His praise I long to speak.

139   O Israel's God, How Good Thou Art

PSALM 73

NEAR UNTO GOD 8 8 9 9 8 8 8 8

Louis Bourgeois, 1551
Harmony from De Vries *Koraalboek*
Adapted by Henry Bruinsma, 1946

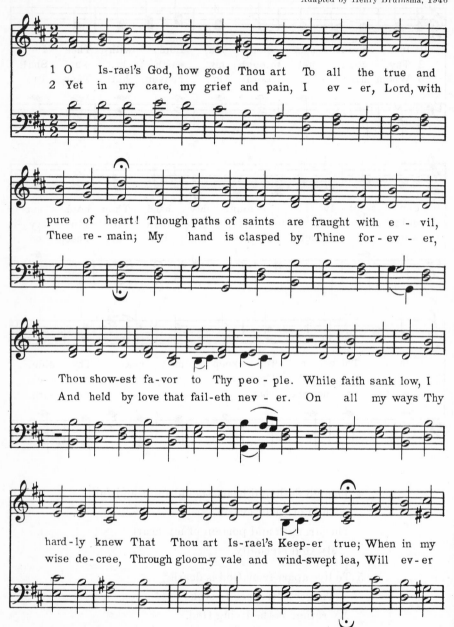

1 O   Is-rael's God, how good Thou art   To all   the true and
2 Yet in   my care, my grief and pain, I   ev - er, Lord, with

pure of heart! Though paths of saints   are fraught with e - vil,
Thee re - main; My   hand is clasped by Thine for - ev - er,

Thou show-est fa - vor to Thy peo - ple. While faith sank low, I
And held by love that fail-eth nev - er. On   all my ways Thy

hard - ly knew That   Thou art Is-rael's Keep-er true; When in my
wise de-cree, Through gloom-y vale and wind-swept lea, Will   ev - er

O Israel's God, How Good Thou Art

PSALM 73

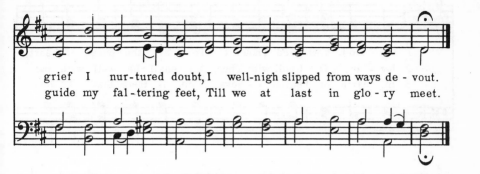

grief I nur-tured doubt, I well-nigh slipped from ways de - vout.
guide my fal - tering feet, Till we at last in glo - ry meet.

3 Whom have I, Lord, but Thee on high?

None else on earth can satisfy

But Thou, O God, my soul's deep yearning;

For Thee my troubled heart is burning.

Though flesh should faint and heart should break,

Thou art my rock that naught can shake;

In life, in death, Thou art my stay,

My strength, my portion, Lord, for aye.

4 All they who wander far from Thee

Will perish in their misery;

Thou hast destroyed the carnal-hearted,

Who from Thy covenant-ways departed.

But unto Thee, my God on high,

'Tis good for me that I draw nigh;

I'll trust Thee, Lord, through all my days,

And publish all Thy works and ways.

William Kuipers, 1931

O God, How Good Thou Art

OLIVET 6 6 4 6 6 6 4

Lowell Mason, 1832

1 O God, how good Thou art To all the pure of heart,
2 Ev - er, O Lord, with Thee, All shall be well with me,
3 In earth or heaven a - bove Who is there that I love

Though life seems vain; Bur-dened with anx-ious care, I groped in
Held by Thy hand; And Thou wilt guide my feet By Thine own
Com - pared with Thee? My heart may faint with fears, But God my

dark de-spair, Till in Thy house of prayer All was made plain.
coun - sel sweet, Till I, for glo - ry meet, In glo - ry stand.
strength ap-pears, And will to end-less years My por - tion be.

4 O it is good that I
May still to God draw nigh,
As oft before;
The Lord Jehovah blest,
My refuge and my rest,
Shall be in praise confessed
Forevermore.

141 O Wherefore Hast Thou Cast Us Off

PSALM 74

LEAF C. M.

Arranged from S. W. B., 1863

1 O where-fore hast Thou cast us off, O
2 Re-mem-ber Thine in-her-it-ance, Thy
3 In ru-in long Thy tem-ple lies; A-

God, our God of old? Why art Thou an-gry with Thy sheep,
Church, re-deemed by grace; Re-mem-ber Zi-on's mount pro-faned,
rise, O God of grace, And see the ru-in foes have wrought

The sheep of Thine own fold, The sheep of Thine own fold?
Thine an-cient dwell-ing-place, Thine an-cient dwell-ing-place.
With-in Thy ho-ly place, With-in Thy ho-ly place.

4 Amid Thy courts are lifted high
  The standards of the foe,
And impious hands with axe and fire
  Have laid Thy temple low.

5 They have profaned the holy place
  Where Thou hast set Thy Name,
The sanctuaries of our God
  Are given to the flame.

6 We see no signs of power divine,
  No prophet speaks for Thee,
And none can tell, and none can know,
  How long these woes shall be.

7 How long, O God, shall blasphemy
  And shame reproach our land?
Why dost Thou not destroy Thy foes
  With Thine almighty hand?

142   O God, Thou Art Our King of Old

PSALM 74   ALBANO C. M.   Vincent Novello, 1800

In moderate time

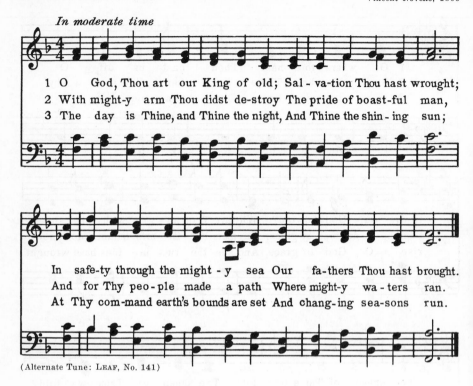

1 O   God, Thou art our King of old; Sal - va-tion Thou hast wrought;
2 With might-y arm Thou didst de-stroy The pride of boast-ful man,
3 The   day is Thine, and Thine the night, And Thine the shin - ing sun;

In safe-ty through the might - y sea Our   fa-thers Thou hast brought.
And for Thy peo-ple made a path Where might-y wa - ters ran.
At Thy com-mand earth's bounds are set And chang-ing sea-sons run.

(Alternate Tune: LEAF, No. 141)

4 Mark how Thine enemies, O Lord,

    Against Thee proudly speak;

  Preserve Thy saints from wicked men,

    Be mindful of the meek.

5 Fulfil, O Lord, Thy covenant,

    Our strong Protector be,

For in the earth are dark abodes

    Of crime and cruelty.

6 Let not Thy saints be put to shame;

    No longer in Thy sight

  Permit Thy foes to vaunt themselves;

    Lord, vindicate the right.

143   To Thee, O God, We Render Thanks

PSALM 75

FARRANT C. M.

Adapted from Richard Farrant, 1530-1580

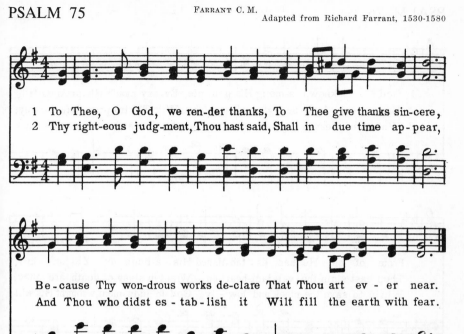

1 To Thee, O God, we ren-der thanks, To Thee give thanks sin-cere,
2 Thy right-eous judg-ment, Thou hast said, Shall in due time ap-pear,

Be-cause Thy won-drous works de-clare That Thou art ev - er near.
And Thou who didst es - tab - lish it Wilt fill the earth with fear.

(Alternate Tune: ST. AGNES, No. 375)

3 Thou teachest meekness to the proud,
    And makest sinners know
  That none is Judge but God alone,
    To honor or bring low.

4 Jehovah holds a cup of wrath,
    And holds it not in vain,
  For all the wicked of the earth
    Its bitter dregs shall drain.

5 The God of Israel I will praise
    And all His glory show;
  The righteous He will high exalt
    And bring the wicked low.

144   God Is Known Among His People

PSALM 76   TEMPLE BORO 8 7 8 7 8 7   F. Pinder

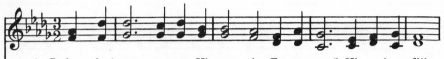

1 God   is known a-mong His peo-ple, Ev-ery mouth His prais-es fill;
2 Ex - cel - lent and glo-rious art Thou, With Thy tro-phies from the fray;
3 When from heaven Thy sen-tence sound-ed, All the earth in fear was still,

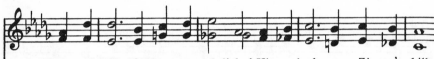

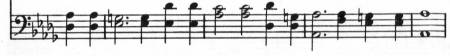

From   of old He has es - tab-lished His a-bode on Zi - on's hill;
Thou hast slain the val-iant-heart-ed, Wrapt in sleep of death are they;
While to save the meek and low - ly   God in judg-ment wrought His will;

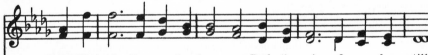

There He broke the sword and ar - row, Bade the noise of war   be   still.
When Thine an- ger once is ris - en, Who can stand in that dread   day?
E'en the wrath of man shall praise Thee, Thy de-signs it shall ful - fil.

4 Vow and pay ye to Jehovah,

Him your God forever own;

All men, bring your gifts before Him,

Worship Him, and Him alone;

Mighty kings obey and fear Him,

Princes bow before His throne.

145

To God Will I Direct My Prayer

PSALM 77

FILLMORE L. M., 6 LINES

Jeremiah Ingalls, 1764-1828

Slowly

1 To God will I di-rect my prayer, And He will make my
2 The thought of God brought me no peace, But rath-er made my
3 Re-call-ing days when faith was bright, When songs of glad-ness

needs His care; I trust Him still, though in my grief No
fears in-crease; With sleep-less eyes and speech-less pain My
filled my night, I pon-dered o'er my griev-ous woes And

an-swer yet has brought re-lief; With hands stretched out through
faint-ing spir-it grieved in vain; The bless-ed-ness of
search-ing ques-tion-ing a-rose: Will God cast off, and

all the night, Un-com-fort-ed I sought for light.
long a-go Made deep-er still my pres-ent woe.
nev-er-more His fa-vor to my soul re-store?

4 I asked in fear and bitterness:
  Will God forsake me in distress?
  Shall I His promise faithless find?
  Has God forgotten to be kind?
  Has He in anger hopelessly
  Removed His love and grace from me?

5 These doubts and fears that troubled me
  Were born of my infirmity;
  Though I am weak, God is most high,
  And on His goodness I rely;
  Of all His wonders I will tell, [dwell.
  And on His deeds my thoughts shall

146 O God, Most Holy Are Thy Ways

PSALM 77   THE LORD'S PRAYER (VATER UNSER) L. M., 6 LINES

Schumann's *Gesangbuch*, 1539

1 O God, most ho-ly are Thy ways, And who like Thee de-
2 O God, from Thee the wa-ters fled, The depths were moved with
3 Thy way was in the sea, O God, Through might-y wa-ters,

serves my praise? Thou on-ly do-est won-drous things, The
might-y dread, The swell-ing clouds their tor-rents poured, And
deep and broad; None un-der-stood but God a-lone, To

whole wide world Thy glo-ry sings; Thine out-stretched arm Thy
o'er the earth the tem-pest roared; 'Mid light-ning's flash and
man Thy foot-steps were. un-known; But safe Thy peo-ple

peo-ple saved, Though sore dis-tressed and long en-slaved.
thun-der's sound Great trem-bling shook the sol-id ground.
Thou didst keep, Al-might-y Shep-herd of Thy sheep.

168

I Thought upon the Days of Old

PSALM 77

SAXONY C. M.

William J. Kirkpatrick, 1838-1921

1 I thought up - on the days of old, The
2 My heart in - quired with anx - ious care, Will
3 For - ev - er shall His prom - ise fail? Has

years de - part - ed long, I held com - mun - ion
God for - ev - er spurn? Shall we no more His
God for - got - ten grace? Has He with - drawn His

with my heart, By night re - called my song.
fa - vor see? Will mer - cy ne'er re - turn?
ten - der love, In an - ger hid His face?

4 These doubts are my infirmity,
My thoughts at once reply;
I call back years of God's right hand,
The years of God Most High.

5 I will commemorate, O Lord,
Thy wondrous deeds of old,
And meditate upon Thy works
Of power and grace untold.

6 O God, most holy is Thy way,
Most perfect, good, and right;
Thou art the only living God,
The God of wondrous might.

148 In My Grievous Tribulation

PSALM 77

REMEMBRANCE 8 8 7 7 D.

Louis Bourgeois, 1551
Harmonized by Henry Bruinsma, 1954

Calmly, smoothly
May be sung in unison

1 In my griev-ous trib-u-la - tion, Hear my cry and sup-pli-ca - tion; O my God, who hear-est prayer, Look on me in all my care. Day and night in my com-plain-ing, Ne'er my mourn-ful voice re-strain-ing,

2 Will the Lord cast off for-ev - er, Ties of cov-enant friend-ship sev - er? Will He show His face no more As He did in days of yore? Will the word, to Is-rael spo-ken By our fa-thers' God, be bro - ken?

In My Grievous Tribulation

PSALM 77

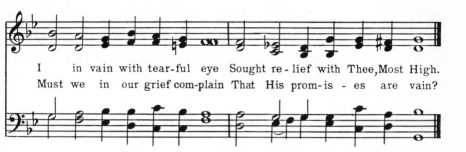

I in vain with tear-ful eye Sought re-lief with Thee, Most High.
Must we in our grief com-plain That His prom-is-es are vain?

3 Shall His wrath, my way attending,
  So I asked in sorrow bending,
  Ever stem His wondrous grace,
  And conceal His kindly face?
  Then my faith, by sorrow chastened,
  Cast out fear and doubt, and hastened
  To reply in nobler strain:
  God will send me joy for pain.

4 I'll remember, O my Savior,
  How the years of joy and favor,
  Like the dew on arid land,
  Came to me from Thy right hand.
  I'll recall, Thy works confessing,
  All the wonders of Thy blessing;
  With my mouth will I proclaim:
  Great and glorious is Thy Name.

5 Holy in Thy habitation
  Are Thy ways, Lord of creation.
  There's no god, O God, like Thee,
  Clothed with strength and majesty.
  Thou eternal art and glorious,
  All Thy wondrous works victorious;
  Let the nations, spread abroad,
  Know that Thou alone art God.

William Kuipers, 1931

149 My People, Give Ear

PSALM 78   Chios 10 10 11 11   Charles H. Gabriel, 1856-1932

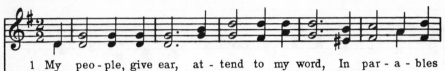

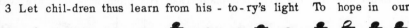

1 My peo-ple, give ear, at-tend to my word, In par-a-bles
2 In-struct-ing our sons, we glad-ly re-cord The prais-es, the
3 Let chil-dren thus learn from his-to-ry's light To hope in our

new deep truths shall be heard; The won-der-ful sto-ry our
works, the might of the Lord, For He has com-mand-ed that
God and walk in His sight, The God of their fa-thers to

fa - thers made known To chil-dren suc-ceed-ing by us must be shown.
what He has done Be passed in tra-di-tion from fa-ther to son.
fear and o - bey, And ne'er like their fa-thers to turn from His way.

4 The story be told, to warn and restrain,
  Of hearts that were hard, rebellious and vain,
  Of soldiers who faltered when battle was near,
  Who kept not God's covenant nor walked in His fear.

5 God's wonderful works to them He had shown,
  His marvelous deeds their fathers had known;
  He made for their pathway the waters divide,
  His glorious pillar of cloud was their guide.

My People, Give Ear

6 He gave them to drink, relieving their thirst,
And forth from the rock caused water to burst;
Yet faithless they tempted their God, and they said,
Can He who gave water supply us with bread?

7 Jehovah was wroth because they forgot
To hope in their God, and trusted Him not;
Yet gracious, He opened the doors of the sky
And rained down the manna in richest supply.

8 With bread from on high their need He supplied,
And more did He do when thankless they sighed:
The strong winds commanding from south and from east,
He sent them abundance of quail for their feast.

9 Though well they were filled, their folly they chose,
Till God in His wrath o'erwhelmed them with woes;
He slew of their strongest and smote their young men,
But still unbelieving, they sinned even then.

10 Because of their sin He smote with His rod,
And then they returned and sought for their God;
Their Rock and Redeemer was God the Most High,
Yet false were their praises, their promise a lie.

11 He gave them the land, a heritage fair;
The nations that dwelt in wickedness there
He drove out before them with great overthrow
And gave to His people the tents of the foe.

12 Again they rebelled and tempted the Lord,
Unfaithful, they turned to idols abhorred,
And God in His anger withdrew from them then,
No longer delighting to dwell among men.

13 He gave them to death in battle, although
His glory and strength were scorned by the foe;
Their young men were fallen, their maidens unwed,
Their priests slain in battle, none wept for the dead.

14 Then mercy awoke, the Lord in His might
Returned, and the foes were scattered in flight;
Again to His people His favor He showed
And chose in Mount Zion to fix His abode.

15 His servant He called, a shepherd of sheep,
From tending his flock, the people to keep;
So David their shepherd with wisdom and might
Protected and fed them and led them aright.

150   Let Children Hear the Mighty Deeds

PSALM 78   WEYMOUTH C. M. D.   Theodore P. Ferris, 1941

With animation

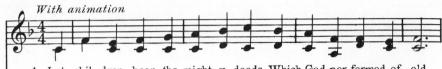

1 Let chil-dren hear the might-y deeds Which God per-formed of old,
2 Our lips shall tell them to our sons, And they a - gain to theirs;

Which in our young-er years we saw And which our fa - thers told.
And gen - er - a - tions yet un-born Must teach them to their heirs;

He bids us make His glo-ries known, The works of power and grace,
Thus shall they learn, in God a - lone Their hope se-cure - ly stands;

That we con - vey His won-ders down Through ev-er-y ris - ing race.
That they may not for - get His works, But hon-or His com-mands.

151   In Thy Heritage the Heathen

PSALM 79   HYFRYDOL 8 7 8 7 D.

Rowland Hugh Prichard, c. 1830

With dignity

1 In Thy her - i - tage the hea-then Now, O God, tri-um-phant stand;
2 O how long a-gainst Thy peo-ple Shall Thine an-ger burn, O Lord?

They de - file Thy ho - ly tem-ple, They de-stroy Thy cho-sen land;.
On Thine en - e - mies, the hea-then, Be Thine in-dig-na-tion poured;

Ruth-less, they have slain Thy ser-vants, They have caused Thy saints to mourn;
Smite the king-doms that de - fy Thee, Call - ing not up - on Thy Name;

In the sight of all a - bout us We en - dure re-proach and scorn.
They have long de-voured Thy peo - ple And have swept Thy land with flame.

3 O remember not against us
  Evil by our fathers wrought;
Haste to help us in Thy mercy,
  Near to ruin we are brought;
Help us, God of our salvation,
  For the glory of Thy Name;
For Thy Name's sake come and save us,
  Take away our sin and shame.

4 Let Thy foes no longer scorn Thee,
  Now avenge Thy servants slain;
Loose the prisoner, save the dying,
  All Thine enemies restrain;
Then Thy flock, Thy chosen people,
  Unto Thee their thanks shall raise,
And to every generation
  We will sing Thy glorious praise.

Remember Not, O God

PSALM 79

GORTON S. M.

Arranged from Beethoven, 1770-1827

1 Re - mem - ber not, O God, The sins of long a - go; In ten - der mer - cy vis - it us, Dis - tressed and hum - bled low.

2 O Lord, our Sav - ior, help, And glo - ri - fy Thy Name; De - liv - er us from all our sins And take a - way our shame.

3 In Thy compassion hear
    Thy prisoner's plaintive sigh,
    And in the greatness of Thy power
    Save those about to die.

4 Then, safe within Thy fold,
    We will exalt Thy Name;
    Our thankful hearts with songs of joy
    Thy goodness will proclaim.

153 Great Shepherd Who Leadest Thy People in Love

PSALM 80   CARITAS 11 11 11 11

Adoniram J. Gordon, 1836-1895

1 Great Shep-herd who lead-est Thy peo-ple in love, 'Mid cher-u-bim
2 O haste, Lord, to hear us and pit-y our woes, Af-flic-tion our
3 A place for Thy peo-ple Thou, Lord, didst pre-pare, Thy vine deep-ly

dwell-ing, shine Thou from a-bove; In might come and save us, Thy
por-tion, de-spised by our foes. O Lord God Al-might-y, in
root-ed re-ward-ed Thy care; Its branch-es like ce-dars, ma-

peo-ple re-store, And we shall be saved when Thy face shines once more.
mer-cy re-store, And we shall be saved when Thy face shines once more.
jes-tic and free, Spread o-ver the moun-tains from riv-er to sea.

4 Thy vineyard no longer Thy tender care knows,
Defenseless, the victim and spoil of her foes;
O turn, we beseech Thee, all glory is Thine,
Look down in Thy mercy and visit Thy vine.

5 The branch of Thy planting is burned and cut down,
Brought nigh to destruction because of Thy frown;
The man of Thy right hand with wisdom endue,
The son of man strengthen Thy pleasure to do.

6 When Thou shalt revive us Thy Name we will praise,
And nevermore turning, depart from Thy ways;
O Lord God Almighty, in mercy restore,
And we shall be saved when Thy face shines once more.

154 O Thou Great Shepherd of Thy Chosen Race

PSALM 80 LANGRAN 10 10 10 10 10 10 James Langran, 1862

1 O Thou great Shep - herd of Thy cho - sen race,
2 How long, O Lord, wilt Thou dis - dain our prayer?

Who lead - est like a flock Thine Is - rael dear,
For Thou hast fed us with the bread of tears,

From out the cher - u - bim re - veal Thy face,
And bit - ter sor - row Thou hast made us share;

Be - fore our host now let Thy might ap - pear.
The na - tions round us mock with scorn - ful jeers.

O Thou Great Shepherd of Thy Chosen Race

PSALM 80

Come Thou, O God, to save us and re - store;
O God of hosts, Thy peo - ple now re - store;

We shall be saved when shines Thy face once more.
We shall be saved when shines Thy face once more.

3 A vine Thou broughtest forth from Egypt's land;
    The nations were thrust out to give it room;
It took deep root, it spread on every hand,
    The hills were covered with its shade and bloom;
Its boughs were like great cedars spreading wide;
They reached the sea, its roots the riverside.

4 Why hast Thou broken down its circling wall
    That they may pluck who pass along the way?
Wild beasts from out the wood destroy it all
    And feed upon Thy vine by night and day.
O God of hosts, we pray Thee now, restore;
We shall be saved when shines Thy face once more.

5 Look down, behold and visit this Thy vine
    Which Thou hast planted with Thine own right hand,
The branch Thou hast made strong and owned as Thine,
    For it is burned with fire, no more to stand;
Thy people perish in Thine anger sore
Because Thy face now shines on them no more.

6 O let Thy hand Thy chosen one sustain,
    The son of man Thou madest strong to be;
So we shall faithful to Thy cause remain;
    Revive Thou us, and we will call on Thee.
Jehovah, God of hosts, again restore:
We shall be saved when shines Thy face once more.

Now to God, Our Strength and Savior

PSALM 81   STOCKWELL 8 7 8 7   Darius E. Jones, 1851

1 Now to God, our Strength and Sav - ior, Ren - der
2 Let the trum - pet, far re - sound - ing, This our
3 I, thy God, re - moved thy bur - dens, When thou

praise and loud - ly sing; In our fa - thers' God re -
fes - tal day pro - claim, By our fa - thers' God ap -
call - edst, set thee free, Proved thee in the thirst - y

joic - ing, All your no - blest mu - sic bring.
point - ed, When from bond - age Is - rael came.
des - ert, In the thun - der an - swered thee.

4 O My people, hear My pleadings;
O that thou wouldst hearken now;
No strange worship shalt thou offer,
Nor to idols shalt thou bow.

Now to God, Our Strength and Savior

PSALM 81

5 I am God the Lord who saved thee,
   And from cruel bondage freed;
   Open wide thy mouth of longing;
   I will satisfy thy need.

6 But My people would not hearken,
   Yea, they would not yield to Me;
   So I left them in their blindness,
   Their own counselors to be.

7 If My people would obey Me,
   Gladly walking in My ways,
   Soon would I, their foes subduing,
   Fill their lips with songs of praise.

8 All the haters of Jehovah
   Shall His clemency implore,
   And the days of those that love Him
   Shall endure forevermore.

9 Yea, with wheat the very finest
   I their hunger will supply,
   Bid the very rocks yield honey
   That shall fully satisfy.

156 Now to God Our King

PSALM 81

TRUMPET 5 6 5 5 5 6

Attributed to Maitre Pierre, 1562
Harmonized by Henry Bruinsma, 1954

Joyfully; may be sung in unison

1 Now to God our King, Joy and strength of Is - rael,
2 This our fes - tal day Ja - cob's God has giv - en;
3 "Hear, my chil - dren, hear," Saith the Lord who bore thee;

Lof - ty an - thems sing; Glo - rious are His ways,
Sol - emn joy dis - play Through-out all the land;
"Nev - er serve nor fear Gods of wood or stone;

To His name give praise With the harp and tim - brel.
This is the com - mand Of the God of heav - en.
I am God a - lone, Wor-ship and a - dore Me."

4 "Open," saith the Lord,
   "Wide thy mouth, believing
This My covenant-word:
'I will, if thou plead,
Fill thine every need,
   All thy wants relieving.' "

5 "O that to My voice
   Israel would hearken!
Then they would rejoice,
Walking in My ways,
Bright and joyous days
   Ne'er a foe would darken."

6 "Most abundant good,
   —If thou wouldst but prove Me—
E'en the choicest food,
Honey from the comb,
Wheat the finest known,
   I would pour upon thee."

Benjamin Essenburg, 1931

157 There Where the Judges Gather

PSALM 82

MEIRIONYDD 7 6 7 6 D.

Welsh Hymn Melody

1 There where the judg - es gath - er A Great - er takes His seat;
2 Deal just - ly with the need - y, Pro - tect the fa - ther - less,
3 He speaks: I named you ru - lers, Sons of the Most High God;

How long, He asks the judg - es, Will ye pro-nounce de - ceit?
De - liv - er the af - flict - ed From those who would dis - tress.
But you shall die as mor - tals, And per - ish by My rod.

How long re - spect the per - sons Of them of ill re - pute?
But you are whol - ly blind - ed, You do not un - der - stand;
A - rise, Thou God of judg - ment, Thy sove-reign-ty make known;

How long neg - lect the or - phaned, The poor and des - ti - tute?
There-fore foun-da - tions tot - ter, In - jus-tice rocks the land.
For Thine shall be the na - tions, The peo - ples Thou shalt own.

Adapted by Henry Zylstra, 1953

158   O God, No Longer Hold Thy Peace

PSALM 83   Forest Green C. M. D.

English Traditional Melody
Arranged by R. Vaughan Williams, 1906

1 O God, no long-er hold Thy peace, No long-er si-lent be;
2 Thine an-cient foes, con-spir-ing still, With one con-sent a-gree,
3 Make them like dust and stub-ble blown Be-fore the whirl-wind dire,

Thine en-e-mies lift up their head To fight Thy saints and Thee.
And they who with Thy peo-ple strive Make war, O God, with Thee.
In ter-ror driven be-fore the storm Of Thy con-sum-ing fire.

A-gainst Thine own, whom Thou dost love, Their craft Thy foes em-ploy;
O God, who in our fa-thers' time Didst smite our foes and Thine,
Con-found them in their sin till they To Thee for par-don fly,

They think to cut Thy peo-ple off, Thy Church they would de-stroy.
So smite Thine en-e-mies to-day Who in their pride com-bine.
Till in dis-may they, trem-bling, own That Thou art God Most High.

From the *English Hymnal*: by permission of the Oxford University Press

159

O Lord of Hosts, How Lovely

PSALM 84

ST. EDITH (ST. HILDA) 7 6 7 6 D.

Justin H. Knecht, 1799, and
Edward Husband, 1871

1 O Lord of hosts, how love - ly Thy tab - er - na - cles are;
2 Be - neath Thy care the spar - row Finds place for peace - ful rest;
3 Blest they who dwell in Zi - on, Whose joy and strength Thou art;

For them my heart is yearn - ing In ban - ish - ment a - far.
To keep her young in safe - ty The swal - low finds a nest;
For - ev - er they will praise Thee, Thy ways are in their heart.

My soul is long - ing, faint - ing, Thy sa - cred courts to see;
Then, Lord, my King Al - might - y, Thy love will shel - ter me;
Though tried, their tears like show - ers Shall fill the springs of peace,

My heart and flesh are cry - ing, O liv - ing God, for Thee.
Be - side Thy ho - ly al - tar My dwell - ing-place shall be.
And all the way to Zi - on Their strength shall still in - crease.

160 Lord God of Hosts, in Mercy

PSALM 84

CRUX CHRISTI 7 6 7 6 D.

Arthur H. Mann, 1897

1 Lord, God of hosts, in mer - cy My sup - pli - ca - tion hear;
2 In Thy blest courts to wor - ship, My God, a sin - gle day
3 A sun and shield for - ev - er Is God, the Lord Most High;

Al - might - y and all - faith - ful, Our fa - thers' God, give ear.
Is bet - ter than a thou-sand While far from Thee I stray.
To those who walk up - right - ly No good will He de - ny.

Our Shield and great De - fend - er, No long - er hide Thy face,
Though in a low - ly sta - tion, The ser - vice of my Lord
His saints, His grace re - ceiv - ing, Shall soon His glo - ry see;

But look up - on Thy ser - vant, A - noint - ed by Thy grace.
I choose a - bove all pleas - ures That sin - ful ways af - ford.
O Lord of hosts, most bless - ed Are they that trust in Thee.

161   O Lord of Hosts, to Thee I Cry

PSALM 84   AUDITE AUDIENTES ME   C. M. D.   Arthur S. Sullivan, 1875

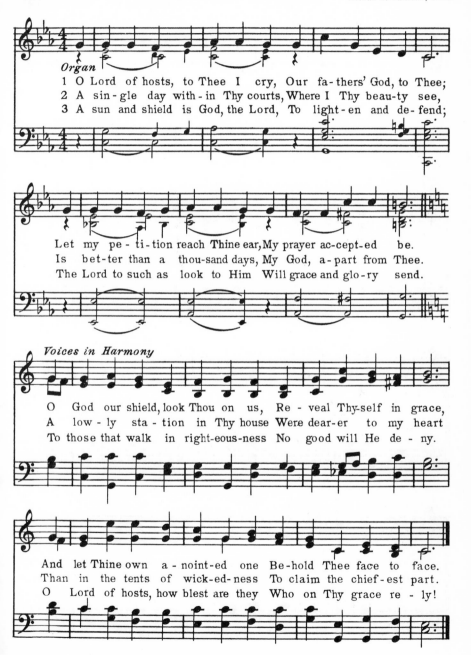

Organ

1 O Lord of hosts, to Thee I cry, Our fa-thers' God, to Thee;
2 A sin-gle day with-in Thy courts, Where I Thy beau-ty see,
3 A sun and shield is God, the Lord, To light-en and de-fend;

Let my pe-ti-tion reach Thine ear, My prayer ac-cept-ed be.
Is bet-ter than a thou-sand days, My God, a-part from Thee.
The Lord to such as look to Him Will grace and glo-ry send.

Voices in Harmony

O God our shield, look Thou on us, Re-veal Thy-self in grace,
A low-ly sta-tion in Thy house Were dear-er to my heart
To those that walk in right-eous-ness No good will He de-ny.

And let Thine own a-noint-ed one Be-hold Thee face to face.
Than in the tents of wick-ed-ness To claim the chief-est part.
O Lord of hosts, how blest are they Who on Thy grace re-ly!

O God of Hosts, O God of Grace

TABERNACLES 8 8 9 8 8 9 8 8

Maitre Pierre, 1562
Harmonized by Henry Bruinsma, 1947

Joyfully; may be sung in unison

1 O God of hosts, O God of grace, How love-ly is Thy
2 The spar-row finds a house to rest, The swal-low deft - ly

ho - ly place, How good and pleas-ant is Thy dwell - ing!
builds her nest, And broods her young hard by Thine al - tar.

My thirst-y soul longs ear-nest-ly, Yea, faints Thy ho - ly courts to see;
O Lord of hosts, my God, my King, With all my soul to Thee I cling!

'Mid fes-tal throngs and mu-sic swell - ing. My heart and flesh cry
Hold Thou my hand, lest I should fal - ter. How blest are they that

O God of Hosts, O God of Grace

PSALM 84

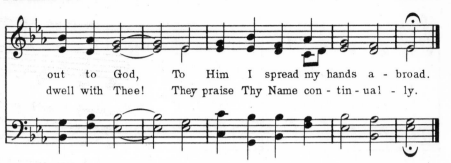

out to God, To Him I spread my hands a - broad.
dwell with Thee! They praise Thy Name con - tin - ual - ly.

3 Blest is the man whose strength Thou art,
  Thy ways are hidden in his heart,
    He treads the highway to Thy dwelling.
  Though passing through a vale of tears,
  Thy grace, O God, to him appears
    With wingèd hope and power impelling.
  The wilderness, by showers blest,
  Is now a pilgrim's vale of rest.

4 From strength to strength Thy children dear
  Go forward, till they all appear
    In Zion's courts, God's holy mountain.
  O how delightful, God of grace,
  The paths of those that seek Thy face,
    And yearn for waters from Thy fountain!
  Jehovah, God of hosts, give ear,
  O Jacob's God, in mercy hear.

5 O God, our shield, with face benign
  Look on Thy servant, wholly Thine,
    And keep him, Lord, Thou great Defender!
  One day passed in Thy house of praise
  Is better than a thousand days
    Spent in the realm of earthly splendor.
  Though only at Thy door I wait,
  No tents of sin give joy so great.

6 O God Jehovah, good and kind,
  On Zion's mount in clouds enshrined,
    Thou art our sun and shield forever.
  To upright souls that seek Thy face
  Thou givest glory, truth, and grace;
    E'en in death's vale Thou failest never.
  O Lord of hosts, how blest is he
  Who puts his stedfast trust in Thee!

William Kuipers, 1931

163 Lord, Thou Hast Greatly Blessed Our Land

PSALM 85

REPENTANCE L. M.

Theodore E. Perkins, born 1831

1 Lord, Thou hast great-ly blessed our land, Thou hast brought
2 O Thou, who in a for-mer day Didst turn Thy
3 O will Thine an-ger nev-er cease, For-ev-er

back our cap-tive band, Thy par-doning grace has
dread-ful wrath a-way, In grace Thy peo-ple,
shall Thy wrath in-crease? Re-vive and quick-en

made us free And cov-ered our in-iq-ui-ty.
Lord, re-turn, And let Thy wrath no long-er burn.
us once more, And Thy sal-va-tion's joy re-store.

4 To us Thy mercy now afford
And show us Thy salvation, Lord;
Yea, Thou wilt answer us in peace,
If from our folly we will cease.

5 The Lord's salvation will appear
To men of faith and godly fear,
And glory in our land shall dwell
When we shall heed God's precepts well.

6 Now truth agrees with mercy mild,
Now law and peace are reconciled;
Behold the truth from earth arise,
With justice shining from the skies.

7 The Lord will send His blessing down,
And harvests all our land shall crown;
Before Him righteousness abides,
And in His steps our feet He guides.

164 Lord, My Petition Heed

PSALM 86   MASON 6 6 4 6 6 6 4   William F. Sherwin, 1826-1888

1 Lord, my pe-ti-tion heed, Now help me in my need,
My Sav-ior be. I am Thy ser-vant, Lord, My trust is
in Thy word, Mer-cy to me af-ford, I cry to Thee.

2 Com-fort Thy ser-vant now, While at Thy throne I bow,
For Thou art love. Thy par-doning grace is free; Sin-ners who
call on Thee Thy ten-der mer-cy see, O God a-bove.

3 Lord, hear me while I pray, While now in trou-ble's day
I seek Thy face. To an-swer, Lord, is Thine; Thou on-ly
art di-vine, Most bright Thy glo-ries shine, O God of grace.

4 By all whom Thou hast made
Be praise and worship paid
 Through earth abroad;
Thy Name be glorified,
There is none great beside,
Matchless Thy works abide,
 For Thou art God.

5 Help me Thy will to do,
Thy truth I will pursue,
 Teach me to fear;
Give me the single eye
Thy Name to glorify,
O Lord, my God Most High,
 With heart sincere.

6 How great Thy love appears
That bade death's gloomy fears
 No more dismay;
O God, to anger slow,
Save me from every foe,
Thy lovingkindness show,
 Thy truth display.

7 Show me Thy mercy true,
Thy servant's strength renew,
 Deliverance send;
To me Thy goodness show,
Thy comfort, Lord, bestow;
Let those that hate me know
 Thou art my Friend.

165 Our Gracious God Has Laid His Firm Foundations

PSALM 87

ZION'S GATES 11 10 10 11

Attributed to Maitre Pierre, 1562
Harmonized by Henry Bruinsma, 1954

Joyfully; may be sung in unison

1 Our gra-cious God has laid His firm foun,-da-tions On Zi-on's
2 What glo-rious things, O cit-y of Je-ho-vah, Are spo-ken
3 The Moor with the Phil-is-tine and the Tyr-ian Shall soon,O

mount, the courts of His de-light; Her gates of splen-dor, bathed in
in me-lo-dious tones of thee! Lo, Ra-hab, e-ven Ba-bel,
Zi-on, throng thy ho-ly gate; In glad-some strains we'll hear her

heaven-ly light, He loves far more than Ja-cob's hab-i-ta-tions.
I will see 'Mid hal-lowed cho-rus sing-ing Hal-le-lu-jah.
sons re-late: "These all were born with-in the walls of Zi-on."

4 God will Himself confirm them with His blessing,
And on the roll of nations He will count
All these as born on Zion's holy mount,
In many tongues one God, one faith confessing.

5 Then shall God's Name with holy adoration
And joyful tones be praised by Israel's throng;
Both harp and voice will blend in swelling song:
"In Zion are the founts of my salvation."

William Kuipers, 1931

166 Zion, Founded on the Mountains

PSALM 87

ZION 8 7 8 7 4 7 4 7

Thomas Hastings, 1830

1 Zi - on, found-ed on the moun-tains, God, thy Mak - er, loves thee well;
2 Hea-then lands and hos-tile peo-ples Soon shall come the Lord to know;
3 When the Lord shall count the na-tions, Sons and daugh-ters He shall see,

He has cho-sen thee, most pre-cious, He de-lights in thee to dwell;
Na-tions born a-gain in Zi - on Shall the Lord's sal-va - tion show;
Born to end-less life in Zi - on, And their joy-ful song shall be:

God's own cit - y, Who can all thy glo - ry tell?
God Al-might - y Shall on Zi - on strength be - stow,
"Bless-ed Zi - on, All our foun-tains are in thee,"

God's own cit - y, Who can all thy glo - ry tell?
God Al-might - y Shall on Zi - on strength be - stow.
"Bless-ed Zi - on, All our foun-tains are in thee."

Zion, on the Holy Hills

GUERNSEY 7 7 7 7 D.

William O. Perkins

1 Zi - on, on the ho - ly hills, God, thy Mak-er, loves thee well;
2 When the Lord the names shall write Of thy sons, a count - less throng,

All thy courts His pres-ence fills, He de-lights in thee to dwell.
God Most High will thee re - quite, He Him-self will make thee strong.

Won-drous shall thy glo - ry be, Cit - y blest of God, the Lord;
Then in song and joy- ful mirth Shall thy ran-somed sons a - gree,

Na - tions shall be born in thee, Un - to life from death re-stored.
Sing-ing forth through-out the earth: "All my foun-tains are in thee."

168 Lord, the God of My Salvation

PSALM 88

IRVING 8 7 8 7 D.

W. Irving Hartshorn

1 Lord, the God of my sal-va-tion, Day and night I cry to Thee;
2 Thou hast brought me down to dark-ness, 'Neath Thy wrath I am op-pressed;
3 Un-to Thee, with hands up-lift-ed, Dai-ly I di-rect my cry;

Let my prayer now find ac-cept-ance, In Thy mer-cy an-swer me.
All the bil-lows of af-flic-tion O-ver-whelm my soul dis-tressed.
Hear, O Lord, my sup-pli-ca-tion, Hear and save me ere I die.

Full of trou-bles and af-flic-tion, Nigh to death my soul is brought,
Thou hast made my friends de-spise me, And com-pan-ion-less I go,
Wilt Thou wait to show Thy won-ders And Thy mer-cy to the dead?

Help-less, like one cast for-ev-er From Thy care and from Thy thought.
Bound, and help-less in my bond-age, Pin-ing in my bit-ter woe.
Let me live to tell Thy prais-es, By Thy lov-ing-kind-ness led.

4 Still, O Lord, renewed each morning
　Unto Thee my prayer shall be;
Cast me not away forever,
　Let me now Thy favor see.
All my life is spent in sorrow,
　Grief and terror always nigh,
Waves of wrath have surged about me;
　Show Thy mercy ere I die.

5 Friend and lover are departed,
　Dark and lonely is my way;
Lord, be Thou my Friend and Helper,
　Still to Thee, O Lord, I pray.
Lord, the God of my salvation,
　Day and night I cry to Thee;
Let my prayer now find acceptance,
　In Thy mercy answer me.

169 My Song Forever Shall Record

PSALM 89

MARYTON L. M.

H. Percy Smith, 1874

1 My song for-ev-er shall re-cord The ten-der
2 I sing of mer-cies that en-dure, For-ev-er
3 Be-hold God's truth and grace dis-played, For He has

mer-cies of the Lord; Thy faith-ful-ness will
build-ed firm and sure, Of faith-ful-ness that
faith-ful cov-enant made, And He has sworn that

I pro-claim, And ev-ery age shall know Thy Name.
nev-er dies, Es-tab-lished change-less in the skies.
Da-vid's son Shall ev-er sit up-on his throne.

4 The heavens shall join in glad accord
To praise Thy wondrous works, O Lord;
Thy faithfulness shall praise command
Where holy ones assembled stand.

5 Who in the heavenly dwellings fair
Can with the Lord Himself compare?
Or who among the mighty shares
The likeness that Jehovah bears?

6 With fear and reverence at His feet
God's holy ones in council meet;
Yea, more than all about His throne
Must He be feared, and He alone.

7 O Thou Jehovah, God of hosts,
What mighty one Thy likeness boasts?
In all Thy works and vast designs
Thy faithfulness forever shines.

8 The swelling sea obeys Thy will,
Its angry waves Thy voice can still;
Thy mighty enemies are slain,
Thy foes resist Thy power in vain.

9 The heavens and earth, by right divine,
The world and all therein, are Thine;
The whole creation's wondrous frame
Proclaims its Maker's glorious Name.

170   Almighty God, Thy Lofty Throne

PSALM 89

WINCHESTER NEW L. M.
Hamburger Musikalisches Handbuch, 1690

1 Al - might - y God, Thy loft - y throne Has jus - tice
2 With bless - ing is the na - tion crowned Whose peo - ple
3 Thy Name with glad - ness they con - fess, Ex - alt - ed

for its cor - ner - stone, And shin - ing bright be -
know the joy - ful sound; They in the light, O
in Thy right - eous - ness; Their fame and might to

fore Thy face Are truth and love and bound - less grace.
Lord, shall live, The light Thy face and fa - vor give.
Thee be - long, For in Thy fa - vor they are strong.

4 All glory unto God we yield,
   Jehovah is our help and shield;
   All praise and honor we will bring
   To Israel's Holy One, our King.

171 In Vision to His Saints God Spake

PSALM 89

JORDAN L. M. D.

Joseph Barnby, 1872

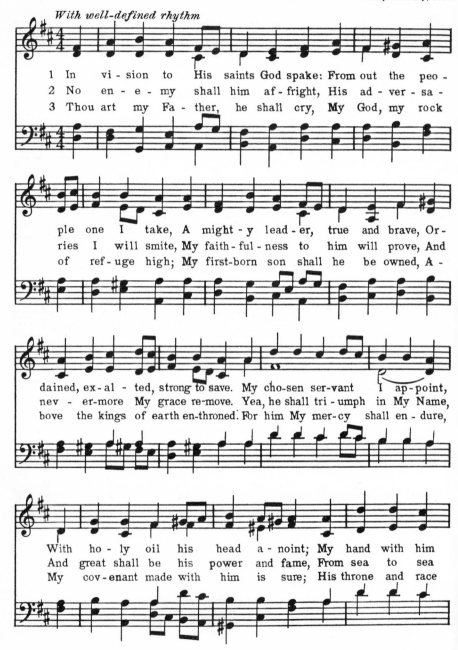

With well-defined rhythm

1 In vi-sion to His saints God spake: From out the peo-
2 No en-e-my shall him af-fright, His ad-ver-sa-
3 Thou art my Fa-ther, he shall cry, My God, my rock

ple one I take, A might-y lead-er, true and brave, Or-
ries I will smite, My faith-ful-ness to him will prove, And
of ref-uge high; My first-born son shall he be owned, A-

dained, ex-al-ted, strong to save. My cho-sen ser-vant I ap-point,
nev-er-more My grace re-move. Yea, he shall tri-umph in My Name,
bove the kings of earth en-throned. For him My mer-cy shall en-dure,

With ho-ly oil his head a-noint; My hand with him
And great shall be his power and fame, From sea to sea
My cov-enant made with him is sure; His throne and race

198

In Vision to His Saints God Spake

PSALM 89

shall still re-main, My arm his strength shall well sus-tain.
his might-y hand Shall hold do-min-ion o'er the land.
I will main-tain For-ev-er, while the heavens re-main.

4 Should sons of his My laws forsake,
My just commands and statutes break,
Then, though My rod their sins reprove,
My mercy I will not remove.
Though they be chastened sore and tried,
My faithfulness shall yet abide;
My plighted word I will not break,
Nor change the promise that I spake.

5 My oath is stedfast, ever sure,
My servant's race shall still endure;
His throne forever firm shall stay
When sun and moon have passed away.
On Thine anointed wrath is poured
As if Thy covenant were abhorred;
Thou hast profaned his kingly crown,
His matchless strength is broken down.

6 He is reproached and spoiled of all,
His enemies upon him fall;
His beauty is consumed away,
Forgotten is his kingly sway.
Cut off in youth, his sacred name
Is covered now with deepest shame;
How long, O Lord, shall wrath abide?
Thy face forever wilt Thou hide?

7 Think on my life; O Lord, take thought;
Hast Thou created man for nought?
What man that lives has power to save
His soul from death, and from the grave?
Where are Thy mercies which of old
Were in Thy promises foretold?
Remember, Lord, the bitter shame
Heaped on Thine own anointed's name.

8 I sing of mercies that endure
Forever builded firm and sure,
Of faithfulness that never dies,
Established changeless in the skies.
Blest be the Lord forevermore,
Whose promise stands from days of yore.
His word is faithful now as then;
Blest be His Name. Amen, Amen.

172 My Mouth Shall Sing for Aye

PSALM 89

SOVEREIGN GRACE 12 12 13 13 13 13

Attributed to Maitre Pierre, 1562
Harmonized by Henry Bruinsma, 1954

May be sung in unison

1 My mouth shall sing for aye Thy ten-der mer-cies, Lord,
2 "With My own cho-sen one, e'en Da-vid," God af-firmed,
3 The heav-ens praise, O Lord, Thy won-ders day and night;
To ev-ery age will I Thy faith-ful-ness re-cord;
"I've made a cov-e-nant, with sa-cred oath con-firmed;
Thy saints on earth ex-tol Thy faith-ful-ness and might;
I know how firm and sure Thy won-drous grace is found-ed,
I've sworn in truth to him, My ser-vant: 'I will sure-ly
Ex-ult-ing-ly they ask: "Who, Lord, with-in Thy dwell-ing,
Es-tab-lished in the skies by love that is un-bound-ed,
Build up thy lus-trous throne through ev-ery age se-cure-ly;
Who of the kings of earth, in car-nal strength ex-cel-ling,

My Mouth Shall Sing for Aye

PSALM 89

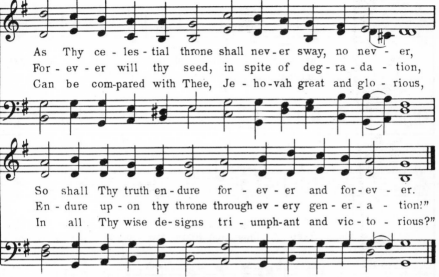

As Thy ce - les - tial throne shall nev - er sway, no nev - er,
For - ev - er will thy seed, in spite of deg - ra - da - tion,
Can be com-pared with Thee, Je - ho-vah great and glo - rious,

So shall Thy truth en - dure for - ev - er and for - ev - er.
En - dure up - on thy throne through ev - ery gen - er - a - tion!"
In all Thy wise de-signs tri - umph-ant and vic - to - rious?"

4 The hosts of heaven, O God, acclaim Thee Lord alone,
And greatly fear Thy Name 'bove all around Thy throne.
Who is there like to Thee, throughout this vast creation,
Jehovah, Lord of hosts, the God of our salvation,
Arrayed like Thee with power and faithfulness astounding,
Constraining saints to praise Thy wondrous grace abounding?

5 How blessed, Lord, are they who know the joyful sound,
Who, when they hear Thy voice, in happiness abound!
With stedfast step they walk, their countenances beaming
With brightness of the light that from Thy face is streaming;
Exalted by Thy might from depths of desolation,
They praise fore'er Thy Name, Thy justice and salvation.

6 Thou art, O God, our boast, the glory of our power;
Thy sovereign grace is e'er our fortress and our tower.
We lift our heads aloft, for God, our shield, is o'er us;
Through Him, through Him alone, whose presence goes before us,
We'll wear the victor's crown, no more by foes assaulted,
We'll triumph through our King, by Israel's God exalted.

7 As long as heaven stands on pillars firm and sure,
So long shall David's seed through endless years endure.
But if his children e'er forsake My law appointed,
And walk not in the ways decreed by Mine Anointed,
Then truly will I come in holy indignation,
And chastise them with rods for all their provocation.

8 Remember, Lord, how frail I am, how few my years;
My life is like a cloud that comes and disappears;
Has man, then, lived in vain? Who can, in death's dark hour,
Escape the dismal grave with all its ruinous power?
O Lord, recall Thy love, Thy words to David spoken,
Sustain us as of yore by covenant-oaths unbroken.

William Kuipers, 1931

173 Lord, Thou Has Been Our Dwelling-place

PSALM 90

St. Chrysostom L.M., 6 Lines

Joseph Barnby, 1871

1 Lord, Thou hast been our dwell-ing-place Through all the a - ges
2 At Thy com-mand man fades and dies And new-born gen - er -

of our race; Be-fore the moun-tains had their birth, Or
a - tions rise; A thou-sand years are passed a - way, And

e - ven Thou hadst formed the earth, From ev - er - last - ing
all to Thee are but a day; Yea, like the watch - es

Thou art God, To ev - er - last - ing our a - bode.
of the night, With Thee the a - ges wing their flight.

(Alternate Tune: St. Catharine, No. 443)

202

Lord, Thou Has Been Our Dwelling-place

PSALM 90

3 Man soon yields up his fleeting breath
Before the swelling tide of death;
Like transient sleep his seasons pass,
His life is like the tender grass,
Luxuriant 'neath the morning sun
And withered ere the day is done.

4 Man in Thine anger is consumed,
And unto grief and sorrow doomed;
Before Thy clear and searching sight
Our secret sins are brought to light;
Beneath Thy wrath we pine and die,
Our life expiring like a sigh.

5 For threescore years and ten we wait,
Or fourscore years if strength be great;
But grief and toil attend life's day,
And soon our spirits fly away;
O who with true and reverent thought
Can fear Thine anger as he ought?

6 O teach Thou us to count our days
And set our hearts on wisdom's ways;
Turn, Lord, to us in our distress,
In pity now Thy servants bless;
Let mercy's dawn dispel our night,
And all our day with joy be bright.

174   O Teach Thou Us to Count Our Days

PSALM 90

SANDS L. M., 7 Lines

William J. Kirkpatrick, 1838-1921

1 O teach Thou us to count our days And set our hearts on wis-dom's
2 O send the day of joy and light, For long has been our sor-row's
3 So let there be on us be-stowed The beau-ty of the Lord our

ways; Turn, Lord, to us in our dis-tress, In pit-y
night; Af - flict-ed through the wea - ry years, We wait un -
God; The work ac - com-plished by our hand Es - tab-lish

now Thy ser-vants bless; Let mer-cy's dawn dis-pel our night,
til Thy help ap - pears; With us and with our sons a - bide,
Thou, and make it stand; Yea, let our hope-ful la - bor be

And all our day with joy be bright, And all our day with joy be bright.
In us let God be glo-ri-fied, In us let God be glo-ri-fied.
Es - tab-lished ev-er-more by Thee, Es-tab-lished ev-er-more by Thee.

175   Lord, Through All the Generations

PSALM 90   EMMELAR (RICHARDS) 8 7 8 7 D.

Arranged from
Henry Brinley Richards, born 1819

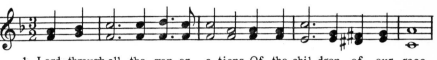

1 Lord, through all the gen-er-a-tions Of the chil-dren of our race,
2 Each suc-ceed-ing gen-er-a-tion At Thy might-y word ap-pears;
3 Long the clouds of e-vil low-er; Bless us now with glad-some days;

In our fears and trib-u-la-tions, Thou hast been our dwell-ing-place.
Thou dost count in time's du-ra-tion One day as a thou-sand years.
Let Thy ser-vants see Thy pow-er, Let their chil-dren learn Thy praise.

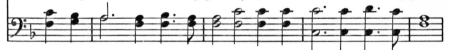

Ere the vast and wide cre-a-tion By Thy word was caused to be,
Death, with swift and sud-den warn-ing, Calls us from life's dream a-way,
On us let the grace and beau-ty Of the Lord our God re-main,

Or the moun-tains held their sta-tion, Thou art God e-ter-nal-ly.
Like the grass, green in the morn-ing, With-ered ere the close of day.
Strength-en us for no-ble du-ty That our work be not in vain.

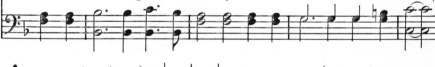

176　　O God, Our Help in Ages Past

PSALM 90　　　　LAFAYETTE C. M.

John B. Herbert, 1852-1927

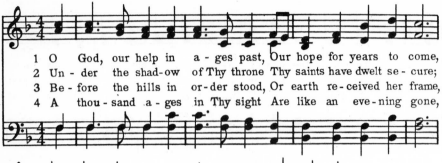

1　O　God, our help in　a - ges past, Our hope for years to come,
2　Un - der　the shad-ow　of Thy throne Thy saints have dwelt se - cure;
3　Be - fore　the hills in　or-der stood, Or earth re - ceived her frame,
4　A　thou - sand .a - ges　in Thy sight Are like an　eve -ning gone,

Our　shel - ter from the storm - y blast, And our　e - ter - nal home.
Suf - fi - cient is Thine arm a - lone, And our de - fense is　sure.
From　ev - er - last - ing Thou art God, To　end - less years the same.
Short　as　the watch that ends the night Be - fore the ris - ing　sun.

5　Time, like an ever-rolling stream,
　　Bears all its sons away;
　They fly forgotten, as a dream
　　Dies at the opening day.

6　O God, our help in ages past,
　　Our hope for years to come,
　Be Thou our guard while troubles last,
　　And our eternal home.

Alternate Tune　　　　ST. ANNE C.M.　　　　William Croft, 1708

177   The Man Who Once Has Found Abode

PSALM 91   Zephyr L. M.

William B. Bradbury, 1816-1868

1 The man who once has found abode With-in the
se - cret place of God Shall with Al - might - y
God a - bide, And in His shad - ow safe - ly hide.

2 I of the Lord my God will say, He is my
ref - uge and my stay; To Him for safe - ty
I will flee, In Him my con - stant trust shall be.

3 The Lord with His pro - tect - ing care Shall keep thee
from the hid - den snare; When fear - ful plagues a -
round pre - vail Thy life the scourge shall not as - sail.

4 Thou shalt beneath His wings abide,
And safe within His care confide;
His faithfulness shall ever be
A sure protection unto thee.

5 No nightly terrors shall alarm,
No deadly shaft by day shall harm,
Nor pestilence that walks by night,
Nor plagues that waste in noonday light.

6 At thy right hand, though thousands die,
No harm shall unto thee come nigh;
But thou, secure, unharmed, shalt see
What wicked men's reward shall be.

178 Because Thy Trust Is God Alone

PSALM 91   UXBRIDGE L. M.   Lowell Mason, 1830

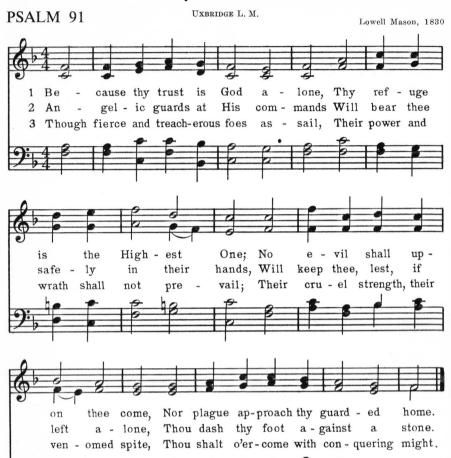

1 Be - cause thy trust is God a - lone, Thy ref - uge
2 An - gel - ic guards at His com - mands Will bear thee
3 Though fierce and treach-erous foes as - sail, Their power and

is the High - est One; No e - vil shall up -
safe - ly in their hands, Will keep thee, lest, if
wrath shall not pre - vail; Their cru - el strength, their

on thee come, Nor plague ap-proach thy guard - ed home.
left a - lone, Thou dash thy foot a - gainst a stone.
ven - omed spite, Thou shalt o'er - come with con - quering might.

4 Because on Me he set his love,
   I will his constant Savior prove,
   And since to him My name is
      known,
   I will exalt him as Mine own.

5 As oft as he shall call on Me,
   Most gracious shall My answer
      be;
   I will be with him in distress,
   And in his trouble I will bless.

6 Complete deliverance I will give,
   And honor him while he shall live;
   Abundant life I will bestow,
   To him, My full salvation show.

179   How Good It Is to Thank the Lord

PSALM 92

CHRISTINE L. M., 6 Lines

Ernest R. Kroeger, 1862-1934

1 How good it is to thank the Lord, And praise to
2 O Lord, with joy my heart ex-pands Be - fore the
3 When as the grass the wick - ed grow, When sin - ners

Thee, Most High, ac-cord, To show Thy love with morn-ing light,
won - ders of Thy hands; Great works, Je-ho-vah, Thou hast wrought,
flour-ish here be-low, Then is there end-less ru - in nigh,

And tell Thy faith - ful - ness each night; Yea, good it
Ex - ceed-ing deep Thine ev - ery thought; A fool - ish
But Thou, O Lord, art throned on high; Thy foes shall

is Thy praise to sing, And all our sweet-est mu - sic bring.
man knows not their worth, Nor he whose mind is of the earth.
fall be - fore Thy might, The wick-ed shall be put to flight.

4 Thou, Lord, hast high exalted me
  With royal strength and dignity;
  With Thine anointing I am blest,
  Thy grace and favor on me rest;
  I thus exult o'er all my foes,
  O'er all that would my cause oppose.

5 The righteous man shall flourish well,
  And in the house of God shall dwell;
  He shall be like a goodly tree,
  And all his life shall fruitful be;
  For righteous is the Lord and just,
  He is my rock, in Him I trust.

180   It Is Good to Sing Thy Praises

PSALM 92   ELLESDIE (DISCIPLE) 8 7 8 7 D.

In Joshua Leavitt's
Christian Lyre, 1831

1 It   is good to sing Thy prais-es And to thank Thee, O Most High,
2 Thou hast filled my heart with glad-ness Thro' the works Thy hands have wrought;
3 But   the good shall live be-fore Thee, Plant-ed in Thy dwell-ing-place,

Show-ing forth Thy lov-ing-kind-ness When the morn-ing lights the sky.
Thou hast made my life vic-to-rious, Great Thy works and deep Thy thought.
Fruit-ful trees and ev-er ver-dant, Nour-ished by   Thy bound-less grace.

It   is good when night is fall-ing Of   Thy faith-ful-ness to tell,
Thou, O Lord, on high ex-alt-ed, Reign-est ev-er-more in might;
In   His good-ness to the right-eous God His right-eous-ness dis-plays;

While with sweet, me-lo-dious prais-es Songs of ad-o-ra-tion swell.
All   Thine en-e-mies shall per-ish, Sin be ban-ished from Thy sight.
God   my rock, my strength and ref-uge, Just and true are all His ways.

Jehovah Sits Enthroned

RIALTO S. M.

George F. Root, 1859

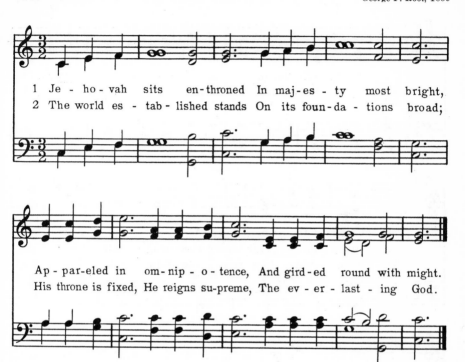

1 Je - ho - vah sits en - throned In maj - es - ty most bright,
2 The world es - tab - lished stands On its foun - da - tions broad;

Ap - par - eled in om - nip - o - tence, And gird - ed round with might.
His throne is fixed, He reigns su - preme, The ev - er - last - ing God.

3 The floods have lifted up
   Their voice in majesty,
  But mighty is the Lord our God
   Above the raging sea.

4 Thy testimonies, Lord,
   In faithfulness excel,
  And holy must Thy servants be
   Who in Thy temple dwell.

182   O Lord, Thou Judge of All the Earth

PSALM 94   BELOIT L. M.   Karl G. Reissiger, 1798-1859

1 O Lord, Thou Judge of all the earth, To whom all
ven - geance doth be - long, A - rise and show Thy
glo - ry forth, Re - quite the proud, con-demn the wrong.

2 How long, O Lord, in boast - ful pride Shall wick - ed
men tri - um - phant stand? How long shall they af -
flict Thy saints And dev - as - tate Thy cho - sen land?

3 The wid - ow and the fa - ther-less They slay, and
help - less stran - gers smite; The faith - ful God they
do not fear, They say the Lord will not re - quite.

4 Be wise, ye fools and brutish men;
　　Shall not He see who formed the eye?
　　Shall not He hear who formed the ear,
　　　　And judge, who reigneth, God Most High?

5 The Lord will judge in righteousness,
　　From Him all truth and knowledge flow;
　　The foolish thoughts of wicked men,
　　　　How vain they are the Lord doth know.

O Lord, Thou Judge of All the Earth

PSALM 94

6 That man is blest whom Thou, O Lord,
  With chastening hand dost teach Thy will,
 For in the day when sinners fall
  That man in peace abideth still.

7 The Lord will not cast off His own,
  Nor His inheritance forsake;
 Just judgment shall at length prevail,
  And upright hearts shall courage take.

8 Who will arise for my defense
  Against the wicked in the land?
 Against iniquity and wrong
  What man for me will valiant stand?

9 Unless the Lord had been my help,
  My life had quickly passed away;
 But when my foot had almost slipped,
  O Lord, Thy mercy was my stay.

10 Amid the doubts that fill my mind
  Thy comforts, Lord, bring joy to me;
 Can wickedness, though throned in might,
  Have fellowship, O Lord, with Thee?

11 The wicked, in their might arrayed,
  Against the righteous join their power,
 But to the Lord I flee for help,
  He is my refuge and my tower.

12 Our God, the refuge of His saints,
  Will fight against iniquity;
 Avenger of the innocent
  The Lord Omnipotent will be.

183 O Come Before the Lord

PSALM 95

St. Petersburg L. M., 6 Lines

Arranged from
Dimítri S. Bortniansky, 1752-1825

1 O come be-fore the Lord, our King, And in His pres-ence let us sing;
2 Al-might-y power the Lord main-tains, Ex-alt-ed o-ver all He reigns;
3 O come and let us wor-ship now, Be-fore our Mak-er let us bow;

Let us in glad and joy-ful lays The rock of our sal-va-tion praise;
He holds the val-leys in His hand, He makes the might-y moun-tains stand;
We are His sheep and He our God, He feeds our souls in pas-tures broad;

Be-fore Him come with thank-ful song, In joy-ful psalms His praise pro-long.
To Him be-long both land and sea, Cre-a-tor of the world is He.
He safe-ly leads us in the way; O come and heed His voice to-day.

4 Take heed and harden not your heart
As did your fathers, nor depart
From God to follow in their ways;
For with complaints instead of praise,
With doubt instead of faith confessed,
They put His mercy to the test.

5 Take heed that ye provoke Him not
As did your fathers, who forgot,
With erring heart, God's holy ways
And grieved Him all their sinful days;
To whom in wrath Jehovah sware,
My promised rest they shall not share.

184   Now with Joyful Exultation

PSALM 95   BEECHER 8 7 8 7 D.

John Zundel, 1870

1 Now with joy-ful ex-ul-ta-tion Let us sing Je-ho-vah's praise,
2 For how great a God, and glo-rious, Is Je-ho-vah whom we sing;

To the rock of our sal-va-tion Loud ho-san-nas let us raise;
O-ver i-dol-gods vic-to-rious, Great is He, our God and King.

Thank-ful trib-ute glad-ly bring-ing, Let us come be-fore Him now,
In His hand are earth's deep plac-es, His the strength of all the hills,

And with psalms His prais-es sing-ing, Joy-ful in His pres-ence bow.
His the sea whose bounds He trac-es, His the land His boun-ty fills.

3 To the Lord, such might revealing,
  Let us come with reverence meet,
And, before our Maker kneeling,
  Let us worship at His feet.
He is our own God and leads us,
  We the people of His care;
With a shepherd's hand He feeds us
  As His flock in pastures fair.

4 While He proffers peace and pardon
  Let us hear His voice to-day,
Lest, if we our hearts should harden,
  We should perish in the way;
Lest to us, so unbelieving,
  He in judgment shall declare:
Ye, so long My Spirit grieving,
  Never in My rest can share.

185

O Come and to Jehovah Sing

PSALM 95

CHOPIN C. M.

Isaac Baker Woodbury, 1854

1 O come and to Je-ho-vah sing, To Him our voic-es raise;
2 Be-fore His pres-ence let us come With praise and thank-ful voice;
3 Je-ho-vah is a might-y King, A-bove all gods His throne;

Let us in our most joy-ful songs The Lord our
Let us sing psalms to Him with grace, With grate-ful
The depths of earth are in His hand, The moun-tains

Sav - ior praise, The Lord our Sav - ior praise.
hearts re - joice, With grate-ful hearts re - joice.
are His own, The moun-tains are His own.

4 To Him the spacious sea belongs,
   He made its waves and tides;
   And by His hand the rising land
   Was formed, and still abides.

5 O come, and bowing down to Him,
   Our worship let us bring;
   Yea, let us kneel before the Lord,
   Our Maker and our King.

186 Sing to the Lord, the Rock of Our Salvation

PSALM 95

PEACE 11 10 11 6

George W. Chadwick, 1890

1 Sing to the Lord, the rock of our sal-va-tion! Sing to the
2 The land and sea are His, for He has made them, The val-leys
3 And we, His peo-ple, sheep of His own pas-ture, Lambs of His

Lord a song of joy and praise! Kneel in His pres-ence,
of the earth, its rug-ged hills; Corn-land and vine-yards
bos-om, whom His hand has fed, Shall we not heark-en

low-ly in thanks-giv-ing! The loft-y psalm up-raise!
and the ol-ive or-chards, All these His mer-cy fills.
to our kind-ly Shep-herd By whom our feet are led?

4 Oh, harden not your hearts, like those who wandered
   The desert forty years to Jordan's strand;
 Humble and comforted, O chosen people,
   Enter the promised land.

Theodore Maynard

217

Sing to the Lord, Sing His Praise

WESLEY 11 10 11 9

Lowell Mason, 1830

1 Sing to the Lord, sing His praise, all ye peo - ples,
2 Tell of His won-drous works, tell of His glo - ry,

New be your song as new hon - ors ye pay;
Till through the na - tions His Name is re - vered;

Sing of His maj - es - ty, bless Him for - ev - er,
Praise and ex - alt Him, for He is al - might - y,

Show His sal - va - tion from day to day.
God o - ver all, let the Lord be feared.

Sing to the Lord, Sing His Praise

PSALM 96

3 Vain are the heathen gods, idols and helpless;
   God made the heavens, and His glory they tell;
Honor and majesty shine out before Him,
   Beauty and strength in His temple dwell.

4 Give unto God Most High glory and honor,
   Come with your offerings and humbly draw near;
In holy beauty now worship Jehovah,
   Tremble before Him with godly fear.

5 Make all the nations know God reigns forever;
   Earth is established as He did decree;
Righteous and just is the King of the nations,
   Judging the people with equity.

6 Let heaven and earth be glad; waves of the ocean,
   Forest and field, exultation express;
For God is coming, the Judge of the nations,
   Coming to judge in His righteousness.

188   Jehovah Reigns As King

PSALM 97   RIGHTEOUS JUDGE 6 6 7 7 6 6 6 6 6

Maitre Pierre, 1562
Harmonized by Seymour Swets, 1954

Triumphantly; may be sung in unison

1 Je - ho - vah reigns as King, To Him all hom - age
2 Con - sum - ing flames de - ploy Be - fore Him, to de -
3 The hills, as wax by fire, Are mol - ten at His

bring; Ye is - lands, earth, and o - cean, Break forth in
stroy His foe - men round a - bout Him, Who vain - ly
ire, When God on His cre - a - tion Pours flam - ing

glad de - vo - tion. Dark clouds of se - cre - cy
seek to flout Him. His light - ning - bolts, when hurled,
in - dig - na - tion. The heavens in awe ex - press

En - shroud His maj - es - ty. The pil - lars of His throne
En - light - ened all the world; Earth saw and quaked with fear,
His per - fect right - eous - ness. Let all the na - tions see

Jehovah Reigns As King

PSALM 97

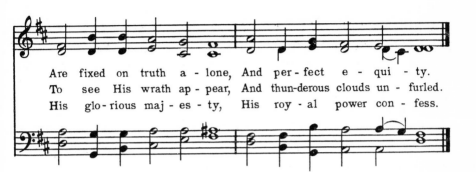

Are fixed on truth a - lone, And per - fect e - qui - ty.
To see His wrath ap - pear, And thun-derous clouds un - furled.
His glo - rious maj - es - ty, His roy - al power con - fess.

4 Confounded be all they
 Who in their folly pray
 To gods of man's creation
 And boast of vain salvation.
 Jehovah, Him we laud,
 For He alone is God.
 Come, all ye gods, draw near,
 And worship Him with fear,
 By His dominion awed.

5 All Zion then rejoiced,
 When in her gates were voiced
 The judgments, O Jehovah,
 Which Thou hast wrought for Judah.
 Her daughters sang with mirth,
 For high above the earth,
 Thou, who art God alone,
 Hast made Thyself a throne
 And magnified Thy worth.

6 Ye lovers of the Lord,
 To Him all praise accord;
 Rejoice in your confession
 And hate all base transgression.
 Jehovah keepeth well
 The saints in Israel;
 He frees them from the snare
 That wicked men prepare,
 And makes them safely dwell.

7 Jehovah's kindly face
 Gives happiness and grace
 To all that are pure-hearted;
 To them is life imparted.
 Rejoice in God, ye just,
 He raised you from the dust;
 Give thanks, ye people all,
 His holy Name recall,
 Repose in Him your trust.

Dewey Westra, 1931

189 Jehovah Reigns; Let Earth Be Glad

PSALM 97

GILEAD L. M.

Arranged from E. N. Mehul, 1763-1817

1 Je - ho - vah reigns; let earth be glad, And all the
2 Con - sum - ing fire de - stroys His foes, A - round the
3 The heavens His right - eous - ness pro - claim, Through earth His

isles their joy make known; With clouds and dark - ness
world His light - nings blaze; The trem-bling earth His
glo - ry shines a - broad; From i - dol - wor - ship

He is clad, On truth and jus - tice rests His throne.
pres - ence knows, The moun-tains melt be - fore His gaze.
turn with shame And bow be - fore the liv - ing God.

4 Thy Church rejoices to behold

Thy judgments in the earth, O Lord;

Thy glory to the world unfold,

Supreme o'er all be Thou adored.

5 All ye that truly love the Lord,

Hate sin, for He is just and pure;

To saints His help He will accord

And keep them in His love secure.

6 For good men light and joy are sown

To bless them in the harvest-time;

Ye saints, your joy in God make known

And ever praise His Name sublime.

190   Sing a New Song to Jehovah

PSALM 98   AUSTRIAN HYMN 8 7 8 7 D.   F. Joseph Haydn, 1797

1 Sing a new song to Je-ho-vah For the won-ders He has wrought,
2 Truth and mer-cy toward His peo-ple He has ev-er kept in mind,
3 Seas and all your ful-ness, thun-der, All earth's peo-ples, now re-joice;

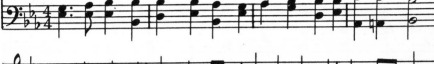

His right hand and arm most ho-ly Tri-umph to His cause have brought.
And His full and free sal-va-tion He has shown to all man-kind.
Floods and hills, in praise u-nit-ing, To the Lord lift up your voice.

In His love and ten-der mer-cy He has made sal-va-tion known,
Sing, O earth, sing to Je-ho-vah, Prais-es to Je-ho-vah sing;
For, be-hold, Je-ho-vah com-eth, Robed in jus-tice and in might;

In the sight of ev-ery na-tion He His right-eous-ness has shown.
With the swell-ing notes of mu-sic Shout be-fore the Lord, the King.
He a-lone will judge the na-tions, And His judg-ment shall be right.

191 Sing, Sing a New Song to Jehovah

PSALM 98

NAVARRE (CORNERSTONE) 9 8 9 8 D.

Louis Bourgeois, 1551
Harmonized by Henry Bruinsma, 1954

Joyfully, flowing
May be sung in unison

1 Sing, sing a new song to Je - ho - vah
2 He has re - mem - bered all His mer - cy,
3 Join to the harp your glad re - joic - ing,
4 Let all the streams in joy - ous u - nion

For all the won - ders He has wrought;
His truth de - clared to Is - ra - el;
A psalm of ad - o - ra - tion bring,
Now clap their hands and praise ac - cord,

His right hand and His arm most ho - ly
The ends of earth have seen His glo - ry;
With trum - pet and the cor - net voic - ing
The hills re - joice in glad com - mun - ion,

The vic - to - ry to Him have brought.
His ways in maj - es - ty ex - cel.
A joy - ful noise to God, the King.
And skip for joy be - fore the Lord.

The Lord has pub - lished His sal - va - tion,
Then make a joy - ful noise be - fore Him,
Let o - ceans roar with all their ful - ness,
He comes, He comes to judge the peo - ple,

His right - eous - ness He has made known;
O all ye earth, His prais - es sing;
The world and they that dwell there - in;
Ar - rayed in truth and eq - ui - ty;

He showed to ev - ery hea - then na - tion
With loud ac - claim let all a - dore Him
Pro - claim Je - ho - vah's power with bold - ness,
The world shall He re - deem from e - vil,

That judg - ment is - sues from His throne.
And let the joy - ful an - thems ring.
Ex - alt Him ev - er and a - gain.
And right - eous shall His judg - ment be.

Dewey Westra, 1931

225

192

Unto God Our Savior

PSALM 98   Repose 6 5 6 5 D.

Anonymous

1 Un - to God our Sav - ior Sing a joy - ful song;
2 Joy - ful, all ye peo - ple, Sing be - fore the Lord;
3 Waves of might - y o - cean, Earth with ful - ness stored,

Won - drous are His do - ings, For His arm is strong.
Shout and sing His prais - es Now in glad ac - cord;
Floods and fields and moun - tains, Sing be - fore the Lord;

He has wrought sal - va - tion, He has made it known,
With the harp and trum - pet Joy - ful prais - es bring;
For He comes with jus - tice, E - vil to re - dress,

And be - fore the na - tions Is His jus - tice shown.
Come, re - joice be - fore Him, God, the Lord, your King.
And to judge the na - tions In His right - eous - ness.

226

God Jehovah Reigns

DOMINUS SANCTUS 5 5 5 5 5 5 6 6

Maitre Pierre, 1562
Harmony from De Vries *Koraalboek*
Adapted by Henry Bruinsma, 1946

1 God Je - ho - vah reigns, His are all do - mains; Trem - ble at His Word,
2 God who rules in state Is in Zi - on great; He ex - cels in worth
3 For God's roy - al might Serves His truth and right; Jus - tice He main - tains,

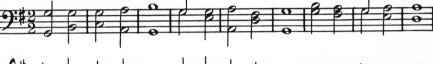

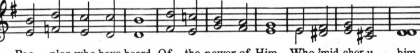

Peo - ples who have heard Of the power of Him Who 'mid cher - u - bim
All that dwell on earth. Hon - or and ac - claim His ex - alt - ed Name,
Right - eous - ly He reigns. Man - i - fest - ing grace To His cho - sen race,

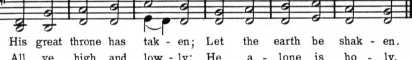

His great throne has tak - en; Let the earth be shak - en.
All ye high and low - ly; He a - lone is ho - ly.
Ja - cob's seed He'll nev - er From His cov - enant sev - er.

4 Then let all accord
Honor to the Lord;
At His footstool bow,
Seek His favor now.
Worship and acclaim
His exalted Name,
All ye high and lowly;
God alone is holy.

Samuel G. Brondsema, 1931

Jehovah Reigns in Majesty

ELLACOMBE C. M. D.

From *Gesangbuch der Herzogl*
Württemberg, 1784

1 Je - ho - vah reigns in maj - es - ty, Let all the na - tions quake;
2 The might - y King loves jus - tice well, And eq - ui - ty or - dains;
3 When priests and proph-ets called on God, He their pe - ti - tions heard;

He dwells be-tween the cher - u - bim, Let earth's foun-da-tions shake.
He rules His peo - ple right-eous-ly And faith - ful-ness main - tains.
His cloud - y pil - lar led them on, And they o-beyed His Word.

Su - preme in Zi - on is the Lord, Ex - alt - ed glo-rious - ly;
O mag - ni - fy the Lord our God, Let Him ex - alt - ed be;
Though send-ing judg-ments for their sins, He par-doned gra-cious - ly;

Ye na - tions, praise His Name with awe, The Ho - ly One is He.
In wor-ship at His foot-stool bow, The Ho - ly One is He.
Ex - alt the Lord and wor-ship Him, The Ho - ly One is He.

195   ## All People That on Earth Do Dwell

PSALM 100   ALL LANDS L. M.   Louis Bourgeois, 1551
Harmony from De Vries *Koraalboek*
Adapted by Henry Bruinsma, 1946

1 All peo-ple that on earth do dwell, Sing
2 Know that the Lord is God in-deed; With-
3 O en-ter then His gates with joy, With-

to the Lord with cheer-ful voice; Him serve with mirth, His
out our aid He did us make; We are His flock, He
in His courts His praise pro-claim; Let thank-ful songs your

praise forth tell, Come ye be-fore Him and re - joice.
doth us feed, And for His sheep He doth us take.
tongues em - ploy, O bless and mag-ni - fy His Name.

(Alternate Tune: OLD HUNDREDTH, No. 280)

4 Because the Lord our God is good,

His mercy is forever sure;

His truth at all times firmly stood,

And shall from age to age endure.

196   Of Mercy and of Justice

PSALM 101   FARMER 7 6 7 6 D.

John Farmer, 1836-1901

1 Of mer-cy and of jus-tice My thank-ful song shall be;
2 On what is base and e-vil I will not set my heart;
3 The faith-ful and the up-right Shall min-is-ter to me;

O Lord, in joy-ful prais-es My song shall rise to Thee.
Trans-gres-sors' ways ab-hor-ring, With them I take no part.
The ly-ing and de-ceit-ful My fa-vor shall not see.

With-in my house I pur-pose To walk in wis-dom's way;
No fro-ward man or e-vil Shall my com-pan-ion be;
I will in dai-ly judg-ment All wick-ed-ness re-ward,

O Lord, I need Thy pres-ence; How long wilt Thou de-lay?
I will not suf-fer slan-der Or pride or treach-er-y.
And cleanse from e-vil-do-ers The cit-y of the Lord.

197 Lord, I Will Sing with Rapturous Rejoicing

PSALM 101

RESOLUTION 11 11 10 4

Louis Bourgeois, 1551
Harmony from De Vries *Koraalboek*
Adapted by Henry Bruinsma, 1946

1 Lord, I will sing with rap-tur-ous re-joic-ing, Thy
jus-tice and Thy lov-ing-kind-ness voic-ing; A joy-ful
psalm, Je-ho-vah, I will raise Un-to Thy praise.

2 I'll wise-ly tread the path-way of per-fec-tion; When
wilt Thou come, O Lord, for my di-rec-tion? I'll walk with-
in my house with per-fect heart, From sin a-part.

3 No wick-ed thing or slan-derous ac-cu-sa-tion Shall
stand be-fore mine eyes with ap-pro-ba-tion; No hate-ful
do-ings of a-pos-ta-sy Shall cleave to me.

4 The froward heart will I not suffer near me,
All evil things will I abhor sincerely;
All who in secret at their neighbors scoff
Will I cut off.

Dewey Westra, 1931

231

198   Thou, O Lord, Art God Alone

PSALM 102   St. George's Windsor (Elvey) 7 7 7 7 D.

George J. Elvey, 1858

1 Thou, O Lord, art God a - lone, Ev - er - last - ing
2 If with love com - pas - sion - ate We, Thy ser - vants,

is Thy throne; Through the a - ges men shall sing
mourn her state, Wilt not Thou, O gra - cious Lord,

Praise to heaven's e - ter - nal King. Thou, en - throned a -
Help in Zi - on's need af - ford? Lord, Thy glo - ry

bove the skies, Wilt for Zi - on's help a - rise;
shall ap - pear, Kings and na - tions then shall fear;

Thou, O Lord, Art God Alone

PSALM 102

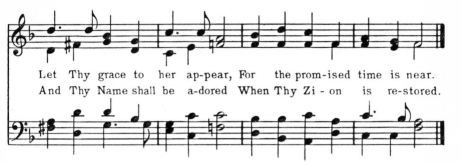

Let Thy grace to her ap-pear, For the prom-ised time is near.
And Thy Name shall be a-dored When Thy Zi - on is re-stored.

3 This all ages shall record
　For the glory of the Lord;
　Thou dost hear the humble prayer,
　For the helpless Thou dost care.
　Thou eternal art, and great,
　Heaven and earth Thou didst create,
　Heaven and earth shall pass away,
　Changeless Thou shalt live for aye.

4 As one lays a garment by,
　Thou wilt change the starry sky
　Like a vesture worn and old;
　But Thy years shall ne'er be told.
　Thou wilt make Thy servants' race
　Ever live before Thy face,
　And forever at Thy side
　Children's children shall abide.

199 Lord, Hear My Prayer

PSALM 102

HOLY COMMUNION L. M. D.

J. Michael Haydn, 1737-1806

1 Lord, hear my prayer and let my cry Have ready access
2 My heart is with-ered like the grass, And I for-get my

un - to Thee; When in dis-tress to Thee I fly,
dai - ly bread; In lone-ly grief my days I pass

O hide not Thou Thy face from me. At-tend, O Lord, to
And sad my thoughts up-on my bed. My foes re-proach me

my de - sire, O haste to an-swer when I pray; For grief con-
all the day, My drink is tears, my bread is grief, For in Thy

Lord, Hear My Prayer

PSALM 102

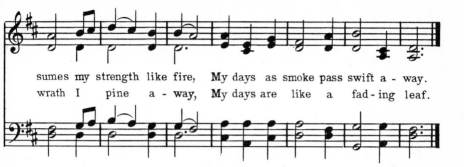

sumes my strength like fire, My days as smoke pass swift a - way.
wrath I pine a - way, My days are like a fad - ing leaf.

3 But Thou, Jehovah, shalt endure,
    Thy throne forever is the same;
And to all generations sure
    Shall be Thy great memorial Name.
The time for Zion's help is near,
    The time appointed in Thy love;
O let Thy gracious aid appear,
    Look Thou in mercy from above.

4 O Lord, regard the prayer of those
    Who love the walls of Zion well,
Whose hearts are heavy for her woes,
    Who sad amid her ruins dwell.
Thy power and glory shall appear,
    And Zion's walls shall be restored;
Then all the kings of earth shall fear
    And heathen nations serve the Lord.

5 The Lord, exalted on His throne,
    Looked down from heaven with pitying eye
To still the lowly captive's moan
    And save His people doomed to die.
All men in Zion shall declare
    His gracious Name with one accord,
When kings and nations gather there
    To serve and worship God the Lord.

200 O Bless the Lord, My Soul, with All Thy Power

PSALM 103

BLESS JEHOVAH 11 11 10 D.

Anonymous, 1539
Harmony from De Vries *Koraalboek*
Adapted by Henry Bruinsma, 1946

1 O bless the Lord, my soul, with all thy pow-er! Ex-alt the
2 O bless the Lord, who all thy need sup-pli-eth! Thy soul with

God who is thy strength and tow-er; Let all with-in me
good He ful-ly sat-is-fi-eth, And, like the ea-gle's,

bless His ho-ly Name. Bless Him who hear-eth all thy
He re-news thy youth. Je-ho-vah do-eth right, for

sup-pli-ca-tion; For-get not thou His kind-ly min-is-
He is ho-ly; His judg-ments for the sore op-pressed and

tra-tion, But all His gra-cious ben-e-fits pro-claim.
low-ly Are done in per-fect right-eous-ness and truth.

236

O Bless the Lord, My Soul, with All Thy Power

PSALM 103

3 He spake to Moses from the midst of thunder,
He brake the bonds of Israel asunder,
   And showed to them His mighty works and ways.
The Lord is gracious and of kind compassion,
He saved His own in truly wondrous fashion,
   To anger slow, He loved them all their days.

4 Jehovah will not chide with us forever
Nor always keep His anger, but deliver
   His people from their sorrows and distress.
He has not crushed the flock of His possession,
Nor dealt with us according to transgression;
   He chastens, but with love and tenderness.

5 Like as a father looketh with compassion
Upon his children, lo, in such a fashion
   The Lord doth look on them that fear and trust.
He knoweth that our frame is weak and humble;
How void of strength, how prone we are to stumble!
   And He is mindful that we are but dust.

6 Lo, as for man, his days are like a shadow,
Like tender grass and flowers of the meadow,
   Whose morning-beauty fadeth with the day;
For when the wind but lightly passeth o'er it
'Tis gone anon and nothing can restore it;
   'Tis found no more, it vanisheth for aye.

7 Jehovah's mercy floweth, like a river,
From everlasting, and abideth ever
   On those that love and worship Him with awe.
His righteousness shall bless the habitations
Of children's children through the generations
   That keep His covenant and obey His law.

8 High in the heavens has Jehovah founded
His lofty throne, by cherubim surrounded;
   And lo, His kingdom ruleth over all!
O bless the Lord, ye angels full of glory,
Ye mighty heroes, famed in sacred story,
   That do His word, obedient to His call!

9 Bless Him, ye hosts, in praises without measure,
Ye ministers of His that do His pleasure;
   Exalt His Name, His majesty extol.
Bless ye Jehovah, all His works in union,
In all the places of His wide dominion;
   Yea, bless the Lord with joy, O thou, my soul!

Dewey Westra, 1931

201 O My Soul, Bless Thou Jehovah

PSALM 103   AUTUMN 8 7 8 7 D.   Francois H. Barthelemon, 1741-1808

1 O my soul, bless thou Je - ho - vah, All with-
2 He with ten - der mer - cies crowns thee, Sat - is -

in me, bless His Name; Bless Je - ho - vah and for -
fies thy full re - quest, So that, like the tire - less

get not All His mer - cies to pro - claim.
ea - gle, Thou with youth re - newed art blessed.

He for - gives all thy trans - gres - sions, Heals thy
Right - eous is the Lord in judg - ment Un - to

O My Soul, Bless Thou Jehovah

PSALM 103

sick - ness - es and pains; He re -
all that, are op - pressed; To His

deems thee from de-struc-tion, And His love thy life sus - tains.
peo - ple He has ev - er Made His good-ness man - i - fest.

3 Yea, the Lord is full of mercy
　　And compassion for distress,
　Slow to anger and abundant
　　In His grace and tenderness.
　He will not be angry alway,
　　Nor will He forever chide;
　Though we oft have sinned against Him,
　　Still His love and grace abide.

4 As the heavens are high above us,
　　Great His love to us has proved;
　Far as east from west is distant,
　　He has all our sins removed.
　As a father loves his children,
　　Feeling pity for their woes,
　So the Lord to those who fear Him
　　Mercy and compassion shows.

Mindful of Our Human Frailty

PSALM 103

Talmar 8 7 8 7

Isaac Baker Woodbury, 1845

1 Mind - ful of our hu - man frail - ty Is the
2 Man is like the ten - der flow - er, And his

God in whom we trust; He whose years are ev - er -
days are like the grass, With-ered where it late - ly

last - ing, He re - mem - bers we are dust.
flour - ished By the blight - ing winds that pass.

3 Changeless is Jehovah's mercy
   Unto those who fear His Name,
  From eternity abiding
   To eternity the same.

4 All the faithful to His covenant
   Shall behold His righteousness;
  He will be their strength and refuge,
   And their children's children bless.

203   In the Heavens the Lord Almighty

PSALM 103   RATHBUN 8 7 8 7   Ithamar Conkey, 1851

1 In the heavens the Lord Al - might - y Fixed His
2 Bless the Lord, ye might - y an - gels, Ye that
3 Bless the Lord, all ye His ser - vants, Min - is -

ev - er - last - ing throne; O - ver all is
heark - en to His voice, All His gra - cious
ters of God Most High; Ye His hosts, that

His do - min - ion, He is God and He a - lone.
word ful - fill - ing, Ev - er bless Him and re - joice.
do His pleas - ure, God your Mak - er glo - ri - fy.

4 Bless the Lord, all things created;
    Be His holy Name adored
    All throughout His wide dominion;
    O my soul, bless thou the Lord.

204　O Come, My Soul, Bless Thou the Lord

PSALM 103　Tidings (Tunbridge) 11 10 11 10, with Refrain

James Walch, 1876

1 O come, my soul, bless thou the Lord thy Mak-er, And all with-
2 Good is the Lord and full of kind com-pas-sion, Most slow to
3 His love is like a fa-ther's to his chil-dren, Ten-der and
4 We fade and die like flowers that grow in beau-ty, Like ten-der

in me, bless His ho-ly Name; Bless thou the Lord, for-get not all His
an-ger, plen-te-ous in love; Rich is His grace to all that hum-bly
kind to all who fear His Name; For well He knows our weak-ness and our
grass that soon will dis-ap-pear; But ev-er-more the love of God is

mer-cies, His par-doning grace and sav-ing love pro-claim.
seek Him, Bound-less and end-less as the heavens a-bove.
frail-ty, He knows that we are dust, He knows our frame.
change-less, Still shown to those who look to Him in fear.

Bless Him, ye

an-gels, won-drous in might, Bless Him, His ser-vants, that in His will de-light.

5 High in the heavens His throne is fixed forever,
His kingdom rules o'er all from pole to pole;
Bless ye the Lord through all His wide dominion,
Bless His most holy Name, O thou my soul.

205
The Tender Love a Father Has

PSALM 103

AVONDALE C.M.

Charles H. Gabriel, 1856-1932

1 The tender love a father has
For all his children dear,
Such love the Lord bestows on them
Who worship Him in fear.

2 The Lord remembers we are dust,
And all our frailty knows;
Man's days are like the tender grass,
And as the flower he grows.

3 The flower is withered by the wind
That smites with blighting breath;
So man is quickly swept away
Before the blast of death.

4 Unchanging is the love of God,
From age to age the same,
Displayed to all who do His will
And reverence His Name.

5 Those who His gracious covenant keep
The Lord will ever bless;
Their children's children shall rejoice
To see His righteousness.

206

My Soul, Bless the Lord!

PSALM 104

HOUGHTON 10 10 11 11

Henry J. Gauntlett, 1861

1 My soul, bless the Lord! the Lord is most great,
2 He rides on the clouds, the wings of the storm,

With glo - ry ar - rayed, ma - jes - tic His state;
The light-ning and wind His mis - sion per - form;

The light is His gar - ment, the skies are His shade,
The earth He has found - ed her sta - tion to keep,

And o - ver the wa - ters His courts He has laid.
And wrapped as a ves - ture a - bout her the deep.

My Soul, Bless the Lord!

PSALM 104

3 O'er mountain and plain the dark waters raged;
His voice they obeyed, the floods were assuaged;
Uplifting the mountains He ordered a bound,
Forbidding the waters to cover the ground.

4 He causes the springs of water to flow
In streams 'mid the hills and valleys below;
Beside them with singing the birds greet the day,
And there the beasts gather their thirst to allay.

5 He waters the hills with rain from the skies,
And plentiful grass and herbs He supplies,
Supplying the cattle, and blessing man's toil
With bread in abundance, with wine and with oil.

6 The trees which the Lord has planted are fed,
And over the earth their branches are spread;
They keep in their shelter the birds of the air,
The life of each creature the Lord makes His care.

7 Thy Spirit, O Lord, makes life to abound,
The earth is renewed, and fruitful the ground;
To God ascribe glory and wisdom and might,
Let God in His creatures forever delight.

8 Rejoicing in God, my thought shall be sweet,
While sinners depart in ruin complete;
My soul, bless Jehovah, His Name be adored,
Come, praise Him, ye people, and worship the Lord.

207 The Seasons Are Fixed by Wisdom Divine

PSALM 104 ASPINWALL 10 10 11 11

Charles H. Gabriel, 1856-1932

1 The sea-sons are fixed by wis-dom di-vine, The slow-chang-ing
2 The Lord makes the night, when, leav-ing their lair, The li-ons creep
3 How man-y and wise Thy works are, O Lord! The earth with the

moon shows forth God's de-sign; The sun in his cir-cuit his
forth, God's boun-ty to share; The Lord makes the morn-ing, when
wealth of wis-dom is stored; The sea bears in safe-ty the

Mak-er o-beys, And run-ning his jour-ney hastes not nor de-lays.
beasts steal a-way And men are be-gin-ning the work of the day.
ships to and fro, And crea-tures un-num-bered it shel-ters be-low.

4 Thy creatures all look to Thee for their food;
  Thy hand opens wide, they gather the good;
  Thy face Thou concealest, in anguish they yearn;
  Their breath Thou withholdest, to dust they return.

5 Thy Spirit, O Lord, makes life to abound,
  The earth is renewed, and fruitful the ground;
  To God ascribe glory and wisdom and might,
  Let God in His creatures forever delight.

The Seasons Are Fixed by Wisdom Divine
PSALM 104

6 Before the Lord's might earth trembles and quakes,
The mountains are rent, and smoke from them breaks;
The Lord I will worship through all of my days,
Yea, while I have being my God I will praise.

7 Rejoicing in God, my thought shall be sweet,
While sinners depart in ruin complete;
My soul, bless Jehovah, His Name be adored,
Come, praise Him, ye people, and worship the Lord.

208 O Lord, How Manifold the Works
PSALM 104

Moline C.M.

William J. Kirkpatrick, 1838-1921

1 O Lord, how man-i-fold the works In wis-dom wrought by Thee;
2 Let God re-joice in all His works, And let His works pro-claim
3 While life shall last, my thank-ful lips A song to God will raise,

The wealth of Thy cre-a-tion fills The earth and might-y sea.
For-ev-er-more their Mak-er's praise And glo-ri-fy His Name.
And while my be-ing I pos-sess, My Mak-er I will praise.

4 My heart shall think upon His grace
In meditation sweet;
My soul, rejoicing in the Lord,
His praises shall repeat.

209   Unto the Lord Lift Thankful Voices

PSALM 105

PIERRE 9 9 8 8 8 8

Maitre Pierre, 1562
Harmonized by H. J. Van Andel, 1954

1 Un - to the Lord lift thank-ful voic - es, Come, wor-ship
2 In joy-ful song your hearts u - nit - ing, His works most

while your soul re-joic - es; Make known His do-ings far and near
mar - vel - ous re - cit - ing, Now glo-ry in His ho-ly Name;

That peo-ples all His Name may fear, And tell, in
Let those that seek Him spread His fame, In - cline their

man-y a joy - ful lay, Of all His won-ders day by day.
hearts to sing His praise, And un - to Him their an - thems raise.

Unto the Lord Lift Thankful Voices

PSALM 105

3 Seek ye Jehovah and His power,
   Seek ye His presence every hour.
   His works, so marvelous and great,
   Remember still, and meditate
   Upon the wonders of His hands,
   The judgments which His mouth commands.

4 Ye seed from Abraham descended,
   To whom His favors were extended,
   And Jacob's children, whom the Lord
   Has chosen, hearken to His word.
   He is the Lord, our Judge divine;
   In all the earth His glories shine.

5 Jehovah's truth will stand forever,
   His covenant-bonds He will not sever;
   The word of grace which He commands
   To thousand generations stands;
   The covenant made in days of old
   With Abraham He doth uphold.

6 The Lord His covenant people planted
   In lands of nations which He granted,
   That they His statutes might observe,
   Nor from His laws might ever swerve.
   Let songs of praise to Him ascend,
   And hallelujahs without end.

Samuel G. Brondsema, 1931

210 O Praise the Lord, His Deeds Make Known

PSALM 105

Spohr C.M.D.

Louis Spohr, 1835

1 O praise the Lord, His deeds make known, And call up-on His Name;
2 Ye chil - dren of God's cov - e - nant, Who of His grace have heard,

Sing ye to Him, His prais-es sing, His won-drous works pro-claim.
For - get not all His won-drous deeds And judg-ments of His word.

Let hearts re-joice that seek the Lord, His ho - ly Name a - dore;
The Lord our God is God a-lone, All lands His judg-ments know;

Seek ye Je-ho-vah and His strength, Seek Him for-ev - er - more.
His prom - ise He re - mem-bers still, While gen-er-a- tions go.

O Praise the Lord, His Deeds Make Known
PSALM 105

3 While yet our fathers were but few,
   Sojourners in the land,
He sware that Canaan should be theirs,
   And made His covenant stand.
He suffered none to do them wrong
   In all their pilgrim way;
Yea, for their sake were kings reproved
   And covered with dismay.

4 His stern command restrained their foes
   And filled them with alarm:
Touch not Mine own anointed ones,
   Nor do My prophets harm.
He wholly broke the staff of bread
   And called for famine sore,
And He prepared His people's way
   By sending one before.

5 Then Joseph, sold to slavery,
   With cruel chains was bound;
Till his prediction came to pass,
   Distress and grief he found.
The king released him from his bonds
   And made him rule the land,
Subjecting chiefs and senators
   To his controlling hand.

6 To Egypt Israel followed then,
   And there grew great and strong,
Until their friends became their foes
   And did them grievous wrong.
God sent His servant Moses then,
   And Aaron, whom He chose;
Great signs and wonders they displayed
   To terrify their foes.

7 In darkness they were taught to fear
   God's great and holy Name;
On man and beast, on vine and field,
   His awful judgment came.
He smote the first-born in the land,
   The chief of all their strength,
Enriched His people with the spoil
   And brought them forth at length.

8 He led them forth in health and strength,
   None weak in all their band,
And Egypt, filled with fear, rejoiced
   To see them leave the land.
He spread a cloud to cover them,
   Most glorious and bright,
And made a fiery pillar shine
   To give them light by night.

9 At their request He sent them quails,
   And bread of heaven bestowed;
And from the rock, to quench their thirst,
   The living waters flowed.
His sacred word to Abraham
   He kept, though waiting long,
And brought His chosen people forth
   With joy and thankful song.

10 The lands and toil of wicked men
   He gave them to possess,
That they might keep His holy laws,
   Jehovah praise and bless.
Let hearts rejoice that seek the Lord,
   His holy Name adore;
Seek ye Jehovah and His strength,
   Seek Him forevermore

211 Praise Ye the Lord, for He Is Good

PSALM 106

BARRE C.M.

Edward Clark, 1871

1 Praise ye   the Lord, for He   is good; Give thanks and bless His Name;
2 What tongue can tell His might-y deeds, His   won-drous works and ways?
3 The   Lord will bless and pros-per those, Yea, blest in - deed are they

His   lov-ing-kind-ness chang-es not, From age to age   the same..
O   who can show His glo - ry forth, Or   ut - ter all   His praise?
Whose ways are just, who con-stant -ly   His right-eous law o - bey.

4 O Lord, remember me in grace,
   Let me salvation see;
   The grace Thou showest to Thy saints,
   That grace reveal to me.

5 Let me behold Thy people's good
   And in their joy rejoice;
   With Thy triumphant heritage
   Let me lift up my voice.

6 In evil we have gone astray,
   And sinful is our race;
   Rebelliously our fathers walked,
   Forgetful of Thy grace.

7 Though they rebelled, yet for their help
   In saving strength He came
   To make His power almighty known
   And glorify His Name.

8 He brought them safely through the sea
   And overwhelmed their foes;
   Their faith was stirred, and for the time
   Their songs of praise arose.

9 Forgetful soon, they tempted God,
   Nor for His counsel cared;
   He sent them leanness in their souls,
   Whilst they earth's bounties shared.

10 With envy they regarded those
   Whom God to them had sent;
   The opening earth, the kindling flame,
   Brought awful punishment.

11 A golden image they adored,
   And worshipped at its shrine;
   Thus they despised the living God
   And scorned His love divine.

Praise Ye the Lord, for He Is Good

PSALM 106

12 Their God and Savior they forgot,
 Their Helper and their Stay,
 But Moses plead the promised grace
 And turned God's wrath away.

13 Yea, they despised the pleasant land,
 The promised land of God,
 And tempted Him to make them fall
 And scatter them abroad.

14 They sacrificed to heathen gods,
 And God their sin repaid;
 Then holy wrath avenged the wrong,
 And so the plague was stayed.

15 The Lord approved the righteous act
 Of him who sin abhorred,
 And honored him forevermore
 With just and great reward.

16 By wicked strife they angered God,
 His wrath they did provoke;
 And stirred by their rebellious cries,
 Their leader rashly spoke.

17 Ensnared, they served the heathen gods,
 And by them were beguiled;
 The blood of children sacrificed
 The very land defiled.

18 Against His own inheritance
 Jehovah's wrath arose,
 His chosen people He condemned
 To serve their heathen foes.

19 Though from their harsh oppressors'
 hand
 Ofttimes He set them free,
 Rebellious still, they were brought low
 In their iniquity.

20 When unto God they cried, He heard
 And turned again His face,
 In boundless love remembering
 The covenant of His grace.

21 He even touched their captors' hearts,
 And made their very foes
 Compassionate and pitiful
 To feel His people's woes.

22 Save us, O Lord, our gracious God,
 From alien lands reclaim,
 That we may triumph in Thy praise
 And bless Thy holy Name.

23 Blessed be the Lord our covenant God,
 All praise to Him accord;
 Let all the people say, Amen.
 Praise ye, praise ye the Lord.

Alternate Tune ST. FLAVIAN C.M. Day's *Psalter*, 1562

212
Praise the Lord, for He Is Good

PSALM 107

HALLE 7 7 7 7 7 7

Arranged by Thomas Hastings, 1784-1872

1 Praise the Lord, for He is good, For His mer - cies ev - er sure
2 From cap - tiv - i - ty re-leased, From the south and from the north,
3 Wan-dering in the wil-der-ness, Far they roamed the des - ert way,

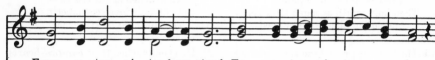

From e - ter - ni - ty have stood, To e - ter - ni - ty en - dure;
From the west and from the east, In His love He brought them forth,
Found no set-tled dwell-ing-place Where in peace se - cure to stay,

Let His ran-somed peo-ple raise Songs to their Re-deem-er's praise.
Ran-somed out of ev - ery land From the ad - ver - sa - ry's hand.
Till with thirst and hun-ger pressed Cour-age sank with-in their breast.

4 To Jehovah then they cried
   In their trouble, and He saved;
He Himself became their Guide.
   Led them to the rest they craved
By a pathway straight and sure,
To a city strong, secure.

5 Sons of men, awake to praise
   God the Lord who reigns above,
Gracious in His works and ways,
   Wondrous in redeeming love;
Longing souls He satisfies.
Hungry hearts with good supplies.

213
Rebels, Who Had Dared to Show

PSALM 107

Dix 7 7 7 7 7 7

Arranged from Conrad Kocher, 1838

1 Reb - els, who had dared to show Proud con-tempt of God Most High, Bound in i - ron and in woe, Shades of death and dark - ness nigh, Hum - bled low with toil and pain, Fell, and looked for help in vain.

2 To Je - ho - vah then they cried In their trou - ble, and He saved, Threw the pris - on o - pen wide Where they lay to death en - slaved, Bade the gloom - y shad - ows flee, Broke their bonds and set them free.

3 Sons of men, a - wake to praise God the Lord who reigns a - bove, Gra - cious in His works and ways, Won - drous in re - deem - ing love; I - ron bars He breaks like clay, And the bra - zen gates give way.

214   Men Who Walk in Folly's Way

PSALM 107   Lux Prima (Gounod) 7 7 7 7 7 7

Charles F. Gounod, 1872

1 Men who walk in fol - ly's way, And to e - vil
2 To Je - ho - vah then they cry In their trou - ble
3 Sons of men, a - wake to praise God the Lord who

turn a - side, Find that sor - row will re - pay
and He saves, Sends com - pas - sion - ate re - ply,
reigns a - bove, Gra - cious in His works and ways,

Those who wis - dom's laws de - fied; Down to death's dark
Gives the health their spir - it craves, Res - cues them with
Won - drous in re - deem - ing love; Let them all thank -

por - tals led, They ab - hor their dai - ly bread.
gra - cious aid From the snares their fol - ly laid.
of - ferings bring, Cel - e - brate His deeds, and sing.

215 They That Traffic on the Sea

PSALM 107

ROSEFIELD 7 7 7 7 7 7

H. A. Cesar Malan, 1834

1 They that traf-fic on the sea, While un-ceas-ing watch they keep,
2 By the bil-lows heaven-ward tossed, Down to dread-ful depths a - gain,
3 To Je - ho - vah then they cry In their trou - ble, and He saves,

See Je - ho - vah's maj - es - ty And His won-ders in the deep;
Trou-bled much, their cour-age lost, Reel - ing, they like drunk-en men
Drives the dark-ness from the sky, Calms the storm and stills the waves,

For He bids the storm-wind fly, Lift - ing o-cean's waves on high.
Find their skill and power o'er-thrown; None can save but God a - lone.
Makes their sad fore-bod - ings cease, To their ha - ven guides in peace.

4 Sons of men, awake to praise
God the Lord who reigns above,
Gracious in His works and ways,
Wondrous in redeeming love;
Praise Him where the people meet,
Praise Him in the elders' seat.

PSALM 107   BREAD OF HEAVEN 7 7 7 7 7 7

William D. Maclagan, 1875

In flowing style

1 Springs and streams no long-er bless All   the dry and thirst-y land;
2 Once   a - gain   the wa-ters well, All   the des-ert blos-soms fair;
3 Now   He bless - es them in-deed, They are great-ly mul - ti-plied;

Fer - tile fields in   ver-dant dress God con-verts to des - ert sand;
There He makes the   hun-gry dwell, There a cit - y they pre-pare,
On   the hills their cat - tle feed, Fast in-creas-ing, spread-ing wide;

For   that they who dwell there- in   Turn to wick- ed-ness and sin.
Plant their vines and sow their fields, And the earth her in-crease yields.
Then a - gain they are brought low   Through op-pres-sion, grief, and woe.

4 His contempt the princes taste;
   Driven out, they helpless fly,
  Wandering in the trackless waste;
   But He lifts the needy high,
  Where no evil shall annoy,
  And with children gives him joy.

5 When His righteous judgments come,
   Strong to bless and to destroy,
  All iniquity is dumb,
   All the righteous sing for joy;
  Who Jehovah wisely heed,
  In His works His mercy read.

217   O Praise the Lord, for He Is Good

PSALM 107   Goshen C.M.D.   German Melody

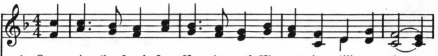

1 O praise the Lord, for He is good, His mer-cies still en - dure;
2 They wan-dered in the wil - der-ness, By want and hun-ger pressed;
3 O praise the Lord, ye sons of men, For all His good-ness shown;

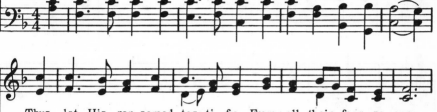

Thus let His ran-somed tes-ti - fy, From all their foes se - cure.
In trou - ble then they cried to God, He saved their souls dis-tressed.
O praise Him for the won-drous works To you He has made known.

He has re-deemed His cap-tive saints From ad-ver - sa-ries' hands,
He made the way be-fore them plain, Him-self be-came their Guide;
The long-ing soul that turns to Him He ful-ly sat - is - fies;

Has gath-ered them and brought them back In peace from hos-tile lands.
He brought them to a cit - y strong Where-in they might a - bide.
He fills with good each hun-gering one That for His mer-cy cries.

My Stedfast Heart, O God

CUTTING 6 6 4 6 6 6 4

William F. Sherwin, 1826-1888

1 My sted-fast heart, O God, Will sound Thy praise a-broad
2 Thy truth and ten-der love Are high as heaven a-bove;

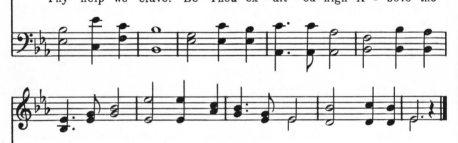

With tune-ful string; The dawn shall hear my song, Thy praise I
Thy help we crave. Be Thou ex-alt-ed high A-bove the

will pro-long, And where Thy peo-ple throng Thanks-giv-ing bring.
loft-y sky; Lest Thy be-lov-ed die, O hear and save.

3 God's word shall surely stand;
His Name through every land
Shall be adored;
Lord, who shall lead our host?
Thine aid we covet most,
In Thee is all our boast,
Strong in the Lord.

219

My Heart Is Fixed, O God

PSALM 108

ST. THOMAS S.M.

Aaron Williams, 1763

1 My heart is fixed, O God, A grate-ful song I raise;
2 A-mong the na-tions, Lord, To Thee my song shall rise;
3 A-bove the heavens, O God, And o-ver all the earth,

A-wake, O harp, in joy-ful strains; A-wake, my soul, to praise.
Thy truth is great a-bove the heavens, Thy mer-cies reach the skies.
Let men ex-alt Thy glo-rious Name And tell Thy match-less worth.

4 Stretch forth Thy mighty hand
　　In answer to our prayer,
　And let Thine own beloved ones
　　Thy great salvation share.

5 The holy God has said,
　　All lands shall own My sway;
　My people shall My glory share,
　　The heathen shall obey.

6 O who will lead our hosts
　　To triumph o'er the foe,
　If Thou shalt cast us off, O God,
　　Nor with our armies go?

7 The help of man is vain,
　　Be Thou our Helper, Lord;
　Through Thee we shall do valiantly
　　If Thou Thine aid afford.

220   O God, Whom I Delight to Praise

PSALM 109   PENTECOST L.M.

William Boyd, 1868

1 O God, whom I de-light to praise, To Thee my
2 A-gainst me slan-derous words are flung From man-y a
3 My good with e - vil they re - pay, My love turns

cry for help I raise; Be Thou my Friend and
false and ly - ing tongue; With-out a cause men
not their hate a - way; The part of ven - geance,

Ad - vo - cate When foes as - sail with bit - ter hate.
hurl at me The shafts of dead - ly en - mi - ty.
Lord, is Thine; To pray, and on - ly pray, is mine.

4 Since love appeals to him in vain,
   The slave of sin let him remain;
   Against him let his foe be turned,
   His sin be judged, his prayer be spurned.

5 Let sudden death upon him break,
   His office let another take,
   His children and his widowed wife
   Pursue the homeless beggar's life.

O God, Whom I Delight to Praise

PSALM 109

6 Let creditors consume his toil
And strangers make his wealth their spoil;
Let none in pity heed his claim;
Cut off his race, blot out his name.

7 His parents' sins be not forgot
Till Thou from earth his memory blot,
Since he remembered not to show
Compassion to the sons of woe.

8 He cursing loved and blessing loathed;
Unblest, with cursing he is clothed;
For thus the justice of the Lord
My adversaries will reward.

9 O God, the Lord, for Thy Name's sake
Let me of Thy good grace partake;
My need is great, and great Thou art
To heal my wounded, stricken heart.

10 With failing strength I fast and pine,
Like shadows swift my days decline,
And when my foes my weakness see
They shake the head in scorn at me.

11 O Lord my God, Thy help I crave,
In Thy great lovingkindness save;
Before my foes Thy mercy show;
That Thou dost help me, make them know.

12 What though they curse, if Thou wilt bless?
Then joy shall banish my distress,
And shame shall overwhelm the foes
Who would Thy servant's way oppose.

13 Thanksgiving to the Lord I raise,
The multitude shall hear my praise,
For by the needy God will stand
To save them from oppression's hand.

221

The Lord unto His Christ Has Said

PSALM 110

ALL SAINTS NEW C.M.D.

Henry S. Cutler, 1872

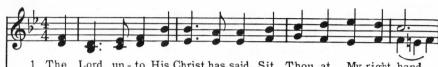

1 The Lord un-to His Christ has said, Sit Thou at My right hand
2 Thy. peo-ple will be glad-ly Thine When Thou shalt come in might,
3 Thou shalt sub-due the kings of earth With God at Thy right hand;

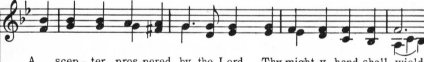

Un-til I make Thine en-e-mies Sub-mit to Thy com-mand.
Like dawn-ing day, like hope-ful youth, With ho-ly beau-ty bright.
The na-tions Thou shalt rule in might And judge in ev-ery land.

A scep-ter pros-pered by the Lord Thy might-y hand shall wield;
A priest-hood that shall nev-er end The Lord has giv-en Thee;
The Christ, re-freshed by liv-ing streams, Shall nei-ther faint nor fall,

From Zi-on Thou shalt rule the world, And all Thy foes shall yield.
This He has sworn, and ev-er-more Ful-filled His word shall be.
And He shall be the glo-rious Head, Ex-alt-ed o-ver all.

222   O Give the Lord Whole-hearted Praise

PSALM 111

GERMANY L.M.
From William Gardiner's *Sacred Melodies*, 1815

1 O give the Lord whole-heart-ed praise, To Him thanks-
2 His saints de-light to search and trace His might-y
3 The won-drous works that God has wrought His peo-ple

giv-ing I will bring; With all His peo-ple
works and won-drous ways; Ma-jes-tic glo-ry,
ev-er keep in mind, His works with grace and

I will raise My voice and of His glo-ry sing.
bound-less grace, And right-eous-ness His work dis-plays.
mer-cy fraught, Re-veal-ing that the Lord is kind.

4 God's promise shall forever stand,
   He cares for those who trust His word;
  Upon His saints His mighty hand
   The wealth of nations has conferred.

5 His works are true and just indeed,
   His precepts are forever sure;
  In truth and righteousness decreed,
   They shall forevermore endure.

6 From Him His saints' redemption came;
   His covenant sure no change can know;
  Let all revere His holy Name
   In heaven above and earth below.

7 In reverence and in godly fear
   Man finds the gate to wisdom's ways;
  The wise His holy Name revere;
   Through endless ages sound His praise.

223 How Blest the Man Who Fears the Lord

PSALM 112

MELCOMBE L.M.

Samuel Webbe, 1782

1 How blest the man who fears the Lord
2 A - bound - ing wealth shall bless his home,

And great - ly loves God's ho - ly will;
His right - eous - ness shall still en - dure,

His chil - dren share his great re - ward,
To him shall light a - rise in gloom,

And bless - ings all their days shall fill.
For he is mer - ci - ful and pure.

How Blest the Man Who Fears the Lord

PSALM 112

3 The man whose hand the weak befriends
   In judgment shall his cause maintain;
A peace unmoved his life attends,
   And long his memory shall remain.

4 Of evil tidings not afraid,
   His trust is in the Lord alone;
His heart is stedfast, undismayed,
   For he shall see his foes o'erthrown.

5 With kind remembrance of the poor,
   For their distress his gifts provide;
His righteousness shall thus endure,
   His name in honor shall abide.

6 To shame the wicked shall be brought,
   While righteous men shall favor gain;
Unrighteous hopes shall come to naught,
   Its due reward shall sin obtain.

224 Praise God, Ye Servants of the Lord

PSALM 113　　ANDRE L.M., 5 Lines

William B. Bradbury, 1816-1868

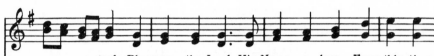

1 Praise God, ye ser-vants of the Lord, Praise, praise His Name with
2 From ris - ing un - to set - ting sun Praised be the Lord, the
3 On whom but God can we re - ly, The Lord our God **who**

one ac-cord; Bless ye the Lord, His Name a-dore From this time
Might-y One; He reigns o'er all, su-preme in might, A - bove the
reigns on high, Who con - de-scends to see and know The things of

forth for - ev - er-more, From this time forth for - ev - er- more.
heavens in glo - ry bright, A - bove the heavens in glo - ry bright.
heaven and earth be - low? The things of heaven and earth be - low?

4 He lifts the poor and makes them great,
　With joy He fills the desolate;
　Praise ye the Lord and bless His Name,
　His mercy and His might proclaim.

5 The barren woman feels His power
　And comes to sacred motherhood,
　Adorns with grace the home of man.
　Sing hallelujah! God is good.

Stanza 5, Wilbert Snow

225 When Israel out of Egypt Went

PSALM 114

VOM HIMMEL HOCH L.M.

Geistliche Lieder, Leipzig, 1539

In moderate time

1 When Is - rael out of E - gypt went, From
2 The sea be - held and fled a - way, The
3 What ail - eth thee, O trou - bled sea? Thou

peo - ple of a speech un - known, The Lord a - mong His
Jor - dan's wa - ters back - ward turned, The loft - y moun - tains
Jor - dan, why thy riv - en tide? Ye moun - tains and ye

peo - ple dwelt, And there He set His roy - al throne.
and the hills With trem - bling awe our God dis - cerned.
lit - tle hills, Why thus dis - mayed on ev - er - y side?

4 O tremble, earth, before the Lord,
In presence of Jehovah fear,
Beneath whose touch the flinty rock
Became a fount of waters clear.

226

Not unto Us, O Lord of Heaven

PSALM 115

GAIRNEY BRIDGE L.M., 6 Lines

Ernest R. Kroeger, 1862-1934

1 Not un-to us, O Lord of heaven, But un-to
2 The i-dol-gods of hea-then lands Are but the
3 Let Is-rael trust in God a-lone, The Lord whose

Thee be glo-ry given; In love and truth Thou dost ful-fil
work of hu-man hands; They can-not see, they can-not speak,
grace and power are known; To Him your full al-le-giance yield,

The coun-sels of Thy sov-ereign will; Though na-tions
Their ears are deaf, their hands are weak; Like them shall
And He will be your help and shield; All those who

fail Thy power to own, Yet Thou dost reign, and Thou a-lone.
be all those who hold To gods of sil-ver and of gold.
fear Him God will bless, His saints have proved His faith-ful-ness.

4 All ye that fear Him and adore,
  The Lord increase you more and more;
  Both great and small who Him confess,
  You and your children He will bless;
  Yea, blest are ye of Him who made
  The heavens, and earth's foundations laid.

5 The heavens are God's since time began,
  But He has given the earth to man;
  The dead praise not the living God,
  But we will sound His praise abroad,
  Yea, we will ever bless His Name;
  Praise ye the Lord, His praise proclaim

227   The Lord Who Has Remembered Us

PSALM 115   St. Anne C.M.   William Croft, 1708

1 The Lord who has re - mem - bered us His bless - ing will be - stow; All those who fear His ho - ly Name, His lov - ing care shall know.

2 For small and great who fear His Name The Lord has good in store; Ye and your chil - dren, blest of God, Shall pros - per more and more.

3 The great Cre - a - tor bless - es you With gifts of bound - less worth; The heavens He claims, but gives to man Do - min - ion in the earth.

4 The silent dead praise not the Lord,
The grave no song can raise;
But we will bless Him evermore,
Let all proclaim His praise.

I Love the Lord, the Fount of Life

PSALM 116

SACRIFICE OF PRAISE 10 11 11·10

Maitre Pierre, 1562
Harmonized by Seymour Swets, 1954

Earnestly; may be sung in unison

1 I love the Lord, the fount of life and grace;
2 The cords of death held me in deep de - spair;
3 I cried, De - liv - er Thou my soul, O Lord!

He hears my voice, my cry and sup - pli - ca - tion,
The pangs of hell, like waves by tem - pest driv - en,
Je - ho - vah heard; I pledge Him my de - vo - tion.

In - clines His ear, gives strength and con - so - la - tion;
Rolled o'er my soul; by grief and sor - row riv - en,
The Lord is just, His grace, wide as the o - cean;

In life, in death, my heart will seek His face.
I turned in my dis - tress to God in prayer.
In bound - less mer - cy He ful - fils His word.

I Love the Lord, the Fount of Life

PSALM 116

4 The Lord preserves the meek most tenderly;
  Brought nigh to death, in Him I found salvation.
  Come, thou my soul, relieved from agitation,
Turn to thy rest; the Lord has favored thee.

5 Thou, O Jehovah, in Thy sovereign grace,
  Hast saved my soul from death and woe appalling,
  Dried all my tears, secured my feet from falling.
Lo, I shall live and walk before Thy face.

6 I have believed, and therefore did I speak
  When I was made to suffer tribulation;
  I said in haste and bitter desperation:
All men are false, 'tis nought but lies they speak.

7 What shall I render to Jehovah now
  For all the riches of His consolation?
  With joy I'll take the cup of His salvation,
And call upon His Name with thankful vow.

8 Before His saints I'll pay my vows to God;
  E'en in death's vale He keepeth me from evil;
  How dear to God the dying of His people!
Praise Him, ye saints, and sound His name abroad.

9 I am, O Lord, Thy servant, bound yet free,
  Thy handmaid's son, whose shackles Thou hast broken:
  Redeemed by grace I'll render as a token
Of gratitude my constant praise to Thee.

10 Jerusalem! Within thy courts I'll praise
  Jehovah's Name; and with a spirit lowly
  Pay all my vows. O Zion, fair and holy,
Come join with me and bless Him all thy days!

William Kuipers, 1931

I Love the Lord, for My Request

PSALM 116

CANONBURY L.M.

Arranged from Robert A. Schumann's
Nachtstücke, No. 4, 1839

1 I love the Lord, for my re - quest And
2 Brought nigh to death and full of grief, The
3 Most kind and right - eous is the Lord, Our

hum - ble plea He makes His care; In Him through life my
Lord's sal - va - tion I be-sought; He heard my cry, He
God is mer - ci - ful in - deed, De-light - ing ev - er

faith shall rest, For He both hears and an - swers prayer.
sent re - lief, My soul from depths of woe He brought.
to af - ford His help to me in time of need.

4 Return unto thy rest, my soul,
  The Lord has richly dealt with thee,
Delivered thee from death's control,
  From sin and sorrow set thee free.

5 Since He has freed mine eyes from tears
  And kept my feet from evil ways,
Redeemed from life's distressing fears,
  With Him I walk, and Him I praise.

6 In my affliction and my pain,
  When fears alarmed and hopes deceived,
I found all human helpers vain,
  But in the Lord my soul believed.

230   What Shall I Render to the Lord

PSALM 116   WALLACE L.M.

Benjamin F. Baker, 1811-1889

1 What shall I ren-der to the Lord For all His ben-e-fits to me? How shall my soul, by grace re-stored, Give wor-thy thanks, O Lord, to Thee?

2 Sal-va-tion's cup of bless.-ing now I take, and call up-on God's Name; Be-fore His saints I pay my vow And here my grat-i-tude pro-claim.

3 His saints the Lord de-lights to save, Their death is pre-cious in His sight; He has re-deemed me from the grave, And in His ser-vice I de-light.

4 With thankful heart I offer now
   My gift, and call upon God's Name;
Before His saints I pay my vow
   And here my gratitude proclaim.

5 Within His house, the house of prayer,
   I dedicate myself to God;
Let all His saints His grace declare
   And join to sound His praise abroad.

231 Praise Jehovah, All Ye Nations

PSALM 117

In Babilone 8 7 8 7 D.

Dutch traditional melody, 1710

1 Praise Je - ho - vah, all ye na - tions, All ye peo - ple,
praise pro - claim; For His grace and lov - ing - kind - ness
O sing prais - es to His Name. For the great - ness of His mer - cy
Con - stant praise to Him ac - cord; Ev - er - more His
truth en - dur - eth; Hal - le - lu - jah, praise the Lord!

232

O Praise the Lord, for He Is Good

PSALM 118

HEAVENLY FOLD C.M.D.

William F. Sherwin, 1826-1888

1 O praise the Lord, for He is good; Let all in heaven a - bove
2 The Lord with me, I will not fear Though hu-man might op-pose;

And all His saints on earth pro-claim His ev - er - last - ing love.
The Lord my Help - er, I shall be Tri - um-phant o'er my foes.

In my dis-tress I called on God; In grace He an - swered me,
No trust in men, or kings of men, Can con - fi-dence af - ford,

Re-moved my bonds, en-larged my place, From trou - ble set me free.
But they are strong, and sure their trust, Whose hope is in the Lord.

3 Though nations compass me about,
    Like swarming hosts of sin,
Yet in the Name of God the Lord
    I shall the victory win.
The Lord has helped and kept me safe
    When foes were fierce and strong;
The Lord my Savior is become,
    He is my strength and song.

4 Salvation's joyful song is heard
    Where'er the righteous dwell;
For them God's hand is strong to save
    And doeth all things well.
I shall not die, but live and tell
    The wonders of the Lord;
He has not given my soul to death,
    But chastened and restored.

Let All Exalt Jehovah's Goodness

PSALM 118

Navarre 9 8 9 8 D.

Louis Bourgeois, 1544
Harmonized by C. Goudimel, 1565

Triumphantly; may be sung in unison

1 Let all ex-alt Je-ho-vah's good-ness, For most com-
pas-sion-ate is He; His mer-cy, ex-cel-lent in ful-ness,
En-dur-eth to e-ter-ni-ty. Let Is-rael praise Je-
ho-vah's good-ness, And say, Ex-alt His maj-es-ty; His mer-cy,

2 Je-ho-vah is my strength and tow-er; He is my
hap-pi-ness and song; He saved me in the try-ing hour,...
Hence shall my mouth His praise pro-long. The voice of glad-ness
and sal-va-tion Is in the tents of right-eous-ness; There do they

Let All Exalt Jehovah's Goodness

PSALM 118

ex - cel - lent in ful - ness, En - du - reth to e - ter - ni - ty.
sing with ad - o - ra - tion; The Lord's right hand is strong to bless.

3 The Lord's right hand is high exalted,
   Jehovah's strong and mighty hand;
The vaunting enemy He halted,
   And made His chosen ones to stand.
I shall not die, but live before Him,
   And all His mighty works declare,
That all may joyfully adore Him
   Who in His lovingkindness share.

4 In truth, the Lord has sorely chastened,
   But not to death delivered me;
In His paternal love He hastened
   To mitigate my misery.
Now open at my salutation
   The gates of truth and righteousness,
And I will enter with elation,
   There to proclaim my thankfulness.

5 The stone the builders had rejected,
   And in contempt refused to own,
To their dismay has been selected
   To be the foremost cornerstone.
This thing is from the Lord Almighty,
   It is a marvel in our eyes;
Man cannot understand it rightly
   Nor fathom it in any wise.

6 This is the day of full salvation
   That God has made and sanctified;
Come, let us voice our jubilation,
   And triumph in the grace supplied.
Save, O Jehovah, we implore Thee,
   Save now Thy people, e'en today;
Prosperity send Thou in mercy,
   And favor us upon our way.

7 Now blessed be the King of Glory,
   That cometh in Jehovah's Name;
Out of His temple we adore Thee,
   And all Thy blessedness proclaim.
The Lord is mighty; He provideth
   A light for us when sore afraid;
Then be our thankful sacrifices
   Upon the sacred altar laid.

8 Thou art my God, I will extol Thee,
   And magnify Thy majesty;
My God, in glory none excel Thee,
   Thy praise be to eternity.
Let all exalt Jehovah's goodness,
   For most compassionate is He;
His mercy, excellent in fulness,
   Endureth to eternity.

Dewey Westra, 1931

234   The Glorious Gates of Righteousness

PSALM 118

ZERAH C.M., 6 Lines

Lowell Mason, 1836

1 The glo-rious gates of right-eous-ness Throw o - pen un - to me,
2 This is Thy tem - ple - gate, O Lord, The just shall en - ter there;
3 The stone re - ject - ed and de-spised Is now the cor-ner-stone;

And I will en - ter them with praise, O Lord, my God, to Thee,
My Sav - ior, I will give Thee thanks, O Thou that hear-est prayer,
How won-drous are the ways of God, Un - fath-omed and un - known,

And I will en - ter them with praise, O Lord, my God, to Thee.
My Sav - ior, I will give Thee thanks, O Thou that hear-est prayer.
How won-drous are the ways of God, Un-fath-omed and un - known!

The Glorious Gates of Righteousness
PSALM 118

4 In this the day that Thou hast made,
   Triumphantly we sing;
Send now prosperity, O Lord,
   O Lord, salvation bring.

5 Hosanna! Ever blest be He
   That cometh in God's Name;
The blessing of Jehovah's house
   Upon you we proclaim.

6 The light of joy to shine on us
   The Lord our God has made;
Now be the precious sacrifice
   Upon His altar laid.

7 O Lord, my God, I praise Thy Name,
   All other names above;
O give Him thanks, for He is good
   And boundless is His love.

8 O praise the Lord, for He is good;
   Let all in heaven above
And all His saints on earth proclaim
   His everlasting love.

235   How Blessed Are the Perfect in the Way

PSALM 119   ROYAL LAW 10 11 10 11 10 11

Louis Bourgeois, 1551
Harmonized by Henry Bruinsma, 1947

Prayerfully; may be sung in unison

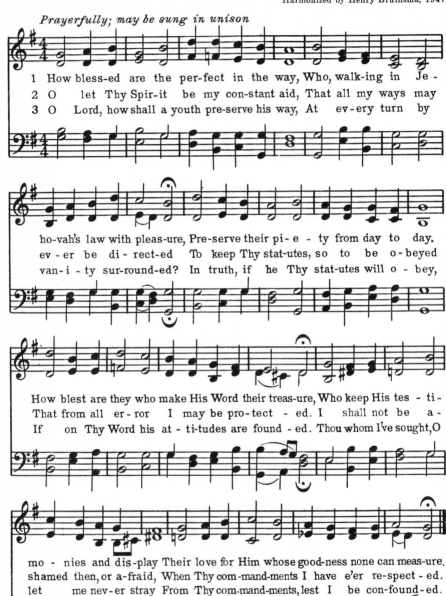

1 How bless-ed are the per-fect in the way, Who, walk-ing in Je-
2 O   let Thy Spir-it be my con-stant aid, That all my ways may
3 O   Lord, how shall a youth pre-serve his way, At   ev-ery turn by

ho-vah's law with pleas-ure, Pre-serve their pi - e - ty from day to day.
ev - er be di - rect-ed To keep Thy stat-utes, so to be o - beyed
van - i - ty sur-round-ed? In truth, if he Thy stat-utes will o - bey,

How blest are they who make His Word their treas-ure, Who keep His tes - ti-
That from all er - ror I may be pro-tect - ed. I   shall not be   a-
If   on Thy Word his at - ti-tudes are found - ed. Thou whom I've sought, O

mo - nies and dis-play Their love for Him whose good-ness none can meas-ure.
shamed then, or a-fraid, When Thy com-mand-ments I have e'er re-spect - ed.
let   me nev-er stray From Thy com-mand-ments, lest I   be con-found-ed.

282

How Blessed Are the Perfect in the Way

PSALM 119

4 Thy precepts have I hid within my heart,
    Lest I should stray and fall into transgression;
O teach Thou me and unto me impart
    Thy statutes for a permanent possession.
In all Thy judgments Thou most righteous art;
    Thy truth I praise in rapturous confession.

5 O teach me, Lord, the way that I should go;
    Then shall Thy servant walk therein forever.
Give understanding all Thy paths to know;
    Then shall I keep Thy law with zealous fervor.
Instruct me in Thy perfect will and, lo,
    I shall observe it with my whole endeavor.

6 O Lord, Thou art my portion and my lot;
    I said that I would keep Thy Word forever,
Though to my sorrow I have oft forgot.
    With all my heart I now entreat Thy favor:
Be merciful to me and chasten not;
    According to Thy Word be Thou my Savior.

7 O how I love Thy law! Yea, Thou canst see
    Through all the day it is my meditation;
By Thy commandments, Lord, Thou madest me
    More wise than all who seek my ruination.
Thy testimonies evermore shall be
    The perfect source of all my inspiration.

8 Thy Word is as a lamp unto my feet,
    A light upon my pathway unto heaven;
I've sworn an oath, which gladly I repeat,
    That I shall keep, as always I have striven,
Thy righteous judgments, holy and complete,
    When unto me Thy helping grace is given.

9 Great peace have they who love Thy perfect law;
    They shall not swerve from paths of consecration;
Their happiness shall be without a flaw.
    Lord, I have ever hoped for Thy salvation;
All Thy commandments I have kept with awe;
    Thy precepts are my daily meditation.

10 Grant life unto my soul, O Lord, I pray;
    Shed still the brightness of Thy presence o'er me;
Then shall I praise Thee in a perfect way,
    Yea, let Thy judgments quicken and restore me.
Thy servant like a sheep has gone astray,
    Yet Thy commandments I will keep before me.

Dewey Westra, 1931

PSALM 119   Appleton L.M.   William Boyce, 1710-1779

1 How blest the per - fect in the way,
2 Yea, they are kept from paths of sin

Who from God's law do not de - part, Who, hold - ing fast the
Who walk in God's ap - point - ed way; Thy pre - cepts Thou hast

Word of truth, Seek Him with un - di - vid - ed heart.
giv - en us That we should faith - ful - ly o - bey.

3 My wavering heart is now resolved
    Thy holy statutes to fulfil;
  No more shall I be brought to shame
    When I regard Thy holy will.

4 To Thee my praise sincere shall rise
    When I Thy righteous judgments learn;
  Forsake me not, but be my Guide,
    And from Thy truth I will not turn.

1 How shall the young di - rect their way? What light shall be their
2 O bless-ed Lord, teach me Thy law, Thy right-eous judg-ments

per-fect guide? Thy Word, O Lord, will safe - ly lead, If in its
I de-clare; Thy tes - ti - mo - nies make me glad, For they are

wis - dom they con-fide. Sin-cere-ly I have sought Thee, Lord,
wealth be - yond com-pare. Up - on Thy pre-cepts and Thy ways

O let me not from Thee de-part; To know Thy will and
My heart will med - i - tate with awe; Thy Word shall be my

keep from sin Thy Word I cher - ish in my heart.
chief de-light, And I will not for - get Thy law.

Thy Servant, Blest by Thee, Shall Live

PSALM 119   St. Martin's C.M.

William Tansur, 1740

1 Thy ser-vant, blest by Thee, shall live And keep Thy
2 A pil-grim in the earth am I, Thy will to
3 Thou dost re-buke the proud, O Lord, Who hate Thy

Word with awe; Lord, o-pen Thou my
me re-veal; To know Thy truth my
ho-ly Name; But since I keep Thy

eyes to see The won-ders of Thy law.
spir-it yearns, Con-sumed with ar-dent zeal.
right-eous law, De-liv-er me from shame.

4 I on Thy statutes meditate,
    Though evil men deride;
  Thy faithful Word is my delight,
    My counselor and guide.

My Grieving Soul Revive, O Lord

PSALM 119 DALEHURST C.M. Arthur Cottman, 1872

Quietly and earnestly

1 My griev-ing soul re-vive, O Lord, Ac-
2 Teach me to know Thy ho-ly way And
3 Keep me from false-hood, let Thy law With

cord-ing to Thy Word; To Thee my ways I
think up-on Thy deeds; In grief I ask for
me in grace a-bide; The way of faith-ful-

have de-clared And Thou my prayer hast heard.
prom-ised grace Ac-cord-ing to my needs.
ness I choose, Thy pre-cepts are my guide.

4 I cleave unto Thy truth, O Lord;
   From shame deliver me;
   In glad obedience I will live
   Through strength bestowed by Thee.

240   **Teach Me, O Lord, Thy Way of Truth**

PSALM 119   BISHOP L.M.

Joseph P. Holbrook, 1822-1888

1 Teach me, O Lord, Thy way of truth, And from it
I will not de - part; That I may sted - fast -
ly o - bey, Give me an un - der - stand - ing heart.

2 In Thy com-mand - ments make me walk, For in Thy
law my joy shall be; Give me a heart that
loves Thy will, From dis - con - tent and en - vy free.

3 Turn Thou mine eyes from van - i - ty, And cause me
in Thy ways to tread; O let Thy ser - vant
prove Thy Word And thus to god - ly fear be led.

4 Turn Thou away reproach and fear;
Thy righteous judgments I confess;
To know Thy precepts I desire;
Revive me in Thy righteousness.

241 Thy Promised Mercies Send to Me

PSALM 119

SARAH C.M.

Charles H. Gabriel, 1901

1 Thy prom - ised mer - cies send to me,
2 My hope is in Thy judg - ment, Lord;
3 And I will walk at lib - er - ty

Thy great sal - va - tion, Lord; So shall I
Take not Thy truth from me, And in Thy
Be - cause Thy truth I seek; Thy truth be -

an - swer those who scoff; My trust is in Thy Word
law for - ev - er - more My dai - ly walk shall be.
fore the kings of earth With bold - ness I will speak.

4 The Lord's commands, which I have loved,
   Shall still new joy impart;
With reverence I will hear Thy laws
   And keep them in my heart.

242
Lord, Thy Word to Me Remember

PSALM 119

WILMOT 8 7 8 7

Carl M. von Weber, 1786-1826
Arranged by Lowell Mason

1 Lord, Thy Word to me re - mem - ber,
2 Mocked by those who are un - right - eous,
3 Wick - ed men, Thy law for - sak - ing,

Thou hast made me hope in Thee; This my com - fort
Still to Thy com - mands I cleave; Think-ing on Thy
Stirred my in - dig - na - tion strong; For in all my

in af - flic - tion, That Thy Word has quick - ened me.
for - mer judg-ments, Help and com - fort I re - ceive.
pil - grim jour - ney Thy com-mand-ments are my song.

4 Thou hast been my meditation
  And Thy law has been my guide;
  I have kept Thy righteous precepts,
  And have found them true and tried.

243

Thou Art My Portion, Lord

PSALM 119

CARLISLE S.M.

C. Lockhart, 1745-1815

1 Thou art my por - tion, Lord; Thy
2 I thought up - on my ways, Thy

words I ev - er heed; With all my heart
tes - ti - mo - nies learned; With ear - nest haste,

Thy grace I seek, Thy prom - is - es I plead.
and wait - ing not, To Thy com - mands I turned.

3 While snares beset my path,
   Thy law I keep in view;
At midnight I will give Thee praise
   For all Thy judgments true.

4 All those who fear Thy Name
   Shall my companions be;
Thy mercy fills the earth, O Lord;
   Thy statutes teach Thou me.

244 Thou, Lord, Hast Dealt Well with Thy Servant

PSALM 119 JANET 9 8 9 8

George C. Stebbins, 1846-1945

1 Thou, Lord, hast dealt well with Thy ser-vant, Thy prom-ise is
faith - ful and just; In - struct me in judg-ment and
knowl - edge, For in Thy com-mand-ments I trust.

2 Be - fore my af - flic-tion I wan-dered, But now Thy good
Word I o - bey; O Thou who art ho - ly and
gra - cious, Now teach me Thy stat - utes, I pray.

3 The proud have as-sailed me with slan - der; Thy pre-cepts shall
still be my guide; Thy law is my joy and my
treas - ure, Though sin - ners may boast in their pride.

4 Affliction has been for my profit,
That I to Thy statutes might hold;
Thy law to my soul is more precious
Than thousands of silver and gold.

292

245   Thou, Who Didst Make and Fashion Me

PSALM 119

HUMILITY L.M.

Samuel P. Tuckerman, 1848

1 Thou, who didst make and fash - ion me, O make me
2 Thou, Lord, art just in all Thy ways, And faith - ful
3 Show mer - cy, Lord, that I may live, For in Thy

wise Thy law to learn; Then they that fear Thee
when Thou chas - tenest me; I pray Thee, let Thy
law is all my joy; While those who wrong me

shall be glad When they my hope in God dis - cern.
prom-ised grace Thy ser-vant's help and com - fort be.
are re - buked, Thy pre-cepts shall my thought em - ploy.

4 Let those that fear Thee turn to me,
Thy truth to them will I proclaim;
Instruct my heart to keep Thy law,
That I may not be put to shame.

246   My Soul for Thy Salvation Faints

PSALM 119   BELMONT C.M.   William Gardiner, 1812

1 My soul for Thy sal - va - tion faints, But still I
2 Thy stat - utes I do not for - get, Though wast - ing
3 The proud, dis - dain - ful of Thy law, En - trap me

hope in Thee; I long to see Thy
grief I know; Thy ser - vant's days are
wrong - ful - ly; O Thou, whose law is

prom - ised help, When Thou shalt com - fort me.
few, O Lord; When wilt Thou judge my foe?
just and true, Help and de - liv - er me.

4 Almost consumed, yet from Thy law
    I have not turned away;
    In lovingkindness give me strength,
    That I may still obey.

247   Forever Settled in the Heavens

PSALM 119

ARCADIA L.M.

Carolyn Beezhold Johnson, 1954

1 For - ev - er set - tled in the heavens, Thy Word, O
2 Thy Word and works un - moved re - main, Thine ev - ery
3 I should have per - ished in my woe Had not I

Lord, shall firm - ly stand; Thy faith - ful - ness shall
pur - pose to ful - fil; All things are Thine and
loved Thy law di - vine; That law I nev - er

nev - er fail; The earth a - bides at Thy com - mand.
Thee o - bey, And all as ser - vants wait Thy will.
can for - get; O save me, Lord, for I am Thine.

(Alternate Tune: DUKE STREET, No. 299)

4 The wicked would destroy my soul,
    But on Thy truth I muse with awe;
    Imperfect I have found all else,
    But boundless is Thy wondrous law.

248　　How I Love Thy Law, O Lord

PSALM 119　　GRANDVILLE 7 7 7 7 D.

Albert Piersma, 1954

1 How I love Thy law, O Lord! Dai-ly joy its truths af-ford;
2 While my heart Thy Word o-beys, I am kept from e - vil ways;

In its con-stant light I go, Wise to con-quer ev - ery foe.
From Thy law, with Thee to guide, I have nev - er turned a - side.

Thy com-mand-ments in my heart Tru - est wis-dom can im - part;
Sweet-er are Thy words to me Than all oth - er good can be;

To mine eyes Thy pre-cepts show Wis-dom more than sa - ges know.
Safe I walk, Thy truth my light, Hat-ing false-hood, lov - ing right.

249 Thy Word Sheds Light upon My Path

PSALM 119

LOUVAN L.M.

Virgil C. Taylor, 1847

1 Thy Word sheds light up-on my path; A shin-ing
2 In my dis-tress I plead with Thee, Send help ac-
3 In dan-ger oft and nigh to death, Thy law re-

light, it guides my feet; Thy right-eous judg-ments
cord-ing to Thy Word; Ac-cept my sac-ri-
mem-bered is mine aid; The wick-ed seek my

to ob-serve My sol-emn vow I now re-peat.
fice of praise And make me know Thy judg-ments, Lord.
o-ver-throw, Yet from Thy truth I have not strayed.

4 Thy precepts are my heritage,
   For daily they my heart rejoice;
   To keep Thy statutes faithfully
   Shall ever be my willing choice.

250   Deceit and Falsehood I Abhor

PSALM 119   STELLA L.M., 6 LINES   Old English Melody

Moderately fast

1 De - ceit and false - hood I ab - hor, But love Thy
2 Ac - cord - ing to Thy gra - cious Word Up - hold me,
3 The fro - ward Thou hast set at nought, Who vain - ly

law, Thy truth re-vealed; My sted-fast hope is in Thy Word;
Lord, de - liv - er me; O do not let me be a-shamed
wan - der from the right; The wick-ed Thou dost count as dross;

Thou art my ref - uge and my shield; The paths of
Of pa - tient hope and trust in Thee; O hold Thou
Thy just de - crees are my de - light; For fear of

sin I have not trod, But kept the pre - cepts of my God.
me, and I shall stand And ev - er fol - low Thy com-mand.
Thee I stand in awe And rev-erence Thy most ho - ly law.

I Have Followed Truth and Justice

PSALM 119   ROBINSON 8 7 8 7 D.   Thomas Hastings, 1787-1872

1 I have fol-lowed truth and jus-tice; Leave me not in deep dis-tress;
2 I am Thine, O give me wis-dom, Make me know Thy truth, I pray;

Be my help and my pro-tec-tion, Let the proud no more op-press.
Sin-ners have de-spised Thy stat-utes; Now, O Lord, Thy power dis-play.

For Thy Word and Thy sal-va-tion, Lord, my eyes with long-ing fail;
Lord, I love Thy good com-mand-ments And es-teem them more than gold;

Teach Thy stat-utes to Thy ser-vant, Let Thy mer-cy now pre-vail.
All Thy pre-cepts are most right-eous; Hat-ing sin, to these I hold.

252 Thy Wondrous Testimonies, Lord

PSALM 119

ST. CRISPIN L.M.

George J. Elvey, 1862

1 Thy won-drous tes - ti - mo - nies, Lord, My soul will keep and
2 I thirst for Thy com-mand-ments, Lord, And for Thy mer - cy
3 Di - rect my foot-steps in Thy Word, From sin's do-min - ion

great - ly praise; Thy Word, by faith - ful lips pro-claimed,
press my claim; O look on me and show the grace
save my soul, From man's op-pres - sion set me free,

To sim - plest minds the truth con - veys.
Dis - played to all who love Thy Name.
That I may yield to Thy con - trol.

4 O make Thy face to shine on me,
   And teach me all Thy laws to keep;
   Because Thy statutes are despised,
   With overwhelming grief I weep.

253   O Lord, Thy Perfect Righteousness

PSALM 119

LAMBETH C.M.

William Schulthes, 1871

1 O Lord, Thy per - fect right - eous - ness
Is in Thy judg - ments shown; In Thy un -
chang - ing faith - ful - ness Thy truth Thou hast made known.

2 Be - cause Thy foes for - get Thy law,
My soul is great - ly stirred; Thy ser - vant
loves the pu - ri - ty Of Thy most ho - ly Word.

3 Though I am humble and despised,
   I strive Thy will to do;
Eternal is Thy righteousness,
   And all Thy law is true.

4 Delight amid distress and pain
   Do Thy commandments give;
Thy Word is righteous evermore,
   Teach me that I may live.

254   O Lord, My Earnest Cry

PSALM 119   WELCOME VOICE S.M.D.   Louis Hartsough, 1872

1 O Lord, my ear-nest cry Thy lis-tening ear has heard;
2 O hear me in Thy grace, In mer - cy quick-en me;

With Thy sal - va - tion an-swer me, And I will keep Thy Word.
The wick - ed plan to do me harm, But they are far from Thee.

At ear - ly dawn I prayed, Thy prom - is - es my trust;
Thou, Lord, art near to me, And true are Thy com-mands;

At night I thought up-on Thy Word, Most ho - ly and most just.
Of old Thy tes - ti-mo-nies show Thy truth e - ter - nal stands.

255 Regard My Grief and Rescue Me

PSALM 119

PRESTON L.M.

William H. Doane, 1831-1915

1 Re - gard my grief and res - cue me, For I do
not for - get Thy laws; As Thou hast prom - ised,
save me, Lord, Re - deem my soul, and plead my cause.

2 Far is sal - va - tion from the men Who do not
seek Thy stat - utes, Lord; Great are Thy mer - cies,
quick - en me Ac - cord - ing to Thy ho - ly Word.

3 I bear the spite of man - y foes; Yet from Thy
law I do not swerve; I saw the faith - less
and was grieved, For they Thy Word do not ob - serve.

4 Behold how I Thy precepts love!
In kindness, Lord, revive Thou me;
The sum of all Thy Word is truth,
Thy Word abides eternally.

256 Though Mighty Foes Assail Me, Lord

PSALM 119

ERSKINE C.M.D.

Charles H. Gabriel, 1856-1932

1 Though might - y foes as-sail me, Lord, I fear not them, but Thee;
2 Great peace has he who loves Thy law, Un-moved, he safe - ly stands;

As bound-less wealth and price-less spoil, Thy Word re - joic - es me
For Thy sal - va - tion I have hoped And fol-lowed Thy com-mands.

De - ceit and false-hood I ab - hor, But in Thy law de - light;
Thy tes - ti - mo - nies I have kept, They are my chief de - light;

Through-out the day I praise Thy Name, For all Thy ways are right.
Ob - ser-vant of Thy law and truth, I walk be - fore Thy sight.

O Let My Supplicating Cry

PSALM 119

ERNAN L.M.

Lowell Mason, 1850

1 O let my sup - pli - cat - ing cry By Thee, my gra - cious
2 In - struct-ed in Thy ho - ly law, To praise Thy Word I
3 For Thy sal - va - tion I have longed, And in Thy law is

Lord, be heard; Give wis - dom and de -
lift my voice; O Lord, be Thou my
my de - light; En - rich my soul with

liv - er me Ac - cor - ding to Thy faith - ful Word.
pres - ent help, For Thy com-mand - ments are my choice.
life di - vine, And help me by Thy judg-ments right.

4 Thy servant like a wandering sheep
    Has lost the path and gone astray;
  Restore my soul and lead me home,
    For Thy commands I would obey.

258 I Cried to God in My Distress

PSALM 120

BABYLON'S STREAMS L.M.

Thomas Campian, 1613

Moderately slow

1 I cried to God in my dis-tress, And by the Lord my
2 What woe for false-hood can a-tone, Or pun-ish the de-
3 A - las for me, whose lot is cast With those who find their

prayer was heard; O save me, Lord, from ly - ing lips And
ceit - ful tongue, The tongue whose speech con-sumes like fire, Whose
joy in strife! With those who hate the paths of peace I

from the false, de - ceit - ful word.
words like dead - ly shafts are flung?
long have dwelt and spent my life.

4 In thought and act I am for peace,
   Peace I pursue and ever seek;
   But those about me are for strife,
   Though I in love and kindness speak.

259 Unto the Hills I Lift Mine Eyes

PSALM 121

KEEPER 8 6 6 8 7 7

Louis Bourgeois, 1551
Harmony from De Vries *Koraalboek*
Adapted by Henry Bruinsma, 1946

1 Un - to the hills I lift mine eyes Whence com-eth all my aid
2 Thy Keep-er slum-bereth not, nor shall He cause thy foot to fail,
3 Je - ho-vah is thy Keep-er aye, A shade on thy right hand

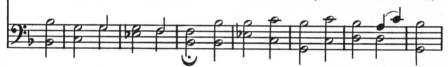

When trou-bled or a - fraid. Je - ho - vah to my help shall rise,
When dan - ger doth as - sail. Lo, He that keep-eth Is - ra - el
Thy safe - ty to com-mand. The moon by night, the sun by day,

He made the earth and heav - en, His aid is free - ly giv - en.
Doth nei - ther sleep nor slum - ber, Naught shall thy soul en - cum - ber.
Shall not af - flict or smite thee, But with their ra-diance light thee.

4 Jehovah will preserve thee when
    The waves of trouble roll;
    He will preserve thy soul.
  When going out or coming in,
    The Lord will thee deliver
    From henceforth and forever.

Dewey Westra, 1931

260

To the Hills I Lift Mine Eyes

PSALM 121

Guide 7 7 7 7 D.

Marcus M. Wells, 1858

1 To the hills I lift mine eyes; Whence shall help for me a - rise?
2 Thy Pro-tec-tor is the Lord, Shade for thee He will af-ford;

From the Lord shall come mine aid, Who the heaven and earth has made.
Nei-ther sun nor moon shall smite, God shall guard by day and night.

He will guide through dan-gers all, Will not suf-fer thee to fall;
He will ev - er keep thy soul, What would harm He will con-trol;

He who safe His peo-ple keeps Slum-bers not and nev - er sleeps.
In the home and by the way He will keep thee day by day.

261   I Lift Up Mine Eyes to the Mountains

PSALM 121   Luzon 9 8 9 8   Dick L. Van Halsema, 1954

1 I lift up mine eyes to the moun - tains, I look to Je - ho - vah for aid; My help is the Lord God Al - might - y; The earth and the heav - ens He made.

2 His vig - il is ten - der and con - stant, And watch-ful the care that He keeps; He suf - fers no harm to be - fall thee And nods not, nor slum-bers, nor sleeps.

3 The Keep-er of Is - ra - el guards thee And keeps thee in path-ways of right; He cir - cles His can - o - py round thee For shel - ter by day and by night.

4 Jehovah will keep thee from evil,
    Thy coming and going He knows;
   Thy soul He preserves unimperiled;
    Look thou to the hills for repose.

Henry Zylstra, 1953

My Soul Was Glad

PSALM 122   Jerusalem's Peace 8 8 8 8 8 8 9 8 8 9

Louis Bourgeois, 1551
Harmonized by Henry Bruinsma, 1954

1 My soul was glad when un - to me They said,
2 Lo, to the ho - ly or - a - cles The tribes
3 Let peace be found with - in thy walls And in

"Come, we will now re - pair Un - to Je - ho -
as - sem - ble from a - broad With thanks un - to
thy pal - a - ces re - pose; Je - ho - vah bless

vah's house of prayer, There to a - dore His ma -
the Name of God, For there His ho - ly pres -
and pros - per those Who dwell with - in thy fa -

jes - ty." Je - ru - sa - lem, where bless - ing waits,
ence dwells. The seats of judg - ment are there - in,
vored halls. For friends and breth - ren I will say,

My Soul Was Glad

PSALM 122

Our feet are stand-ing in Thy gates, Here shall we bring
The thrones of Da-vid's roy-al kin, There sit the rul-
"Let peace a-bide in thee for aye, May nought dis-turb

our sup-pli-ca-tions. Je-ru-sa-lem is builders of the na-tion. Pros-per-i-ty shall be
thee now or ev-er." By rea-son of His tem-

ed well, It is the pride of Is-ra-el,
to them That love thee, O Je-ru-sa-lem,
ple fair And for the mer-cy prof-fered there,

Se-cure-ly knit are its foun-da-tions.
Who make thy peace their sup-pli-ca-tion.
Will I in-voke thy good for-ev-er.

Dewey Westra, 1931

263   With Joy and Gladness in My Soul

PSALM 122   HARVEY'S CHANT C.M., 5 Lines

William B. Bradbury, 1853

1 With joy and glad-ness in my soul I hear the call to prayer; Let us go up to God's own house And bow be-fore Him there, And bow be-fore Him there.

2 We stand with-in thy sa-cred walls, O Zi-on, blest for aye, Where-in the peo-ple of the Lord U-nit-ed hom-age pay, U-nit-ed hom-age pay.

3 They come to learn Je-ho-vah's will, His might-y deeds to own, For there is judg-ment's roy-al seat, Mes-si-ah's king-ly throne, Mes-si-ah's king-ly throne.

4 O pray that Zion may be blest
And have abundant peace,
For all that love thee in their hearts
Shall prosper and increase.

5 I pray the Lord that peace may still
Within thy walls abound,
And ever in thy palaces
Prosperity be found.

6 Yea, for the sake of friends and kin,
My heart desires thy peace,
And for the house of God the Lord
My care shall never cease.

264 My Heart Was Glad to Hear the Welcome Sound

PSALM 122

MORECAMBE 10 10 10 10

Frederick C. Atkinson, 1880

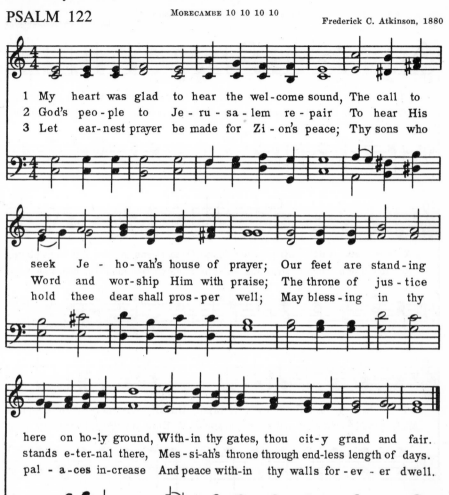

1 My heart was glad to hear the wel-come sound, The call to
2 God's peo-ple to Je - ru - sa - lem re - pair To hear His
3 Let ear-nest prayer be made for Zi - on's peace; Thy sons who

seek Je - ho-vah's house of prayer; Our feet are stand-ing
Word and wor-ship Him with praise; The throne of jus - tice
hold thee dear shall pros - per well; May bless-ing in thy

here on ho-ly ground, With-in thy gates, thou cit-y grand and fair.
stands e-ter-nal there, Mes - si-ah's throne through end-less length of days.
pal - a -ces in-crease And peace with-in thy walls for - ev - er dwell.

4 For all my brethren and companions' sakes
    My prayer shall be, Let peace in thee abide;
  Since God the Lord in thee His dwelling makes,
    To thee my love shall never be denied.

265 To Thee, O Lord, I Lift Mine Eyes

PSALM 123   PAXTANG L.M., 6 Lines, with Refrain   Robert Lowry, 1826-1899

1 To Thee, O Lord, I lift mine eyes, O Thou en-throned a-bove the skies;
2 O Lord, our God, Thy mer-cy show, For man's con-tempt and scorn we know;

As ser-vants watch their mas-ter's hand, Or maid-ens by their mis-tress stand,
Re-proach and shame Thy saints en-dure From wick-ed men who dwell se-cure;

So   to   the Lord our eyes we raise, Un-til His mer-cy He dis-plays.
Man's proud con-tempt and scorn we know; O Lord, our God, Thy mer-cy show.

REFRAIN

To Thee, O Lord, I lift mine eyes, O Thou en-throned a-bove the skies.

266

Now Israel May Say

PSALM 124   Old 124th 10 10 10 10 10   Louis Bourgeois, 1551

1 Now Is - ra - el may say, and that in truth, If that the
2 Yea, when their wrath a - gainst us fierce-ly rose, The swell - ing
3 Blest be the Lord who made us not their prey; As from the

Lord had not our right main-tained, If that the Lord had
tide had o'er us spread its wave, The rag - ing stream had
snare a bird es - cap - eth free, Their net is rent and

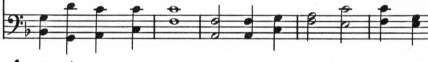

not with us re-mained, When cru - el men a - gainst us
then be-come our grave, The surg - ing flood, in proud - ly
so es-caped are we. Our on - ly help is in Je -

rose to strive, We sure - ly had been swal-lowed up a - live.
swell-ing roll, Most sure - ly then had o - ver-whelmed our soul.
ho - vah's Name, Who made the earth and all the heaven - ly frame.

315

267

All Who with Heart Confiding

PSALM 125

KNOWHEAD 7 6 7 6 D.

Charles H. Gabriel, 1856-1932

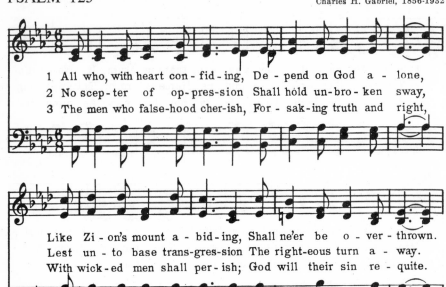

1 All who, with heart con - fid - ing, De - pend on God a - lone,
2 No scep - ter of op - pres - sion Shall hold un - bro - ken sway,
3 The men who false-hood cher-ish, For - sak-ing truth and right,

Like Zi - on's mount a - bid - ing, Shall ne'er be o - ver - thrown.
Lest un - to base trans-gres-sion The right-eous turn a - way.
With wick - ed men shall per - ish; God will their sin re - quite.

Like Zi - on's cit - y, bound - ed By guard-ing moun-tains broad,
Thy fa - vor be im-part - ed To god - ly men, O Lord;
From sin Thy saints de-fend - ing, Their joy, O Lord, in - crease,

His peo - ple are sur-round - ed For - ev - er by their God.
Bless all that are pure-heart - ed, The good with good re - ward.
With mer - cy nev - er end - ing And ev - er - last - ing peace.

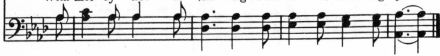

When Zion in Her Low Estate

MELMORE L.M.

W. Martin, 1864

1 When Zi - on in her low es - tate Was
2 The Lord, in great - ly bless - ing us, Be -
3 O Lord, re - fresh us by Thy grace, Re -

brought from bond - age by the Lord, In ec - sta -
fore the world His power dis-plays; Yea, great things
vive and quick - en all our powers, As fail - ing

sy we sang for joy, By grace and won-drous love re-stored.
God has done for us And filled our hearts with joy and praise.
streams are made to flow, Re - plen-ished by a - bun-dant showers.

4 The sower, bearing precious seed,
   May weep as in his toil he grieves,
   But he shall come again with joy
   In harvest time with golden sheaves.

269   Unless the Lord the House Shall Build

PSALM 127   ILLA L.M.   Lowell Mason, 1841

1 Un - less the Lord the house shall build, The wea - ry
2 In vain you rise ere morn - ing break, And late your
3 Lo, chil - dren are a great re - ward, A gift from

build - ers toil in vain; Un - less the Lord the
night - ly vig - ils keep, And of the bread of
God in ve - ry truth; With ar - rows is his

cit - y shield, The guards a use - less watch main - tain.
toil par - take; God gives to His be - lov - ed sleep.
quiv - er stored Who joys in chil - dren of his youth

4 And blest the man whose age is cheered
    By stalwart sons and daughters fair;
   No enemies by him are feared,
    No lack of love, no want of care.

270   Blest the Man That Fears Jehovah

PSALM 128   GALILEE (JUDE) 8 7 8 7   William H. Jude, 1887

1 Blest the man that fears Je - ho - vah, Walk - ing
2 In thy wife thou shalt have glad - ness, She shall
3 Joy - ful chil - dren, sons and daugh - ters, Shall a -

ev - er in His ways; By thy toil thou shalt be
fill thy home with good, Hap - py in her lov - ing
bout thy ta - ble meet, Ol - ive plants, in strength and

pros - pered And be hap - py all thy days.
ser - vice And the joys of moth - er - hood.
beau - ty, Full of hope and prom - ise sweet.

4 Lo, on him that fears Jehovah
  Shall this blessedness attend,
For Jehovah out of Zion
  Shall to thee His blessing send.

5 Thou shalt see God's kingdom prosper
  All thy days, till life shall cease,
Thou shalt see thy children's children;
  On Thy people, Lord, be peace.

271   Through All the Years, May Israel Say

PSALM 129   HUMILITY L.M.   Samuel P. Tuckerman, 1848

1 Through all the years, may Is-rael say, My bit-ter
2 Though scars of con-flict and dis-tress Re-main to
3 The foes of Zi-on shall be brought To hope-less

foes have oft as-sailed, Have sought my hurt in
tell of tri-als past, Je-ho-vah in His
flight and put to shame; Their wick-ed plans shall

fierce ar-ray, Yet o-ver me have not pre-vailed.
right-eous-ness Has safe-ly brought us through at last.
come to nought And all man-kind for-get their name.

4 To them no kindly friend shall say,
    God bless you now and speed you well;
No grateful heart for them shall pray,
    May God's rich blessing on you dwell.

272   Out of the Depths of Sadness

PSALM 130   CONTRITION 7 6 7 6 D.   Louis Bourgeois, 1542
Harmony from De Vries *Koraalboek*
Adapted by Henry Bruinsma, 1946

1 Out of the depths of sad-ness, O Lord, I cried to Thee;
2 If Thou shouldst mark trans-gres-sion, O Lord, who then could stand?

Thou who canst fill with glad-ness, Lend now Thine ear to me.
For e - vil and op - pres - sion Are found on ev - ery hand.

O Fount of con - so - la - tion, At - tend un - to my cry,
But Thou dost par - don ful - ly All our in - iq - ui - ty,

Hear Thou my sup - pli - ca - tion And to my help draw nigh.
That we may serve Thee tru - ly And fear Thy maj - es - ty.

3 I wait for God to hide me;
   My soul, with longing stirred,
Shall hope, whate'er betide me,
   In His unfailing word.
My soul waits for Jehovah
   With more intense desire
Than watchers for the morning
   To dawn of day aspire.

4 Hope in the Lord, O nation!
   For with Him there is grace
And plenteous salvation
   For all who seek His face.
He shall redeem His people,
   His chosen Israel,
From all their sin and evil,
   And all their gloom dispel.

Dewey Westra, 1931

273 From out the Depths I Cry

PSALM 130   SANDON 10 4 10 4 10 10

Charles H. Purday, 1799-1885

1 From out the depths I cry, O Lord, to Thee; Lord, hear my call.
2 I wait for God, the Lord, and on His word My hope re - lies;
3 Hope in the Lord, ye wait-ing saints, and He Will well pro - vide;

I love Thee, Lord, for Thou dost heed my plea,
My soul still waits and looks un - to the Lord
For mer - cy and re - demp - tion full and free

For - giv - ing all. If Thou shouldst mark our sins, who then could stand?
Till light a - rise. I look for Him to drive a - way my night,
With Him a - bide. From sin and e - vil, might - y though they seem,

But grace and mer - cy dwell at Thy right hand.
Yea, more than watch - men look for morn - ing light.
His arm al - might - y will His saints re - deem.

322

274

From the Depths Do I Invoke Thee

PSALM 130   EVENING PRAYER 8 7 8 7

George C. Stebbins, 1878

1 From the depths do I in - voke Thee; Lord, to
2 Lord, if Thou shouldst mark trans - gres - sions, In Thy
3 For Je - ho - vah I am wait - ing And my

me in - cline Thine ear; To my voice be Thou at -
pres - ence who shall stand? But with Thee there is for -
hope is in His Word, In His Word of prom - ise

ten - tive And my sup - pli - ca - tion hear.
give - ness, That Thy Name may fear com - mand.
giv - en; Yea, my soul waits for the Lord.

4 For the Lord my soul is waiting
   More than watchers in the night,
   More than they for morning watching,
   Watching for the morning light.

5 Hope in God, ye waiting people;
   Mercies great with Him abound;
   With the Lord a full redemption
   From the guilt of sin is found.

275   From the Depths My Prayer Ascendeth

PSALM 130   Bullinger 8 5 8 3   Ethelbert W. Bullinger, 1877

1 From the depths my prayer ascendeth
2 None can stand unscathed and blameless
3 Lord, my hope is in Thy promise,

Unto God on high;   Hear, O
In Thy judgment just,   But the
And I wait for Thee   More than

Lord, my supplication And my cry.
con-trite in Thy mercy Humbly trust.
they who watch for morning, Light to see.

4 With the Lord is tender mercy,
    And redeeming love;
Israel, look for full salvation
    From above.

276   Not Haughty Is My Heart

PSALM 131   TRENTHAM S.M.   Robert Jackson, 1894

1 Not haugh - ty is my heart, Not loft - y is my pride; I do not seek to know the things God's wis - dom has de - nied.

2 With child - like trust, O Lord, In Thee I calm - ly rest, Con - tent - ed as a lit - tle child Up - on its moth - er's breast.

3 Ye peo - ple of the Lord, In Him a - lone con - fide; From this time forth and ev - er - more His wis - dom be your guide.

277   Gracious Lord, Remember David

PSALM 132   ULSTER 8 7 8 7 D.   Robert Lowry, 1875

1 Gra-cious Lord, re-mem-ber Da-vid, How he made Thy house his care,
2 Far a - way God's ark was rest-ing, It is with His peo -ple now;

How he vowed to seek no pleas-ure Till Thy house he should pre-pare.
We will go in - to His tem-ple, At His foot-stool we will bow.

Lord, re-mem-ber his de - vo-tion; Rest-less in his courts he trod
With the ark, Thy might re-veal-ing, En - ter, Lord, in - to Thy rest;

Till he found a hab - i - ta-tion Fit for Is-rael's might-y God,
Let Thy priests be clothed with jus-tice, Let Thy joy-ful saints be blest,

Gracious Lord, Remember David

PSALM 132

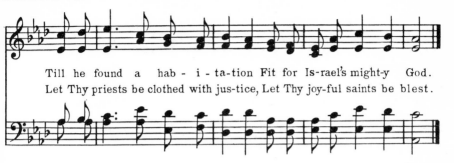

Till he found a hab - i - ta-tion Fit for Is-rael's might-y God.
Let Thy priests be clothed with jus-tice, Let Thy joy-ful saints be blest.

3 Let the king behold Thy favor
    For Thy servant David's sake,
  Unto whom a sacred promise.
      Sure and faithful, Thou didst make.
  If his children keep Thy covenant
      And Thy testimony own,
  Then, as Thou, O Lord, hast promised,
      They shall sit upon his throne.

4 Thou, the Lord, hast chosen Zion,
      Thou hast ever loved her well;
  This My resting-place forever.
      Here, Thou say'st, I choose to dwell.
  Surely I will bless and help her,
      Feed her poor, her saints make glad,
  And her priests shall stand before Me
      In salvation's garments clad.

5 I will cause the might of David
      Ever more and more to grow;
  On the path of Mine Anointed
      I will make a lamp to glow.
  All His enemies shall perish,
      I will cover them with shame;
  But His crown shall ever flourish;
      Blessed be His holy Name.

278   How Good and Pleasant Is the Sight

PSALM 133   Pressly 8 8 6 D.

Charles H. Gabriel, 1856-1932

1 How good and pleas-ant is the sight When breth - ren
2 Such love in peace and joy dis - tils, As o'er the
3 How good and pleas - ant is the sight When breth - ren

make it their de - light To dwell in blest ac - cord;
slopes of Her-mon's hills Re - fresh - ing dew de - scends;
make it their de - light To dwell in blest ac - cord;

Such love is like a - noint - ing oil That con - se -
The Lord com-mands His bless - ing there, And they that
The Lord com-mands His bless - ing there, And they that

crates for ho - ly toil The ser - vants of the Lord.
walk in love shall share In life that nev - er ends.
walk in love shall share In life that nev - er ends.

279   Behold, How Pleasant and How Good

PSALM 133   SUCH A FRIEND 8 7 8 7 D.   George C. Stebbins, 1878

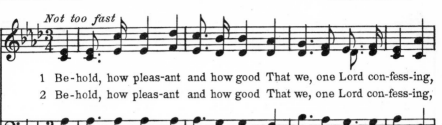

1 Be-hold, how pleas-ant and how good That we, one Lord con-fess-ing,
2 Be-hold, how pleas-ant and how good That we, one Lord con-fess-ing,

To-geth-er dwell in broth-er-hood, Our u - ni-ty ex-press-ing;
To-geth-er dwell in broth-er-hood, Our u - ni-ty ex-press-ing;

'Tis like the oil on Aa-ron's head, The seal of or - di - na - tion,
'Tis like the dew from Her-mon fair On Zi-on's hill de-scend-ing;

That o'er his robes the sweet-ness shed Of per-fect con-se-cra-tion.
The Lord com-mands His bless-ing there In life that is un-end-ing.

280   O Bless Our God with One Accord

PSALM 134   OLD HUNDREDTH L.M.   Louis Bourgeois, 1551

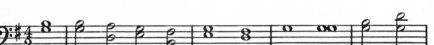

1 O bless our God with one ac - cord, Ye faith - ful
2 Lift up your hands, in prayer draw nigh Un - to His
3 Je - ho - vah bless thee from a - bove, From Zi - on

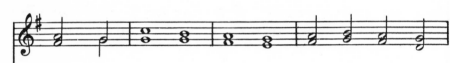

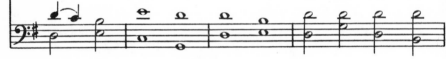

ser - vants of the Lord, Who in His house do
sanc - tu - a - ry high; Bless ye the Lord, kneel
in His bound - less love, Our God, who heaven and

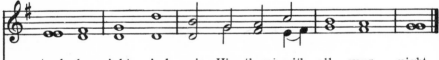

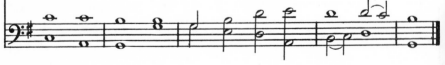

stand by night; And praise Him there with all your might.
at His feet, And wor-ship Him with rev - erence meet.
earth did frame; Blest be His great and ho - ly Name.

Lambertus J. Lamberts, 1928

281   O Praise Ye the Name of Jehovah

PSALM 135   JANET 9 8 9 8   George C. Stebbins, 1846-1945

1 O praise ye the Name of Je - ho - vah, Pro -
2 O praise ye the Lord for His good - ness; 'Tis

claim ye His glo - ry a - broad; O praise Him, ye ser-vants ap-
pleas-ant His prais-es to sing; His peo - ple, His cho-sen and

point - ed To stand in the house of our God.
pre - cious, Your prais - es with grat - i - tude bring.

3 I know that the Lord is almighty,
   Supreme in dominion is He,
Performing His will and good pleasure
In heaven and in earth and the sea.

4 His hand guides the clouds in their
     courses,
   The lightning flames forth at His will,
The wind and the rain He releases
His sovereign designs to fulfil.

5 To ransom His people from bondage
   Great wonders and signs He displayed;
He smote all the first-born of Egypt,
Till Pharaoh made haste and obeyed.

6 Great nations and kings that opposed Him
   Were smitten by God's mighty hand;
Their riches He gave to His people,
And made them inherit the land.

7 Thy name shall abide, O Jehovah,
   Through all generations renowned;
The Lord is the Judge of His people,
His mercies forever abound.

8 Men's idols of gold and of silver
   Can speak not, nor hearken, nor see;
Like them shall their makers be
     helpless,
Unblest shall their worshippers be.

9 Ye people who worship Jehovah,
   His praises with gladness proclaim;
His servants, and all ye that fear Him,
Sing praise to His glorious Name.

10 O Church of our God, sing His praises,
   For with you and in you He dwells;
O sing Hallelujahs before Him,
Whose glory all praises excels.

282   Exalt the Lord, His Praise Proclaim

PSALM 135

CREATION L.M.D.

Arranged from F. Joseph Haydn, 1798

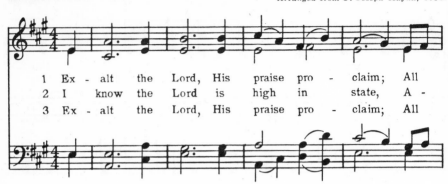

1 Ex - alt the Lord, His praise pro - claim; All
2 I know the Lord is high in state, A -
3 Ex - alt the Lord, His praise pro - claim; All

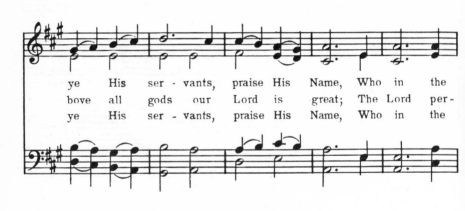

ye His ser - vants, praise His Name, Who in the
bove all gods our Lord is great; The Lord per -
ye His ser - vants, praise His Name, Who in the

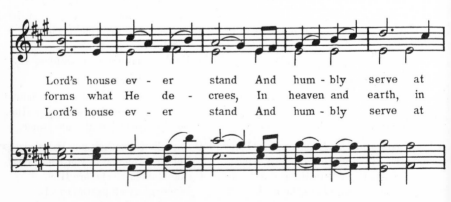

Lord's house ev - er stand And hum - bly serve at
forms what He de - crees, In heaven and earth, in
Lord's house ev - er stand And hum - bly serve at

Exalt the Lord, His Praise Proclaim

PSALM 135

His com - mand. The Lord is good, His praise pro-claim;
depths and seas. He makes the va - pors to as - cend
His com - mand. For - ev - er praise and bless His Name,

Since it is pleas - ant, praise His Name;
In clouds from earth's re - mot - est end;
And in the Church His praise pro - claim;

His peo - ple for His own He takes
The light - nings flash at His com - mand,
In Zi - on is His dwell - ing - place;

And His pe - cu - liar treas - ure makes.
He holds the tem - pest in His hand.
Praise ye the Lord, show forth His grace.

283   Now May All in Brotherhood

PSALM 136   REMEIN 7 7 7 7 D.   Johannes Dirk Plekker, 1954

1 Now may all in bro - ther - hood Praise the Lord, for
2 Tune your thanks with sound - ing chords To ex - tol the
3 He or - dained the arch - ing sky, Spoke the word that

He is good. With most heart - felt songs of laud
Lord of Lords; By the won - ders of His hand
holds it high; Made the wa - ters of the deep,

Glo - ri - fy our gra - cious God. For His mer - cy
He main - tains His just com - mand. For His mer - cy
Fixed the bounds which they must keep. For His mer - cy

will en - dure, Ev - er faith - ful, ev - er sure; For His mer - cy
will en - dure, Ev - er faith - ful, ev - er sure; For His mer - cy
will en - dure, Ev - er faith - ful, ev - er sure; For His mer - cy

Now May All in Brotherhood

PSALM 136

will en-dure, Ev-er faith-ful, ev-er sure.
will en-dure, Ev-er faith-ful, ev-er sure.
will en-dure, Ev-er faith-ful, ev-er sure.

4 Filled the world with radiance bright,
Fashioned heaven's orbs of light;
Made the sun, whose golden rays
Regulate the passing days.
For His mercy will endure,
Ever faithful, ever sure.

5 Made the moon and stars to gleam
Through the night with silvery beam;
Struck down Egypt's eldest born,
Smiting them 'twixt eve and morn.
For His mercy will endure,
Ever faithful, ever sure.

6 His right hand and outstretched arm
Led the slaves past reach of harm;
Cleft the Red Sea flood in two,
Guided Israel safely through.
For His mercy will endure,
Ever faithful, ever sure.

7 Overwhelmed therein the foe,
Drowned therein proud Pharaoh;
Through the trackless waste He led
Israel's folk and gave them bread.
For His mercy will endure,
Ever faithful, ever sure.

8 Smote the kings who barred the way,
Great and mighty kings were they:
Sihon, lord of Hamor's coast,
Og, whose might was Bashan's boast.
For His mercy will endure,
Ever faithful, ever sure.

9 And the land that bore their yoke
Gave He to His chosen folk,
He remembered all our woes,
Snatched us from the clutch of foes.
For His mercy will endure,
Ever faithful, ever sure.

10 He sustains and saves from dearth
All who dwell upon the earth;
Let high thanks be ever given
To the Lord of earth and heaven.
For His mercy will endure,
Ever faithful, ever sure.

Harry Mayer, 1940

284   Give Thanks to God, for Good Is He

PSALM 136   Constance 8 7 8 7 D.   Arthur S. Sullivan, 1875

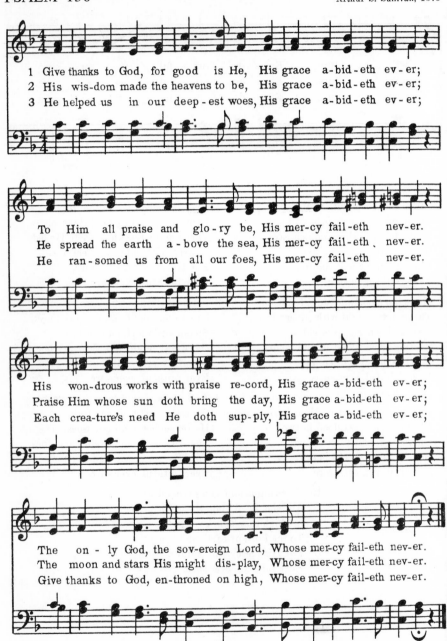

1 Give thanks to God, for good is He, His grace a-bid-eth ev-er;
2 His wis-dom made the heavens to be, His grace a-bid-eth ev-er;
3 He helped us in our deep-est woes, His grace a-bid-eth ev-er;

To Him all praise and glo-ry be, His mer-cy fail-eth nev-er.
He spread the earth a-bove the sea, His mer-cy fail-eth nev-er.
He ran-somed us from all our foes, His mer-cy fail-eth nev-er.

His won-drous works with praise re-cord, His grace a-bid-eth ev-er;
Praise Him whose sun doth bring the day, His grace a-bid-eth ev-er;
Each crea-ture's need He doth sup-ply, His grace a-bid-eth ev-er;

The on-ly God, the sov-ereign Lord, Whose mer-cy fail-eth nev-er.
The moon and stars His might dis-play, Whose mer-cy fail-eth nev-er.
Give thanks to God, en-throned on high, Whose mer-cy fail-eth nev-er.

285   By Babel's Streams We Sat and Wept

PSALM 137   OLIVE'S BROW L.M.

William B. Bradbury, 1853

1 By Babel's streams we sat and wept, For memory
2 There our rude captors, flushed with pride, A song re-
3 Not songs but sighs to us belong When Zion's

still to Zion clung; The winds alone our
quired to mock our wrongs; Our spoilers called for
walls in ruin lie; How shall we sing Je-

harp-strings swept, That on the drooping willows hung.
mirth and cried, Come, sing us one of Zion's songs.
hovah's song While in an alien land we die?

4 O Zion fair, God's holy hill,
    Wherein our God delights to dwell,
Let my right hand forget her skill
    If I forget to love thee well.

5 If I do not remember thee,
    Then let my tongue from utterance cease,
If any earthly joy to me
    Be dear as Zion's joy and peace.

6 Remember, Lord, the dreadful day
    Of Zion's cruel overthrow;
How happy he who shall repay
    The bitter hatred of her foe.

286 With Grateful Heart My Thanks I Bring

PSALM 138

THE SOLID ROCK L.M., 7 Lines

William B. Bradbury, 1868

1 With grate-ful heart my thanks I bring, Be -
2 I cried to Thee and Thou didst save, Thy

fore the great Thy praise I sing; I wor-ship in Thy
Word of grace new cour-age gave; The kings of earth shall

ho - ly place And praise Thee for Thy truth and grace;
thank Thee, Lord, For they have heard Thy won-drous Word;

For truth and grace to-geth-er shine In Thy most ho-ly
Yea, they shall come with songs of praise, For great and glo-rious

With Grateful Heart My Thanks I Bring

Word di - vine, In Thy most ho - ly Word di - vine.
are Thy ways, For great and glo - rious are Thy ways.

3 O Lord, enthroned in glory bright,
  Thou reignest in the heavenly height;
  The proud in vain Thy favor seek,
  But Thou hast mercy for the meek;
  Through trouble though my pathway be,
  Thou wilt revive and strengthen me.

4 Thou wilt stretch forth Thy mighty arm
  To save me when my foes alarm;
  The work Thou hast for me begun
  Shall by Thy grace be fully done;
  Forever mercy dwells with Thee;
  O Lord, my Maker, think on me.

287   With All My Heart Will I Record

PSALM 138

JUBILATION 8 9 8 9 D.

Louis Bourgeois, 1543
Harmonized by Henry Bruinsma, 1946

With strength; may be sung in unison

1 With all my heart will I re-cord Thy praise, O
2 O God, when-e'er I cried to Thee, Thou heard-est

Lord, and ex-al-ta-tion; Be-fore the gods with
me and didst de-liv-er; For by Thy strength, when

joy-ful song Will I pro-long My ad-o-ra-tion. I'll
sore a-fraid, My soul was stayed, O gra-cious Giv-er. The

wor-ship toward Thy ho-ly place And for Thy
kings of earth in one ac-cord Shall thank Thee,

With All My Heart Will I Record

PSALM 138

grace and truth ex - tol   Thee; A - bove Thy Name, Thou, Lord Most
Lord, with praise un - bro - ken; When o - ver all   the earth is

High,   Didst mag - ni - fy   Thy Word so   ho - ly.
heard   The   won - drous Word which Thou hast   spo - ken.

3 They all shall sing in joyful lays
 And laud His ways with jubilation;
For great is God in majesty,
 The Lord is He of all creation.
Jehovah looketh from on high
 With kindly eye upon the lowly,
But knoweth those from far who hide
 In sinful pride their ways unholy.

4 Lord, though I walk 'mid troubles sore,
 Thou wilt restore my faltering spirit;
Though angry foes my soul alarm,
 Thy mighty arm will save and cheer it.
Yea, thou wilt finish perfectly
 What Thou for me hast undertaken;
May not Thy works, in mercy wrought,
 E'er come to naught or be forsaken.

Dewey Westra, 1931

288 Lord, Thou Hast Searched Me

PSALM 139

WOODWORTH L.M.

William B. Bradbury, 1849

1 Lord, Thou hast searched me and dost know Wher-e'er I
2 My words from Thee I can-not hide, I feel Thy
3 Where can I go a-part from Thee, Or whith-er

rest, wher-e'er I go; Thou know-est all that
power on ev-ery side; O won-drous knowl-edge,
from Thy pres-ence flee? In heaven? It is Thy

I have planned, And all my ways are in Thy hand.
aw-ful might, Un-fath-omed depth, un-meas-ured height!
dwell-ing fair; In death's a-bode? Lo, Thou art there.

4 If I the wings of morning take,
And far away my dwelling make,
The hand that leadeth me is Thine,
And my support Thy power divine.

5 If deepest darkness cover me,
The darkness hideth not from Thee;
To Thee both night and day are bright,
The darkness shineth as the light.

All That I Am I Owe to Thee

PSALM 139

FEDERAL STREET, L.M.

Henry K. Oliver, 1832

1 All that I am I owe to Thee, Thy wis-dom,
Lord, has fash-ioned me; I give my Mak-er
thank-ful praise, Whose won-drous works my soul a-maze.

2 Ere in-to be-ing I was brought, Thine eye did
see, and in Thy thought My life in all its
per-fect plan Was or-dered ere my days be-gan.

3 Thy thoughts, O God, how man-i-fold, More pre-cious
un-to me than gold! I muse on their in-
fin-i-ty, A-wak-ing, I am still with Thee.

4 The wicked Thou wilt surely slay,
From me let sinners turn away;
They speak against the Name divine,
I count God's enemies as mine.

5 Search me, O God, my heart discern,
Try me, my inmost thought to learn;
And lead me, if in sin I stray,
To choose the everlasting way.

290   O Lord, My Inmost Heart and Thought

PSALM 139   BINGHAM C.M.   Anonymous

1 O Lord, my in-most heart and thought Thy search-ing eye doth see; Wher-e'er I rest, wher-e'er I go, My ways are known to Thee.

2 Each spo-ken word, each si-lent thought, Thou, Lord, dost un-der-stand; Be-fore me and be-hind art Thou, Re-strain-ing by Thy hand.

3 If I the wings of morn-ing take To some re-mot-est land, Still I shall be up-held by Thee And guid-ed by Thy hand.

4 From Thee, O Lord, I cannot hide,
    Though darkness cover me;
    The darkness and the light of day
    Are both alike to Thee.

5 Search me, O God, and know my heart,
    Try me, my thoughts to know;
    O lead me, if in sin I stray,
    In paths of life to go.

Deliver Me from Evil

MUNICH 7 6 7 6 D.

Meiningen *Gesangbuch*, 1693

1 De - liv - er me from e - vil, Pre-serve me, Lord, from wrong;
2 O Lord, I have con-fessed Thee To be my God a - lone;
3 Let e - vil smite the e - vil, And cause their o - ver - throw;

A - gainst the foes that gath - er Be Thou my Help - er strong;
O hear my sup - pli - ca - tion And be Thy mer - cy shown;
The need - y and af - flict - ed The Lord will help, I know;

From those who plot to hurt me And spread the treach-erous snare,
O God the Lord, my Sav - ior, My shield a - mid the strife,
Thy saints, re-deemed from e - vil, Their thanks to Thee shall give;

Pre-serve me, Lord, and keep me Safe-guard-ed in Thy care.
Let not the wick - ed tri - umph Who plot a - gainst my life.
The right-eous and the up-right Shall in Thy pres - ence live.

292   O Lord, Make Haste to Hear My Cry

PSALM 141   Quebec (Hesperus) L.M.

Henry Baker, 1862

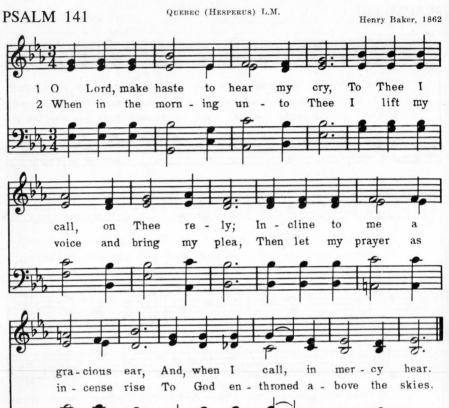

1 O Lord, make haste to hear my cry, To Thee I
call, on Thee re - ly; In - cline to me a
gra - cious ear, And, when I call, in mer - cy hear.

2 When in the morn - ing un - to Thee I lift my
voice and bring my plea, Then let my prayer as
in - cense rise To God en - throned a - bove the skies.

3 When unto Thee I look and pray
With lifted hands at close of day,
Then as the evening sacrifice
Let my request accepted rise.

4 Guard Thou my thoughts, I Thee im-
    plore,
And of my lips keep Thou the door;
Nor leave my sinful heart to stray
Where evil footsteps lead the way.

5 O righteous God, Thy chastisement,
Though sent through foes, in love is sent;
Though grievous, it will profit me,
A healing ointment it shall be.

6 While wickedness my foes devise,
To Thee my constant prayer shall rise;
When their injustice is o'erthrown
My gentleness shall still be shown.

7 Brought nigh to death and sore dis-
    tressed,
O Lord, my God, in Thee I rest;
Forsake me not, I look to Thee,
Let me Thy great salvation see.

8 Themselves entangled in their snare,
Their own defeat my foes prepare;
O keep me, Lord, nor let me fall,
Protect and lead me safe through all.

293   To God My Earnest Voice I Raise

PSALM 142   HAMBURG L.M.

Arranged from a Gregorian Chant
by Lowell Mason, 1824

1 To God my ear - nest voice I raise, To God my
2 When gloom and sor - row com - pass me, The path I
3 All un - pro - tect - ed, lo, I stand, No friend - ly

voice im - plor - ing prays; Be - fore His face my
take is known to Thee, And all the toils that
guard - ian at my hand, No place of flight or

grief I show And tell my trou - ble and my woe.
foes do lay To snare Thy ser - vant in his way.
ref - uge near, And none to whom my soul is dear.

4 O Lord, my Savior, now to Thee,
Without a hope besides, I flee,
To Thee, my shelter from the strife,
My portion in the land of life.

5 Be Thou my help when troubles throng,
For I am weak and foes are strong;
My captive soul from prison bring,
And thankful praises I will sing.

6 The righteous then shall gather round
To share the blessing I have found,
Their hearts made glad because they see
How richly God has dealt with me.

294   Lord, Hear Me in Distress

PSALM 143   Denby 6 6 6 6 D.

Charles J. Dale, 1904

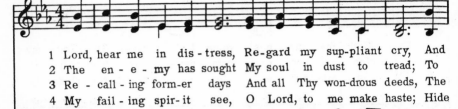

1 Lord, hear me in dis-tress, Re-gard my sup-pliant cry, And
2 The en-e-my has sought My soul in dust to tread; To
3 Re-call-ing form-er days And all Thy won-drous deeds, The
4 My fail-ing spir-it see, O Lord, to me make haste; Hide

in Thy faith-ful-ness And right-eous-ness re-ply. In judg-ment do not cause Thy
dark-ness I am brought, For-got-ten as the dead. My spir-it, crushed with grief, Is
mem-ory of Thy ways To hope and com-fort leads. To Thee I stretch my hands, Let
not Thy face from me, Lest bit-ter death I taste. O let the morn re-turn, Let

ser-vant to be tried; Be-fore Thy ho-ly laws No man is jus-ti-fied.
sad and o-ver-borne; My heart finds no re-lief, But des-o-late I mourn.
me not plead in vain; I wait as wea-ry lands Wait for re-fresh-ing rain.
mer-cy light my day; For Thee in faith I yearn, O guide me in the way.

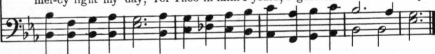

5 Lord, save me from my foe,
   To Thee for help I flee;
Teach me Thy way to know,
   I have no God but Thee.
By Thy good Spirit led
   From trouble and distress,
My erring feet shall tread
   The path of uprightness.

6 O Lord, for Thy Name's sake
   Revive my fainting heart;
My soul from trouble take,
   For just and true Thou art.
Remove mine enemy,
   My cruel foe reward;
In mercy rescue me
   Who am Thy servant, Lord.

295 When Morning Lights the Eastern Skies

PSALM 143

LYNTON C.M.

Arthur J. Jamouneau, 1904

1 When morn - ing lights the east - ern skies,
2 Teach me the way that I should go;
3 Thou art my God, to Thee I pray,

O Lord, Thy mer - cy show; On Thee a - lone my
I lift my soul to Thee; For ref - uge from my
Teach me Thy will to heed; And in the right and

hope re - lies, Let me Thy kind - ness know.
cru - el foe To Thee, O Lord, I flee.
per - fect way May Thy good Spir - it lead.

4 For Thy Name's sake, O gracious Lord,
Revive my soul and bless,
And in Thy faithfulness and love
Redeem me from distress.

296

Thrice Blest Be Jehovah

PSALM 144

Sᴛ. Dᴇɴɪᴏ 11 11 11 11

Welsh Melody, adapted 1839

1 Thrice blest be Je - ho - vah, The rock of my
2 O Lord, what are mor-tals That Thou shouldst be -
3 Bend low Thine arched heav-ens, Come, Lord, from on

might; He girds me for bat - tle And nerves me to
stow At - ten - tion up - on them Wher - ev - er they
high, And touch the great moun-tains Till smoke shall thence

fight; My mer - cy and strong-hold, My shield and my
go? Man is but a va - por, His brief earth - ly
fly; Flash forth Thy fierce light-nings And scat - ter the

tower, He hum-bled my foe-men, Es - tab-lished my power.
stay Is but as a shad-ow That fleet-eth a - way.
foe, Send out Thy sharp ar - rows And whelm him in woe.

Thrice Blest Be Jehovah

PSALM 144

4 Reach down out of heaven
    My Helper to be,
From floods and barbarians,
    Lord, rescue Thou me;
Their tongues speak me falsely
    And truth they despise,
Their right hand they hold forth
    To swear to their lies.

5 A song never rendered
    Before I will sing,
And laud Thee with music
    On many a string;
Thou biddest kings triumph;
    Thy hand hath, O Lord,
Kept David, Thy servant,
    From hurt by the sword.

6 Reach down out of heaven
    And rescue Thou me,
From threat of barbarians,
    O Lord, set me free,
Whose tongues speak me falsely
    And truth they despise,
Whose right hand is held forth
    To swear to their lies.

7 Our sons be like saplings
    In youth grown apace,
Our daughters, carved pillars
    Excelling in grace;
Our garners be brimming,
    Our flocks in the field,
Increasing by thousands,
    Then thousandfold yield.

8 Our rulers established,
    No raids, no retreats;
No outcry of panic
    Be heard in the streets.
How happy the people
    On whom is outpoured
Such blessing; how happy
    Whose God is the Lord!

Harry Mayer, 1940

297   O Happy Land, Whose Sons in Youth

PSALM 144   SHORTLE 8 8 6   8 8 6 6

Charles G. Goodrich, born 1869

1 O hap-py land, whose sons in youth, In stur-dy strength and
2 O hap-py land, when flock and field Their rich, a - bun - dant
3 O hap-py peo - ple, fa-vored land, To whom the Lord with

no - ble truth, Like plants in vig - or spring; Whose daugh-ters fair, a
in-crease yield, And bless-ings mul-ti - ply; When plen - ty all thy
lib-eral hand Has thus His good-ness shown; Yea, sure - ly is that

queen - ly race, Are like the cor - ner - stones that grace
peo - ple share, And no in - vad - ing foe is there,
peo - ple blest By whom Je - ho - vah is con - fessed

The pal - ace of a king, The pal - ace of a king.
And no dis - tress-ful cry, And no dis - tress - ful cry.
To be their God a - lone, To be their God a - lone.

352

298   I Will Extol Thee, O My God

PSALM 145

GERARD C.M.D.

Arranged by Arthur S. Sullivan, 1871

1 I will ex-tol Thee, O my God, And praise Thee, O my King;
2 Each gen - e - ra - tion to the next Shall tes - ti - mo-ny bear,
3 Thy might-y acts and ter - ri - ble Shall men with awe con - fess;

Yea, ev-ery day and ev - er-more Thy prais-es I will sing.
And to Thy praise, from age to age, Thy won-drous acts de-clare.
Of Thy great good-ness they shall sing, And per-fect right-eous-ness.

Great is the Lord, our might-y God, And great-ly to be praised;
Up - on Thy glo-rious maj-es - ty And hon - or I will dwell,
Most gra-cious and com-pas - sion-ate Is God who reigns a - bove;

His great-ness is un - search - a - ble, A - bove all glo - ry raised.
And all Thy grand and glo-rious works And all Thy great-ness tell.
His wrath is ev - er slow to rise, Un-bound-ed is His love.

299   O Lord, Thou Art My God and King

PSALM 145   DUKE STREET L.M.   John Hatton, died 1793

1 O Lord, Thou art my God and King, And I will
2 The Lord is great-ly to be praised, His great-ness
3 Up-on Thy glo-rious maj-es-ty And won-drous
4 Thy match-less good-ness and Thy grace Thy peo-ple

ev-er bless Thy Name; I will ex-tol Thee
is be-yond our thought; From age to age the
works my mind shall dwell; Thy deeds shall fill the
shall com-mem-o-rate, And all Thy truth and

ev-ery day, And ev-er-more Thy praise pro-claim.
sons of men Shall tell the won-ders God has wrought.
world with awe, And of Thy great-ness I will tell.
right-eous-ness My joy-ful song shall cel-e-brate.

5 The Lord our God is rich in grace,
   Most tender and compassionate;
His anger is most slow to rise,
   His lovingkindness is most great.

6 The Lord is good in all His ways,
   His creatures know His constant care;
To all His works His love extends,
   All men His tender mercies share.

7 Thy works shall give Thee thanks, O Lord,
   Thy saints Thy mighty acts shall show,
Till o'er the earth the sons of men
   Thy kingdom, power and glory know.

8 Eternal is Thy kingdom, Lord,
   Forever strong and ever sure;
While generations rise and die,
   Shall Thy dominion still endure.

300   The Lord Upholds the Faltering Feet

PSALM 145

NAZARETH L.M.D.

Theodore E. Perkins, born 1831

1 The Lord up-holds the fal-tering feet And makes the weak se-cure-ly stand;
2 The Lord is just in all His ways, In all His works the Lord is kind,
3 His great sal-va-tion they shall know Who love the Lord's most ho-ly Name;

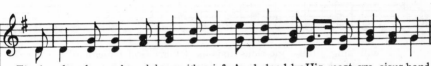

The bur-dened ones, bowed down with grief, Are helped by His most gra-cious hand.
And all that call on Him in truth In Him a pres-ent Help-er find.
The wick-ed He will o-ver-throw And put His en - e-mies to shame.

The eyes of all up-on Thee wait, By Thee their wants are all sup-plied;
He will ful-fil the heart's de-sire Of those that fear Him and o-bey;
My mouth shall speak the glo-rious praise Of Him whom heaven and earth a-dore;

Thine o-pen hand is boun-ti-ful, And ev - ery soul is sat - is-fied.
Their cry the Lord will sure-ly hear, And He will save them when they pray.
Let all ex-alt His ho-ly Name For - ev - er and for - ev - er-more.

301 Hallelujah, Praise Jehovah

PSALM 146

RIPLEY 8 7 8 7 D.

From a Gregorian Chant
Arranged by Lowell Mason, 1839

1 Hal-le-lu-jah, praise Je-ho-vah, O my soul, Je-ho-vah praise;
2 Hap-py is the man that choos-es Is-rael's God to be his aid;

I will sing the glo-rious prais-es Of my God through all my days.
He is blest whose hope of bless-ing On the Lord his God is stayed.

Put no con-fi-dence in prin-ces, Nor for help on man de-pend;
Heaven and earth the Lord cre-at-ed, Seas and all that they con-tain;

He shall die, to dust re-turn-ing, And his pur-pos-es shall end.
He de-liv-ers from op-pres-sion, Right-eous-ness He will main-tain.

3 Food He daily gives the hungry,
Sets the mourning prisoner free,
Raises those bowed down with anguish,
Makes the sightless eyes to see.
Well Jehovah loves the righteous,
And the stranger He befriends,
Helps the fatherless and widow,
Judgment on the wicked sends.

4 Hallelujah, praise Jehovah,
O my soul, Jehovah praise;
I will sing the glorious praises
Of my God through all my days.
Over all God reigns forever,
Through all ages He is King;
Unto Him, thy God, O Zion,
Joyful hallelujahs sing.

302   Praise Ye the Lord, for It Is Good

PSALM 147   Minerva C.M.D.   John H. Stockton, 1813-1877

1 Praise ye the Lord, for it is good To sing un-to our God;
2 Our Lord is great, He calls by name And counts the stars of night;
3 No hu-man might, no earth-ly pride De-lights the Lord a-bove;

'Tis right and pleas-ant for His saints To tell His praise a-broad.
His wis-dom is un-search-a-ble, And won-drous is His might.
In them that fear Him He de-lights, In them that trust His love.

The Lord our God builds up His Church, He seeks her wan-dering sons;
The Lord up-holds the poor and meek, He brings the wick-ed low;
O Zi-on, praise the Lord thy God, His won-drous love con-fess;

He binds their wounds and gen-tly heals The bro-ken-heart-ed ones.
Sing praise to Him and give Him thanks And all His good-ness show.
He is thy glo-ry and thy strength, He will thy chil-dren bless.

303

O Sing Ye Hallelujah

PSALM 147

HARTFORD 7 6 7 6 D.

John B. Dykes, 1877

1 O sing ye Hal - le - lu - jah! 'Tis good our God to praise;
2 The star - ry hosts He num - bers, He calls them all by name;

'Tis pleas-ant and be - com - ing To Him our songs to raise;
His great-ness and His wis - dom His won-drous works pro - claim;

He builds the walls of Zi - on, He seeks her wan-dering sons;
The meek He lifts to hon - or, He hum - bles sin - ful pride.

He binds their wounds and com-forts The bro - ken-heart - ed ones.
Give thanks to Him and ut - ter His prais - es far and wide.

O Sing Ye Hallelujah

3 The heavens with clouds He covers,
    He sends the cheering rain;
The slopes of all the mountains
    He fills with grass and grain;
To beast and bird His goodness
    Their daily food supplies;
He cares for all His creatures,
    Attentive to their cries.

4 No human power delights Him,
    No earthly pomp or pride;
He loves the meek who fear Him
    And in His love confide;
Then praise thy God, O Zion,
    His gracious aid confess;
He gives thee peace and plenty,
    His gifts thy children bless.

5 He sends His swift commandment,
    And snow and ice enfold
The world, and none are able
    To stand before His cold.
Again He gives commandment:
    The winds of summer blow,
The snow and ice are melted,
    Again the waters flow.

6 His statutes and His judgments
    He makes His people know;
To them as to no others
    His grace He loves to show;
For matchless grace and mercy
    Your grateful praises bring;
To Him give thanks forever,
    And Hallelujah sing.

304 Hallelujah, Praise Jehovah

PSALM 148

KIRKPATRICK 8 7 8 7 D. with Refrain
William J. Kirkpatrick, 1838-1921

1 Hal - le - lu - jah, praise Je-ho-vah, From the heav-ens praise His Name;
2 Let them prais-es give Je-ho-vah, They were made at His com-mand;
3 All ye fruit-ful trees and ce-dars, All ye hills and moun-tains high,

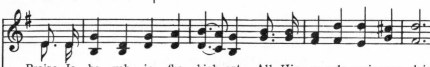

Praise Je - ho - vah in the high-est, All His an-gels, praise pro-claim.
Them for - ev - er He es - tab-lished, His de-cree shall ev - er stand.
Creep-ing things and beasts and cat - tle, Birds that in the heav-ens fly,

All His hosts, to-geth-er praise Him, Sun and moon and stars on high;
From the earth, O praise Je - ho - vah, All ye seas, ye mon-sters all,
Kings of earth, and all ye peo-ple, Prin-ces great, earth's judg-es all;

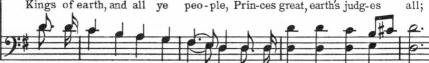

Praise Him, O ye heavens of heav-ens, And ye floods a-bove the sky.
Fire and hail and snow and va-pors, Storm-y winds that hear His call.
Praise His Name, young men and maid-ens, A - ged men, and chil-dren small.

Hallelujah, Praise Jehovah

REFRAIN *(May be sung after 3rd stanza only)*

Let them prais - - es give Je - ho - vah, For His
Let them prais - es

Name a - lone is high, And His glo - - ry is ex -
And His glo - ry

pp

alt - ed, And His glo - - ry is ex - alt - ed, And His
And His glo - ry

p

ff

glo - - ry is ex - alt - ed, Far a - bove the earth and sky.
And His glo - ry

305   Praise the Lord in Heavenly Places

PSALM 148   LYDIA 8 7 8 7

George C. Stebbins, 1846-1945

1 Praise the Lord in heaven-ly plac - es, Ye His
2 Let the sky and clouds for - ev - er Praise His
3 In the earth let all things praise Him, Seas and

hosts and an - gels bright; Sun and moon, de - clare His
glo - rious maj - es - ty; At His word they were cre -
all that they con - tain, Storm - y winds that do His

glo - ry, Praise Him, all ye stars of light.
at - ed, Or - dered by His firm de - cree.
pleas - ure, Hail and light - ning, snow and rain.

4 Hills and mountains, praise your Maker,
    Praise Him, all ye flocks and herds,
Woods and fields and fruitful vineyards,
    Creeping things and flying birds.

5 Kings and princes, bow before Him,
    Earthly judges, give Him praise,
All ye people, tell His glory,
    Old and young, your voices raise.

6 Praise His Name with praise unending,
    For His Name alone is great;
Over heaven and earth exalted,
    Reigns the Lord in kingly state.

7 He has greatly blessed His people,
    Therefore, all ye saints, give praise;
Chosen of the Lord and precious,
    Thankful hallelujahs raise.

306 O Praise Ye the Lord

PSALM 149   HANOVER (CROFT) 10 10 11 11   William Croft, 1678-1727

1 O praise ye the Lord And sing a new song,
2 With tim - brel and harp And joy - ful ac - claim,

A - mid all His saints His prais - es pro - long;
With glad - ness and mirth, Sing praise to His Name;

The praise of their Mak - er His peo - ple shall sing,
For God in His peo - ple His pleas - ure doth seek,

And chil - dren of Zi - on Re - joice in their King.
With robes of sal - va - tion He cloth - eth the meek.

3 In glory exult,
  Ye saints of the Lord;
With songs in the night
  High praises accord;
Go forth in His service,
  Be strong in His might
To conquer all evil
  And stand for the right.

4 For this is His word:
  His saints shall not fail,
But over the earth
  Their power shall prevail;
All kingdoms and nations
  Shall yield to their sway.
To God give the glory
  And praise Him for aye.

363

307

Ye Who His Temple Throng

PSALM 149   TRINITY (ITALIAN HYMN) 6 6 4 6 6 6 4

Felice de Giardini, 1769

1 Ye who His tem-ple throng, Je - ho-vah's praise pro - long,
2 O let His Name em-ploy Your ev - ery note of joy,
3 Ye saints, your joy pro-claim And glo-ry in the Name.

New an-thems sing; Ye saints, with joy de-clare Your Mak-er's
His prais-es speak; He looks with lov-ing face Up - on His
Of God a - bove; And when the day-light dies, Ere sleep shall

lov - ing care, And let the chil-dren there Joy in their King.
cho - sen race, And will with ev - ery grace A - dorn the meek.
close your eyes, Let praise to God a - rise For all His love.

308

Hallelujah! Praise Ye God!

PSALM 150

GLORIA 7 7 7 7 8 7 7 8

Maitre Pierre, 1562
Harmony from De Vries *Koraalboek*
Adapted by Henry Bruinsma, 1946

1 Hal - le - lu - jah! Praise ye God! In His tem - ple shout His laud,
2 Praise Him with the trum-pet-sound, Let Je - ho - vah's praise a-bound,
3 Let the clash-ing cym-bals ring To the praise of God, the King,

Praise Him in the wide ex - tent Of His spa-cious fir - ma - ment,
Praise Him with the psal - ter - y, Harp un - to His maj - es - ty,
Praise Him with a might - y sound, Let your voic - es shake the ground

Sing Je - ho-vah's praise up-right-ly; Praise Him for the plen - i - tude
Praise Him with the pipe and tim-brel; Praise Him with stringed in-stru-ments,
With the prais-es of Je - ho-vah; All that breathe, ex - alt the Lord,

Of His bound-less mag-ni-tude, Praise Him for His deeds so might-y.
Or-gan forth His ex - cel-lence, Praise Him with the sound-ing cym - bal.
All ye men, His fame re-cord; Great is God! Sing: Hal-le - lu - jah!

Dewey Westra, 1931

309
Hallelujah! Hallelujah!

PSALM 150

WELLESLEY 8 7 8 7

Lizzie S. Tourjee, 1878

1 Hal - le - lu - jah! Hal - le - lu - jah! In His
2 Hal - le - lu - jah! Praise Je - ho - vah For His
3 Hal - le - lu - jah! Praise Je - ho - vah With the

tem - ple God be praised; In the high and heaven - ly
might - y acts of fame; Ex - cel - lent His might and
trum - pet's joy - ful sound; Praise with harp and praise with

plac - es Be the sound - ing an - them raised.
great - ness; Fit - ting prais - es then pro - claim.
vi - ol, Let His glo - rious praise a - bound.

4 Hallelujah! Praise Jehovah,
　　With the flute His praises sing;
　Praise Him with the clanging cymbals,
　　Let them with His praises ring.

5 Hallelujah! Hallelujah!
　　All that breathe, Jehovah praise;
　Let the voices God has given
　　Joyful anthems to Him raise.

Hallelujah! Hallelujah!

SICILIAN MARINERS 8 7 8 7

Sicilian Melody

1 Hal - le - lu - jah! Hal - le - lu - jah! Earth and
2 Hal - le - lu - jah! Hal - le - lu - jah! Mag - ni -

heaven in sweet ac - cord Join to sound Je -
fy Je - ho - vah's Name; Praise the liv - ing

ho - vah's prais - es, Tell the glo - ry of the Lord.
God, your Mak - er, All that breathe, His praise pro - claim.

HYMNS

311

We Praise Thee, O God

KREMSER 12 11 12 11

Netherlands Folk Song
From *The Collection* by A. Valerius, 1625
Arranged by Edward Kremser, 1838-1914

1 We praise Thee, O God, our Re-deem-er, Cre-a-tor,
2 We wor-ship Thee, God of our fa-thers, we bless Thee;
3 With voic-es u-nit-ed our prais-es we of-fer,

In grate-ful de-vo-tion our trib-ute we bring;
Through life's storm and tem-pest our Guide hast Thou been;
To Thee, great Je-ho-vah, glad an-thems we raise;

We lay it be-fore Thee, we kneel and a-dore Thee,
When per-ils o'er-take us, es-cape Thou wilt make us,
Thy strong arm will guide us, our God is be-side us,

We bless Thy ho-ly Name, glad prais-es we sing.
And with Thy help, O Lord, our bat-tles we win.
To Thee, our great Re-deem-er, for-ev-er be praise.

A. Valerius, 1625
Tr. Julia Bulkley Cady, 1882

312   We Gather Together

KREMSER 12 11 12 11

Netherlands Folk Song
From *The Collection* by A. Valerius, 1625
Arranged by Edward Kremser, 1838-1914

1 We gath - er to - geth - er to ask the Lord's bless-ing;
2 Be - side us to guide us, our God with us join - ing,
3 We all do ex - tol Thee, Thou Lead - er tri - um - phant,

He chast - ens and hast - ens His will to make known;
Or - dain - ing, main - tain - ing His king - dom di - vine;
And pray that Thou still our De - fend - er wilt be.

The wick - ed op - press - ing now cease from dis - tress-ing;
So from the be - gin - ning the fight we were win - ning;
Let Thy con - gre - ga - tion es - cape trib - u - la - tion;

Sing prais - es to His Name; He for - gets not His own.
Thou, Lord, wast at our side; all glo - ry be Thine!
Thy Name be ev - er praised! O Lord, make us free!

Tr. Theodore Baker

313

We Praise Thee, O God

HANOVER (CROFT) 10 10 11 11

William Croft, 1678-1727

1 We praise Thee, O God, our Lord and our King;
2 We praise Thee, O God, for Thy guid-ing hand,

Ac-cept Thou the praise we grate-ful-ly bring;
In lead-ing Thy Church to free-dom's fair land;

Thanks-giv-ing and wor-ship we of-fer to Thee,
Through sore per-se-cu-tion our fa-thers here came,

Thou Rul-er of na-tions, in whom we are free.
Where free and un-fet-tered they wor-shipped Thy Name.

3 We praise Thee, O God, for years of increase,
For faith unassailed, prosperity, peace;
United we offer our anthem of praise
To Thee, our Supporter, our Ancient of Days.

4 We pray Thee, O Christ, our Savior and Friend,
From error and strife Thy Zion defend;
Breathe on us, we pray Thee, O Spirit of Love,
And fit us for union with Thy Church above.

Ambrose M. Schmidt, 1857

Come, Thou Fount of Every Blessing

NETTLETON 8 7 8 7 D.

Asahel Nettleton, 1825

1 Come, Thou Fount of ev-ery bless-ing, Tune my heart to sing Thy grace;
2 Here I raise my Eb-en-e-zer; Hith-er by Thy help I'm come;
3 O to grace how great a debt-or Dai-ly I'm con-strained to be;

Streams of mer-cy, nev-er ceas-ing, Call for songs of loud-est praise.
And I hope, by Thy good pleas-ure, Safe-ly to ar-rive at home.
Let Thy good-ness, like a fet-ter, Bind my wan-dering heart to Thee.

Teach me some me-lo-dious son-net, Sung by flam-ing tongues a-bove;
Je-sus sought me when a stran-ger, Wan-dering from the fold of God;
Prone to wan-der, Lord, I feel it, Prone to leave the God I love;

Praise the mount—I'm fixed up-on it— Mount of Thy re-deem-ing love.
He, to res-cue me from dan-ger, In-ter-posed His pre-cious blood.
Here's my heart, O take and seal it, Seal it for Thy courts a-bove.

Robert Robinson, 1758

315   O Worship the King, All-glorious Above

LYONS 10 10 11 11

J. Michael Haydn, 1770

1 O worship the King, all-glorious above,
O gratefully sing His power and His love;
Our Shield and Defender, the Ancient of Days,
Pavilioned in splendor, and girded with praise.

2 O tell of His might, O sing of His grace,
Whose robe is the light, whose canopy space.
His chariots of wrath the deep thunderclouds form,
And dark is His path on the wings of the storm.

3 Thy bountiful care what tongue can recite?
It breathes in the air, it shines in the light;
It streams from the hills, it descends to the plain,
And sweetly distils in the dew and the rain.

4 Frail children of dust, and feeble as frail,
In Thee do we trust, nor find Thee to fail.
Thy mercies how tender, how firm to the end!
Our Maker, Defender, Redeemer, and Friend!

Robert Grant, 1833

316   Now Thank We All Our God

NUN DANKET 6 7 6 7 6 6 6 6   Johann Crüger, 1647

1 Now thank we all our God With heart and hands and voic - es
2 O may this boun-teous God Through all our life be near us,
3 All praise and thanks to God The Fa-ther now be giv - en,

Who won-drous things has done, In whom His world re - joic - es;
With ev - er joy - ful hearts And bless - ed peace to cheer us,
The Son, and Him who reigns With them in high-est heav - en,

Who, from our moth-ers' arms, Has blessed us on our way
And keep us in His grace, And guide us when per - plexed,
The one e - ter-nal God, Whom earth and heaven a - dore;

With count-less gifts of love, And still is ours to - day.
And free us from all ills In this world and the next.
For thus it was, is now, And shall be ev - er - more.

Martin Rinkart, 1648
Tr. Catherine Winkworth, 1858

373

Come, Thou Almighty King

TRINITY (ITALIAN HYMN) 6 6 4 6 6 6 4

Felice de Giardini, 1769

1 Come, Thou Al-might-y King, Help us Thy Name to sing,
2 Come, Thou In-car-nate Word, Gird on Thy might-y sword,
3 Come, Ho-ly Com-fort-er, Thy sa-cred wit-ness bear

Help us to praise. Fa-ther, all-glo-ri-ous, O'er all vic-
Scat-ter Thy foes. Let Thine al-might-y aid Our sure de-
In this glad hour. Thou who al-might-y art, Now rule in

to-ri-ous, Come and reign o-ver us, An-cient of Days.
fense be made, Our souls on Thee be stayed; Thy won-ders show.
ev-ery heart, And ne'er from us de-part, Spir-it of power.

4 To the great One in Three
  Eternal praises be
    Hence evermore.
  His sovereign majesty
  May we in glory see,
  And to eternity
    Love and adore.

Anonymous, 1757

318

Holy, Holy, Holy!

NICEA 11 12 12 10

John B. Dykes, 1861

1 Ho - ly, Ho - ly, Ho - ly! Lord God Al - might - y!
2 Ho - ly, Ho - ly, Ho - ly! All the saints a - dore Thee,

Ear - ly in the morn - ing our song shall rise to Thee;
Cast - ing down their gold - en crowns a - round the glass - y sea;

Ho - ly, Ho - ly, Ho - ly! Mer - ci - ful and might - y!
Cher - u - bim and sera - phim fall - ing down be - fore Thee,

God in Three Per - sons, bless - ed Trin - i - ty!
Who wert and art and ev - er - more shalt be.

3 Holy, Holy, Holy! Though the darkness hide Thee,
Though the eye of sinful man Thy glory may not see,
Only Thou art holy; there is none beside Thee,
Perfect in power, in love, and purity.

4 Holy, Holy, Holy! Lord God Almighty!
All Thy works shall praise Thy Name, in earth and sky and sea;
Holy, Holy, Holy! Merciful and Mighty!
God in Three Persons, blessed Trinity!

Reginald Heber, 1827

319 All Glory Be to Thee, Most High

ALLEIN GOTT 8 7 8 7 8 8 7

Ascribed to Nicolaus Decius, 1539

1 All glo-ry be to Thee, Most High, To Thee all ad-o-ra - tion; In grace and truth Thou draw-est nigh To of-fer us sal-va - tion; Thou show-est Thy good will to men, And peace shall reign on earth a-gain; We praise Thy Name for-ev - er.

2 We praise, we wor-ship Thee, we trust, And give Thee thanks for-ev - er, O Fa-ther, for Thy rule is just And wise, and chang-es nev - er; Thy hand al-might-y o'er us reigns, Thou do - est what Thy will or-dains; 'Tis well for us Thou rul - est.

3 O Jesus Christ, our God and Lord,
   Son of the Heavenly Father,
O Thou who hast our peace restored,
   The straying sheep dost gather,
Thou Lamb of God, to Thee on high
Out of the depths we sinners cry:
   Have mercy on us, Jesus!

4 O Holy Spirit, precious gift,
   Thou Comforter unfailing,
From Satan's snares our souls uplift,
   And let Thy power, availing,
Avert our woes and calm our dread.
For us the Savior's blood was shed;
   We trust in Thee to save us.

Latin Hymn

376

320   # Safely Through Another Week

Dix 7 7 7 7 7 7

Arranged from Conrad Kocher, 1838

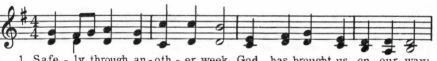

1 Safe - ly through an - oth - er week God has brought us on our way;
2 While we pray for par-doning grace, Through the dear Re-deem-er's name,
3 Here we come Thy Name to praise; Let us feel Thy pres-ence near;

Let us now a bless-ing seek, Wait-ing in His courts to - day;
Show Thy rec - on - cil - ed face; Take a - way our sin and shame;
May Thy glo - ry meet our eyes While we in Thy house ap - pear;

Day of all the week the best, Em-blem of e - ter - nal rest.
From our earth-ly cares set free, May we rest this day in Thee.
Here af - ford us, Lord, a taste Of our ev - er - last - ing feast.

4 May Thy gospel's joyful sound
    Conquer sinners, comfort saints;
May the fruits of grace abound,
    Bring relief for all complaints;
Thus may all our Sabbaths prove,
Till we join the Church above.

John Newton, 1774

321   O Day of Rest and Gladness

Mendebras 7 6 7 6 D.   German Melody
Arranged by Lowell Mason, 1839

1 O day of rest and glad-ness, O day of joy and light,
2 On thee, at the cre - a - tion, The light first had its birth;

O balm of care and sad-ness, Most beau-ti - ful, most bright;
On thee, for our sal - va - tion, Christ rose from depths of earth;

On thee the high and low - ly Through a - ges joined in tune,
On thee our Lord vic - to-rious The Spir - it sent from heaven;

Sing, Ho - ly, Ho - ly, Ho - ly, To the great God Tri - une.
And thus on thee, most glo-rious, A tri - ple light was given.

3 Today on weary nations
    The heavenly manna falls;
To holy convocations
    The silver trumpet calls,
Where gospel light is glowing
    With pure and radiant beams,
And living water flowing
    With soul-refreshing streams.

4 New graces ever gaining
    From this our day of rest,
We reach the rest remaining
    To spirits of the blest.
To Holy Ghost be praises,
    To Father, and to Son;
The Church her voice upraises
    To Thee, blest Three in One.

Christopher Wordsworth, 1862

322 When Morning Gilds the Skies

LAUDES DOMINI 6 6 6 6 6 6

Joseph Barnby, 1868

1 When morn-ing gilds the skies, My heart a-wak-ing cries, May
2 Does sad-ness fill my mind? A sol-ace here I find, May
3 Ye na-tions of man-kind, In this your con-cord find, May

Je-sus Christ be praised! A-like at work and prayer To
Je-sus Christ be praised! Or fades my earth-ly bliss? My
Je-sus Christ be praised! Let all the earth a-round Ring

Je-sus I re-pair; May Je-sus Christ be praised!
com-fort still is this, May Je-sus Christ be praised!
joy-ous with the sound, May Je-sus Christ be praised! A-men.

4 Be this, while life is mine,
My canticle divine,
  May Jesus Christ be praised!
Be this the eternal song,
Through all the ages long,
  May Jesus Christ be praised!

German, 19th Cent.
Tr. Edward Caswall, 1854

323   Father, Again in Jesus' Name We Meet

LANGRAN 10 10 10 10

James Langran, 1862

1 Fa - ther, a - gain in Je - sus' Name we meet
2 O we would bless Thee for Thy cease - less care
3 A - las, un - worth - y of Thy bound - less love,

And bow in pen - i - tence be - neath Thy feet;
And all Thy works from day to day de - clare;
Too oft our feet from Thee, our Fa - ther, rove;

A - gain to Thee our fee - ble voic - es raise
Is not our life with hour - ly mer - cies crowned?
But now, en - cour - aged by Thy voice, we come,

To sue for mer - cy and to sing Thy praise.
Does not Thine arm en - cir - cle us a - round?
Re - turn - ing sin - ners, to a Fa - ther's home.

4 O by that Name in whom all fulness dwells,
O by that love which every love excels,
O by that blood so freely shed for sin,
Open blest mercy's gate and take us in.

Lucy E. G. Whitmore, 1824

God Himself Is with Us

ARNSBERG 6 6 8 D. 3 3 6 6
Joachim Neander's *Bundes-Lieder*, 1680

1 God Him-self is with us: Let us now a-dore Him, And with
2 God Him-self is with us: Hear the harps re-sound-ing! See the
3 O Thou Fount of bless-ing, Pur-i-fy my spir-it, Trust-ing

awe ap-pear be-fore Him. God is in His tem-ple, All with-in keep
crowds the throne sur-round-ing! "Ho-ly, ho-ly, ho-ly," Hear the hymn as-
on-ly in Thy mer-it. Like the ho-ly an-gels Who be-hold Thy

si-lence, Pros-trate lie with deep-est rev-erence. Him a-lone God we own,
cend-ing, An-gels, saints, their voic-es blend-ing! Bow Thine ear To us here:
glo-ry, May I cease-less-ly a-dore Thee, And in all, Great and small,

Him, our God and Sav-ior; Praise His Name for-ev-er.
Hear, O Christ, the prais-es That Thy Church now rais-es.
Seek to do most near-ly What Thou lov-est dear-ly. A-men.

Gerhardt Tersteegen, 1729
Tr. John Miller and Frederick Foster, 1789

325 Lord, Dismiss Us with Thy Blessing

SICILIAN MARINERS 8 7 8 7 8 7

Sicilian Melody

1 Lord, dis-miss us with Thy bless-ing; Fill our hearts with
2 Thanks we give and ad-o-ra-tion For Thy gos-pel's
3 Of Thy love some gra-cious to-ken Grant us, Lord, be-

joy and peace; Let us each, Thy love pos-sess-ing,
joy-ful sound; May the fruits of Thy sal-va-tion
fore we go; Bless Thy Word which has been spo-ken,

Tri-umph in re-deem-ing grace; O re-fresh us,
In our hearts and lives a-bound; Ev-er faith-ful,
Life and peace on all be-stow; O di-rect us

O re-fresh us, Trav-eling through this wil-der-ness.
ev-er faith-ful To the truth may we be found.
and pro-tect us In the paths we do not know.

John Fawcett, 1740-1817
Stanza 3, Thomas Kelly, 1804

326 Savior, Again to Thy Dear Name We Raise

ELLERS 10 10 10 10

Edward J. Hopkins, 1868

1 Sav - ior, a - gain to Thy dear Name we raise With one ac-
2 Grant us Thy peace up - on our home-ward way; With Thee be-
3 Grant us Thy peace, Lord, through the com-ing night; Turn Thou for

cord our part - ing hymn of praise; We stand to bless Thee
gan, with Thee shall end the day; Guard Thou the lips from
us its dark-ness in - to light; From harm and dan - ger

ere our wor-ship cease, And now, de-part - ing, wait Thy word of peace.
sin, the hearts from shame, That in this house have called up-on Thy Name.
keep Thy chil-dren free, For dark and light are both a-like to Thee.

4 Grant us Thy peace throughout our earthly life,
Our balm in sorrow, and our stay in strife;
Then, when Thy voice shall bid our conflict cease,
Call us, O Lord, to Thine eternal peace.

John Ellerton, 1866

327   Praise to the Lord, the Almighty

Lᴏʙᴇ ᴅᴇɴ Hᴇʀʀᴇɴ 14 14 4 7 8

From *Praxis Pietatis Melica*, 1668

1 Praise to the Lord, the Al-might-y, the King of cre-a - tion!
2 Praise to the Lord, who o'er all things so won-drous-ly reign - eth,
3 Praise to the Lord, O let all that is in me a - dore Him!

O my soul, praise Him, for He is thy health and sal-va - tion!
Shel-ters thee un-der His wings, yea, so gen-tly sus-tain - eth!
All that hath life and breath, come now with prais-es be-fore Him.

All ye who hear, Now to His tem-ple draw near;
Hast thou not seen How thy de-sires e'er have been
Let the a - men Sound from His peo-ple a - gain,

Join me in glad ad-o-ra - tion!
Grant-ed in what He or-dain - eth?
Glad-ly for aye we a-dore - Him.

Joachim Neander, 1680
Adapted from Psalms 103 and 150

384

328 My God, How Wonderful Thou Art

ST. ETHELDREDA C.M.

T. Turton, 1780-1864

1 My God, how won-der-ful Thou art, Thy maj-es-ty, how bright! How beau-ti-ful Thy mer-cy-seat In depths of burn-ing light!

2 O how I fear Thee, liv-ing God, With deep-est, ten-derest fears; And wor-ship Thee with trem-bling hope And pen-i-ten-tial tears!

3 Yet I may love Thee too, O Lord, Al-might-y as Thou art; For Thou hast stooped to ask of me The love of my poor heart.

4 No earthly father loves like Thee,
   No mother, half so mild,
   Bears and forbears as Thou hast done
   With me, Thy sinful child.

5 Father of Jesus, Love Divine,
   What rapture will it be,
   Prostrate before Thy throne to lie,
   And gaze and gaze on Thee!

Frederick W. Faber, 1848

385

329 **O Love of God, How Strong and True**

LOUVAN L.M.

Virgil C. Taylor, 1847

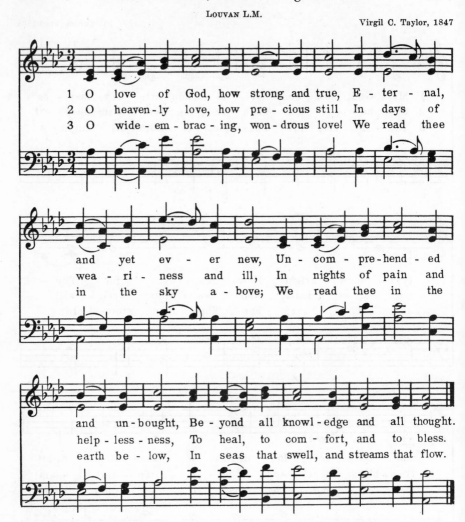

1 O love of God, how strong and true, E - ter - nal, and yet ev - er new, Un - com - pre-hend - ed and un - bought, Be - yond all knowl - edge and all thought.

2 O heaven-ly love, how pre - cious still In days of wea - ri - ness and ill, In nights of pain and help - less - ness, To heal, to com - fort, and to bless.

3 O wide - em - brac - ing, won - drous love! We read thee in the sky a - bove; We read thee in the earth be - low, In seas that swell, and streams that flow.

4 We read thee best in Him who came
To bear for us the cross of shame;
Sent by the Father from on high,
Our life to live, our death to die.

5 We read thy power to bless and save,
E'en in the darkness of the grave;
Still more in resurrection-light
We read the fulness of thy might.

6 O love of God, our shield and stay
Through all the perils of our way;
Eternal love, in thee we rest,
Forever safe, forever blest.

Horatius Bonar, 1861

330   O Jesus, We Adore Thee

MEIRIONYDD 7 6 7 6 D.

William Lloyd, 1840

1 O   Je - sus, we   a - dore Thee, Up - on the cross, our King!
2 Yet   doth the world dis-dain Thee, Still pass-ing by   the cross:
3 O   glo - rious King, we bless Thee, No   long-er   pass Thee by;

We   bow   our hearts be-fore Thee, Thy gra-cious Name we sing.
Lord, may   our hearts re-tain Thee, All else we   count but loss.
O   Je - sus, we   con-fess Thee, The Son en - throned on high.

That Name hath brought sal-va - tion, That Name in   life   our   stay,
Ah,   Lord, our sins ar-raigned Thee, And nailed Thee to   the   tree;
Lord, grant to   us   re - mis - sion; Life through Thy death re - store;

Our peace, our con-so - la - tion, When life shall fade a - way.
Our pride, O Lord, dis-dained Thee; Yet deign our hope to   be.
Yea, grant us the fru - i - tion Of life for - ev - er - more.

Arthur T. Russell, 1851

387

O Come, O Come, Emmanuel

VENI EMMANUEL 8 8 8 8 8 8

Plainsong, 13th century

1 O come, O come, Em-man - u - el, And ran-som cap-tive
2 O come, Thou Branch of Jes - se's stem, Un - to Thine own, and
3 O come, Thou Bright and Morn - ing Star, And bring us com-fort

Is - ra - el, That mourns in lone-ly ex - ile here,
res - cue them! From depths of hell Thy peo - ple save,
from a - far! Dis - pel the shad-ows of the night,

REFRAIN

Un - til the Son of God ap-pear.
And give them vic-to-ry o'er the grave. Re-joice! Re-joice! Em -
And turn our dark-ness in - to light.

man - u - el Shall come to thee, O Is - ra - el.

Alternate Tune: ST. PETERSBURG, No. 183

4 O come, Thou Lord of David's key!
  The gate of heaven unfolds to Thee;
  Make safe for us the heavenward road,
  And bar the way to death's abode.

5 O come, O come, Thou Lord of might,
  Who to Thy tribes from Sinai's height
  In olden time didst give the law
  In cloud and majesty and awe.

Latin, 12th century
Tr. John Mason Neale, 1861

332 My Soul Doth Magnify the Lord

PENTECOST L.M.

William Boyd, 1868

1 My soul doth mag - ni - fy the Lord; In Him my
2 All gen - er - a - tions from hence-forth Shall now my
3 His mer - cy shall a - bide on them That fear the

spir - it doth re - joice, For He be - held my
bless - ed - ness pro - claim, For He has done great
Lord from age to age; He has re - vealed His

low es - tate, And in His love made me His choice.
things to me; Might - y and ho - ly is His Name.
might - y arm, Rout - ing the haugh - ty in their rage.

4 He has abased the mighty ones,
   Exalted those of low degree;
He filled the hungry souls with good,
   And smote the rich with poverty.

5 He helped His servant Israel,
   In honor of His mercy sure;
E'en as He spake to Abraham
   And to His seed forevermore.

Song of Mary, Luke 1:46-55
Adapted by Dewey Westra, 1931

389

Blest Be the God of Israel

BENEDICTUS 8 8 8 8 8 8 7 10 8 10

Anonymous, 1566
Harmonized by Dick L. Van Halsema, 1958

1 Blest be the God of Is - ra - el, The Lord who vis - it -
2 He prom-ised us that He would save From all who for our

ed His own; Who by His gra-cious prov - i - dence Re - demp-tion
ru - in wait, And from the hands of them that rave A - gainst us

un - to us made known. With-in His ser - vant Da-vid's tent
with a war - ring hate, To show the mer - cy once fore - told

Has He to us, His peo-ple, sent A horn of full sal - va - tion;
Un - to our fa - thers, and up-hold His ho - ly cov-enant with us,

Blest Be the God of Israel

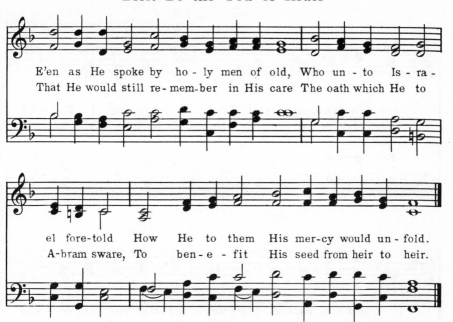

E'en as He spoke by ho - ly men of old, Who un - to Is - ra -
That He would still re - mem - ber in His care The oath which He to

el fore-told How He to them His mer-cy would un - fold.
A-bram sware, To ben - e - fit His seed from heir to heir.

3 He spoke that He would strength command,
  And grant to us when foemen near,
That we, delivered from their hand,
  Might worship Him without a fear,
And walk before Him faithfully
In righteousness and sanctity,
  While life to us is given.
And thou, O child, so shall they say of thee,
"The prophet of the Lord is he,"
For thou shalt go before Christ's majesty.

4 Yea, thou shalt make salvation known,
  That we may be revived again,
Receiving favor as His own,
  In free remission of our sin,
Through God's compassion and His love
Whereby the Dayspring from above
  Has visited His people;
To lighten them that in the darkness hide,
And in the shades of death abide;
Our feet into the way of peace to guide.

Song of Zacharias, Luke 1:67-79
Adapted by Dewey Westra, 1931

334 Now May Thy Servant, Lord

NUNC DIMITTIS 6 6 7 D.

Louis Bourgeois, 1549
Harmony from Claude Goudimel, c. 1505-1572

1 Now may Thy ser - vant, Lord, Ac - cord - ing to Thy word,
2 Thou didst for all pre - pare This Gift, so great, so rare,

De - part in ex - ul - ta - tion. My rest shall be se - rene,
That peo-ples might a - dore Thee; A light to show the way

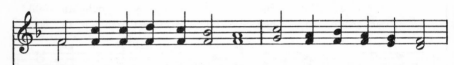

For lo, mine eyes have seen Thy won-der-ful sal - va - tion.
To na - tions gone a - stray, And un - to Is - rael's glo - ry.

Song of Simeon, Luke 2:28-32
Adapted by Dewey Westra, 1931

392

335   Come, Thou Long-expected Jesus

Stuttgart 8 7 8 7

Psalmodia Sacra, Gotha, 1715

1 Come, Thou long - ex - pect - ed Je - sus, Born to set Thy
2 Is - rael's strength and con - so - la - tion, Hope of all the
3 Born Thy peo - ple to de - liv - er, Born a Child, and

peo - ple free; From our fears and sins re - lease us;
earth Thou art; Dear de - sire of ev - ery na - tion,
yet a King, Born to reign in us for - ev - er,

Let us find our rest in Thee.
Joy of ev - ery long - ing heart.
Now Thy gra - cious King - dom bring. A - men.

4 By Thine own eternal Spirit
   Rule in all our hearts alone;
By Thine all-sufficient merit
   Raise us to Thy glorious throne.   Amen.

Charles Wesley, 1744

336   How Bright Appears the Morning Star

WIE SCHÖN LEUCHTET 8 8 7 D. 4 8 4 8

Philip Nicolai, 1599
Arranged by J. S. Bach, c. 1730

With breadth; may be sung in unison

1 How bright ap-pears the Morn-ing Star, With mer-cy beam-ing
2 Though cir-cled by the hosts on high, He deigned to cast a

from a-far; The host of heaven re-joic - es;
pit-ying eye Up-on His help-less crea - ture;

O Right-eous Branch, O Jes-se's Rod! Thou Son of Man and
The whole cre-a-tion's Head and Lord, By high-est ser-a -

Son of God! We, too, will lift our voic - es:
phim a-dored, As-sumed our ve-ry na - ture.

How Bright Appears the Morning Star

Je - sus, Je - sus! Ho - ly, ho - ly, yet most low - ly,
Je - sus, grant us, Through Thy mer - it to in - her - it

Draw Thou near us; Great Em-man-uel, come and hear us.
Thy sal - va - tion; Hear, O hear our sup - pli - ca - tion. A-men.

3 Rejoice, ye heavens; thou earth, reply;
   With praise, ye sinners, fill the sky,
      For this His incarnation.
   Incarnate God, put forth Thy power,
   Ride on, ride on, great Conqueror
      Till all know Thy salvation.
         Amen, Amen!
         Hallelujah! Hallelujah!
         Praise be given
         Evermore by earth and heaven. Amen.

Philip Nicolai, 1599
Tr. William Mercer, 1859

337 Joy to the World!

ANTIOCH C.M., 6 Lines

Lowell Mason, 1830

1 Joy to the world! the Lord is come. Let earth re-
2 Joy to the earth! the Sav-ior reigns. Let men their
3 He rules the world with truth and grace, And makes the

ceive her King; Let ev-ery heart pre-pare Him room,
songs em-ploy, While fields and floods, rocks, hills, and plains
na-tions prove The glo-ries of His right-eous-ness

And heaven and na-ture sing, And heaven and na-ture
Re-peat the sound-ing joy, Re-peat the sound-ing
And won-ders of His love, And won-ders of His

1 And heaven and na-ture sing, And

sing, And heaven, and heav-en and na-ture sing.
joy, Re-peat, re-peat the sound-ing joy.
love, And won-ders, won-ders of His love.
heaven and na-ture sing,

Isaac Watts, 1719

396

338 While Shepherds Watched Their Flocks by Night

CHRISTMAS C.M., 5 Lines

George F. Handel, 1728

1 While shep-herds watched their flocks by night, All seat - ed
2 "Fear not," said he — for might - y dread Had seized their
3 "To you, in Da - vid's town this day, Is born of

on the ground, The an - gel of the Lord came down,
trou - bled mind — "Glad ti - dings of great joy I bring
Da - vid's line The Sav - ior, who is Christ the Lord,

And glo - ry shone a - round, And glo - ry shone a - round.
To you and all man - kind, To you and all man-kind.
And this shall be the sign: And this shall be the sign:

4 "The heavenly Babe you there shall find
To human view displayed,
All meanly wrapped in swaddling bands,
And in a manger laid."

5 Thus spake the seraph, and forthwith
Appeared a shining throng
Of angels praising God, who thus
Addressed their joyful song:

6 "All glory be to God on high,
And to the earth be peace;
Good will henceforth, from heaven to men,
Begin and never cease!"

Nahum Tate, 1702

339 Hark! the Herald Angels Sing

MENDELSSOHN 7 7 7 7 D., with Refrain

Arranged from Mendelssohn
by William H. Cummings, 1850

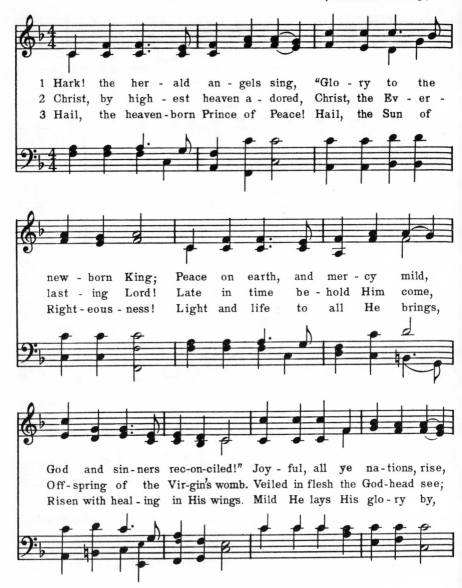

1 Hark! the her - ald an - gels sing, "Glo - ry to the
2 Christ, by high - est heaven a - dored, Christ, the Ev - er -
3 Hail, the heaven - born Prince of Peace! Hail, the Sun of

new - born King; Peace on earth, and mer - cy mild,
last - ing Lord! Late in time be - hold Him come,
Right - eous - ness! Light and life to all He brings,

God and sin - ners rec - on - ciled!" Joy - ful, all ye na - tions, rise,
Off - spring of the Vir - gin's womb. Veiled in flesh the God - head see;
Risen with heal - ing in His wings. Mild He lays His glo - ry by,

Hark! the Herald Angels Sing

Join the tri-umph of the skies; With th'an-gel-ic
Hail th'In-car-nate De-i-ty, Pleased as man with
Born that man no more may die, Born to raise the

host pro-claim, "Christ is born in Beth-le-hem!"
men to dwell, Je-sus, our Em-man-u-el.
sons of earth, Born to give them sec-ond birth.

REFRAIN

Hark! the her-ald an-gels sing, "Glo-ry to the new-born King."
Hark! the her-ald an-gels sing, "Glo-ry to the new-born King."
Hark! the her-ald an-gels sing, "Glo-ry to the new-born King."

Charles Wesley, 1739, altered

340   Angels, from the Realms of Glory

REGENT SQUARE 8 7 8 7 8 7

Henry Smart, 1867

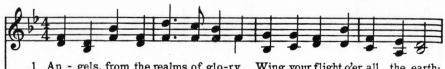

1 An - gels, from the realms of glo-ry,   Wing your flight o'er all the earth;
2 Shep-herds, in the fields a - bid-ing, Watch-ing o'er your flocks by night,
3 Sa - ges, leave your con-tem-pla-tions, Bright-er vi - sions beam a - far;

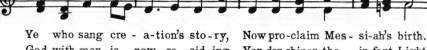

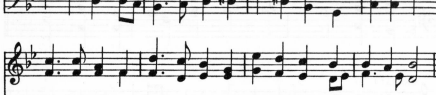

Ye who sang cre - a-tion's sto - ry, Now pro-claim Mes - si-ah's birth.
God with man is now re - sid-ing, Yon-der shines the in-fant Light.
Seek the great De-sire of na-tions; Ye have seen His na - tal star.

Come and wor-ship, Come and wor-ship, Wor-ship Christ, the new-born King.
Come and wor-ship, Come and wor-ship, Wor-ship Christ, the new-born King.
Come and wor-ship, Come and wor-ship, Wor-ship Christ, the new-born King.

4 Saints, in humble prayer now bending,
    Watching long in hope and fear,
Suddenly the Lord, descending,
    In His temple shall appear.
Come and worship, come and worship,
Worship Christ, the new-born King.

5 Saints and angels join in praising
    Thee, the Father, Spirit, Son,
Evermore their voices raising
    To th' Eternal Three in One.
Come and worship, come and worship,
Worship Christ, the new-born King.

James Montgomery, 1816, 1825

341   O Come, All Ye Faithful

ADESTE FIDELES 12 10 11, with Refrain
In J. F. Wade's *Cantus Diversi*, 1751

1 O come, all ye faith-ful, joy-ful and tri-um-phant! O come ye,
2 O sing, choirs of an-gels, sing in ex-ul-ta-tion, O sing, all
3 O Sav-ior, we greet Thee, born this hap-py morn-ing; O Je-sus,

O come ye to Beth-le-hem! Come and be-hold Him, born the
ye bright hosts of heav-en a-bove: "Glo-ry to God, all glo-ry
to Thee be all glo-ry given, Word of the Fa-ther, now in

REFRAIN

King of an-gels.
in the high-est." O come, let us a-dore Him, O come, let
flesh ap-pear-ing.

us a-dore Him, O come, let us a-dore Him, Christ the Lord.

Latin, 18th Century
Tr. Frederick Oakeley, 1841

342   Silent Night! Holy Night!

STILLE NACHT   Irregular

Franz Gruber, 1818

1 Si - lent night! Ho - ly night! All is calm,
2 Si - lent night! Ho - ly night! Shep-herds quake
3 Si - lent night! Ho - ly night! Son of God,

all is bright 'Round yon vir - gin moth - er and child!
at the sight! Glo - ries stream from heaven a - far,
love's pure light Ra - diant beams from Thy ho - ly face

Ho - ly in - fant so ten - der and mild, Sleep in heav - en - ly
Heaven-ly hosts sing: "Al - le - lu - ia! Christ the Sav - ior is
With the dawn of re - deem - ing grace, Je - sus, Lord, at Thy

peace,   Sleep   in heav - en - ly   peace.
born!   Christ   the Sav - ior is   born!"
birth!   Je - sus, Lord, at Thy   birth!

Joseph Mohr, 1818

343   Brightest and Best of the Sons

Morning Star 11 10 11 10

John P. Harding, 1861

1 Bright-est and best of the sons of the morn-ing,
2 Say, shall we yield Him, in cost-ly de-vo-tion,
3 Vain-ly we of-fer each am-ple ob-la-tion,

Dawn on our dark-ness and lend us Thine aid;
O dors of E-dom and of-ferings di-vine:
Vain-ly with gifts would His fa-vor se-cure;

Star of the east, the ho-ri-zon a-dorn-ing,
Gems of the moun-tain and pearls of the o-cean,
Rich-er by far is the heart's ad-o-ra-tion,

Guide where our in-fant Re-deem-er is laid.
Myrrh from the for-est, or gold from the mine?
Dear-er to God are the prayers of the poor.

Reginald Heber, 1811

403

344   Break Forth, O Beauteous Heavenly Light

SCHOP 8 7 8 7 8 8 7 7

Johann Schop, 1641
Harmonized by J. S. Bach
in the *Christmas Oratorio*

Joyously; may be sung in unison

1 Break forth, O beau-teous heaven-ly light, And ush-er in the morn - ing; Ye shep-herds, shrink not with af-fright, But hear the an-gel's warn - ing. This Child, now weak in in - fan - cy, Our con - fi - dence and joy shall be: The power of Sa - tan break - ing, Our peace e-ter-nal mak - ing.

Johann Rist, 1641

345   From Heaven Above to Earth I Come

VOM HIMMEL HOCH L.M.

Geistliche Lieder
Leipzig, 1539

In moderate time

1 From heaven a - bove to earth I come To bring good news to ev - ery home; Glad ti - dings of great joy I bring, Where-of I now will say and sing:

2 To you this night is born a Child Of Ma - ry, cho - sen Vir - gin mild; This lit - tle Child of low - ly birth Shall be the joy of all the earth.

3 This is the Christ, our God and Lord, Who in all need shall aid 'af - ford; He will Him - self your Sav - ior be, From all your sins to set you free.

4 These are the tokens ye shall mark:
The swaddling clothes and manger dark;
There ye shall find the Infant laid,
By whom the heavens and earth were
made.

5 Glory to God in highest heaven,
Who unto us His Son hath given!
While angels sing with pious mirth
A glad new year to all the earth.

Martin Luther, 1535

346 Christians, Awake, Salute the Happy Morn

YORKSHIRE 10 10 10 10 10 10

John Wainwright, 1750

1 Christ - ians, a - wake, sa - lute the hap - py morn
2 Then to the watch - ful shep - herds it was told,
3 He spake; and straight - way the ce - les - tial choir

Where - on the Sav - ior of the world was born.
Who heard th'an - gel - ic her - ald's voice, "Be - hold,
In hymns of joy, un - known be - fore, con - spire;

Rise to a - dore the mys - ter - y of love
I bring good ti - dings of a Sav - ior's birth
The prais - es of re - deem - ing love they sang,

Which hosts of an - gels chant - ed from a - bove;
To you and all the na - tions up - on earth;
And heaven's whole orb with al - le - lu - ias rang.

Christians, Awake, Salute the Happy Morn

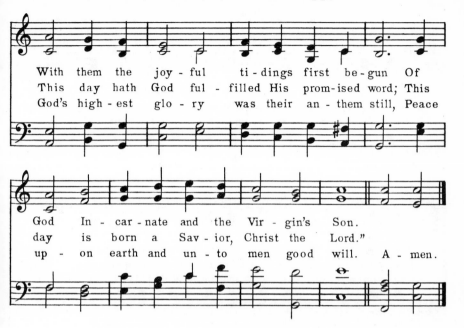

With them the joy - ful ti - dings first be - gun Of
This day hath God ful - filled His prom-ised word; This
God's high - est glo - ry was their an - them still, Peace

God In - car - nate and the Vir - gin's Son.
day is born a Sav - ior, Christ the Lord."
up - on earth and un - to men good will. A - men.

4 To Bethl'em straight th' enlightened shepherds ran
To see the wonder God had wrought for man,
And found, with Joseph and the blessed maid,
Her Son, the Savior, in a manger laid;
Then to their flocks, still praising God, return,
And their glad hearts with holy rapture burn.

5 Oh, may we keep and ponder in our mind
God's wondrous love in saving lost mankind!
Trace we the Babe, who hath retrieved our loss,
From His poor manger to His bitter cross,
Tread in His steps, assisted by His grace,
Till our imperfect state God doth replace.

6 Then may we hope, angelic hosts among,
To sing, redeemed, a glad triumphal song:
He that was born upon this joyful day
Around us all His glory shall display.
Saved by His love, incessant we shall sing
Eternal praise to heaven's almighty King.   Amen.

John Byrom, c. 1749

347   Thine Arm, O Lord, in Days of Old

SPOHR C.M.D.

Louis Spohr, 1835

1 Thine arm, O Lord, in days of old Was strong to heal and save;
2 And lo, Thy touch brought life and health, Gave speech and strength and sight;
3 Be Thou our great De - liv - erer still, Thou Lord of life and death;

It tri -umphed o'er dis-ease and death, O'er dark-ness and the grave.
Lo, youth re-newed and fren-zy calmed Owned Thee, the Lord of Light.
Re - store and quick - en, soothe and bless With Thine al-might-y breath.

To Thee they went: the blind, the dumb, The pal - sied, and the lame,
And now, O Lord, be near to bless, Al - might - y as of yore,
To hands that work and eyes that see Give wis-dom's heaven-ly lore,

The lep - er with his taint-ed life, The sick with fe-vered frame.
In crowd-ed streets, by rest-less couch, As by Gen-nes-areth's shore.
That whole and sick, and weak and strong May praise Thee ev - er - more.

E. H. Plumptre, 1866

408

348 All Glory, Laud, and Honor

ST. THEODULPH 7 6 7 6 D.

Melchior Teschner, 1615

1 All glo-ry, laud, and hon - or To Thee, Re-deem-er, King,
2 The com-pa-ny of an - gels Are prais-ing Thee on high,
3 To Thee be-fore Thy pas - sion They sang their hymns of praise;

To whom the lips of chil - dren Made sweet ho-san-nas ring.
And mor-tal men, and all things Cre - at - ed, make re - ply.
To Thee, now high ex - alt - ed, Our mel - o - dy we raise.

Thou art the King of Is - ra-el, Thou, Da-vid's roy - al Son,
The peo-ple of the He-brews With palms be-fore Thee went;
Thou didst ac - cept their prais-es; Ac - cept the prayers we bring,

Who in the Lord's Name com - est, The King and Bless-ed One.
Our praise and prayer and an - thems Be - fore Thee we pre - sent.
Who in all good de - light - est, Thou good and gra-cious King.

Theodulph of Orleans, c. 820
Tr. John Mason Neale, 1854

349 ## Hosanna, Loud Hosanna

ELLACOMBE 7 6 7 6 D.

From *Gesangbuch der Herzogl*
Württemberg, 1784

1 Ho - san - na, loud ho - san - na, The lit - tle chil-dren sang;
2 From O - liv - et they fol - lowed, 'Mid an ex - ult - ant crowd,
3 "Ho - san - na in the high - est!" That an - cient song we sing,

Through pil-lared court and tem - ple The love - ly an - them rang;
The vic - tor palm branch wav - ing, And chant-ing clear and loud;
For Christ is our Re - deem - er, The Lord of Heaven, our King.

To Je - sus, who had blessed them, Close fold - ed to His breast,
The Lord of men and an - gels Rode on in low - ly state;
O may we ev - er praise Him With heart and life and voice,

The chil - dren sang their prais - es, The sim-plest and the best.
Nor scorned that lit - tle chil - dren Should on His bid-ding wait.
And in His bliss-ful pres - ence E - ter - nal - ly re - joice.

Jennette Threlfall, 1873

350 When I Survey the Wondrous Cross

HAMBURG L.M.

Arranged from a Gregorian Chant
by Lowell Mason, 1824

1 When I sur-vey the won-drous cross On which the
2 For-bid it, Lord, that I should boast, Save in the
3 See from His head, His hands, His feet, Sor-row and

Prince of Glo-ry died, My rich-est gain I
death of Christ, my God! All the vain things that
love flow min-gled down; Did e'er such love and

count but loss, And pour con-tempt on all my pride.
charm me most, I sac-ri-fice them through His blood.
sor-row meet, Or thorns com-pose so rich a crown?

4 Were the whole realm of nature mine,
    That were a present far too small;
    Love so amazing, so divine,
    Demands my soul, my life, my all.

Isaac Watts, 1707

351   Ah, Dearest Jesus, How Hast Thou Offended

HERZLIEBSTER JESU 11 11 11 5

Johann Crüger, 1640

1 Ah, dear-est Je-sus, how hast Thou of-fend-ed, That man to
2 Who was the guilt-y? Who brought this up-on Thee? A - las, my
3 For me, dear Je-sus, was Thine in - car - na - tion, Thy mor-tal

judge Thee hath in hate pre - tend - ed? By foes de - rid - ed,
trea - son, Je-sus, hath un - done Thee! 'Twas I, Lord Je - sus,
sor - row, and Thy life's o - bla - tion; Thy death of an - guish

by Thine own re - ject - ed, O most af-flict - ed!
I it was de-nied Thee; I cru - ci - fied Thee.
and thy bit-ter pas - sion, For my sal - va - tion. A - men.

4 Therefore, dear Jesus, since I cannot pay Thee,
    I do adore Thee, and will ever pray Thee,
    Think on Thy pity and Thy love unswerving,
    Not my deserving.

Johann Heermann, 1630
Tr. Robert Bridges, 1899

352 Alas! and Did My Savior Bleed

AVON (MARTYRDOM) C.M.

Hugh Wilson, 1766-1824

1 A - las! and did my Sav - ior bleed, And
2 Was it for crimes that I have done He
3 Well might the sun in dark - ness hide, And

did my Sov - ereign die? Would He de - vote that
groaned up - on the tree? A - maz - ing pit - y,
shut his glo - ries in, When Christ, the might - y

sa - cred head For such a worm as I?
grace un - known, And love be - yond de - gree!
Mak - er, died For man the crea - ture's sin.

4 Thus might I hide my blushing face
While His dear cross appears;
Dissolve, my heart, in thankfulness!
And melt, mine eyes, to tears!

Isaac Watts, 1707

353 Beneath the Cross of Jesus

St. Christopher 7 6 8 6 8 6 8 6

Frederick C. Maker, 1881

1 Be-neath the cross of Je - sus I fain would take my stand,
2 Up - on that cross of Je - sus Mine eye at times can see
3 I take, O cross, thy shad - ow For my a - bid - ing place;

The shad-ow of a might - y rock With-in a wea - ry land,
The ver - y dy - ing form of One Who suf-fered there for me;
I ask no oth - er sun-shine than The sun-shine of His face;

A home with-in the wil - der-ness, A rest up - on the way,
And from my smit-ten heart with tears, Two won-ders I con - fess:
Con - tent to let the world go by, To know no gain nor loss,

From the burn-ing of the noon-tide heat, And the bur-den of the day.
The won-ders of His glo-rious love And my un-worth-i-ness.
My sin-ful self my on - ly shame, My glo-ry all, the cross.

Elizabeth C. Clephane, 1868

354 Jesus, Keep Me Near the Cross

NEAR THE CROSS 7 6 7 6, with Refrain

William H. Doane, 1831-1915

1 Je - sus, keep me near the cross; There a pre-cious foun-tain,
2 To the cross, a trem-bling soul, Love and mer-cy brought me;
3 Near the cross! O Lamb of God, Bring its scenes be-fore me;

Free to all, a heal-ing stream, Flows from Cal-vary's moun-tain.
There the Bright and Morn-ing Star Sheds its beams a - round me.
Help me walk from day to day With its shad-ows o'er me.

REFRAIN

In the cross, in the cross Be my glo - ry ev - er,

Till my rap-tured soul shall find Rest be-yond the riv - er.

4 Near the cross I'll watch and wait,
   Hoping, trusting ever,
   Till I reach the golden strand
   Just beyond the river.

Fanny J. Crosby, 1869

355 O Sacred Head, Now Wounded

PASSION CHORALE 7 6 7 6 D.

H. L. Hassler, 1564-1612
Adapted and harmonized by
Johann Sebastian Bach, 1729

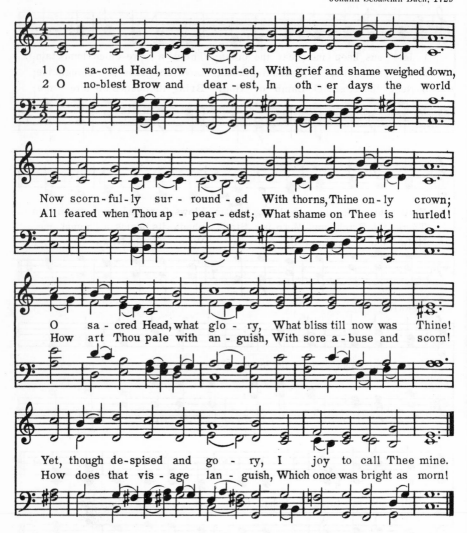

1 O sa-cred Head, now wound-ed, With grief and shame weighed down,
2 O no-blest Brow and dear-est, In oth-er days the world

Now scorn-ful-ly sur-round-ed With thorns, Thine on-ly crown;
All feared when Thou ap-pear-edst; What shame on Thee is hurled!

O sa-cred Head, what glo-ry, What bliss till now was Thine!
How art Thou pale with an-guish, With sore a-buse and scorn!

Yet, though de-spised and go-ry, I joy to call Thee mine.
How does that vis-age lan-guish, Which once was bright as morn!

3 What Thou, my Lord, hast suffered
Was all for sinners' gain;
Mine, mine was the transgression,
But Thine the deadly pain.
Lo, here I fall, my Savior,
'Tis I deserve Thy place;
Look on me with Thy favor,
Vouchsafe to me Thy grace.

4 What language shall I borrow
To thank Thee, dearest Friend,
For this Thy dying sorrow,
Thy pity without end?
O make me Thine forever;
And should I fainting be,
Lord, let me never, never
Outlive my love to Thee.

Bernard of Clairvaux, 1091-1153
Tr. James W. Alexander, 1830

356   ## Christ the Lord Is Risen Today

EASTER HYMN 7 7 7 7, with Alleluia

Lyra Davidica, 1708

1 "Christ the Lord is risen to day," Al - - le - lu - ia!
2 Lives a-gain our glo-rious King; Al - - le - lu - ia!

Sons of men and an-gels say; Al - - le - lu - ia!
Where, O death, is now thy sting? Al - - le - lu - ia!

Raise your joys and tri-umphs high; Al - - le - lu - ia!
Once He died, our souls to save; Al - - le - lu - ia!

Sing, ye heavens, and earth re-ply. Al - le - lu - ia!
Where thy vic - to - ry, O grave? Al - le - lu - ia!

3 Love's redeeming work is done;
    Alleluia!
Fought the fight, the battle won;
    Alleluia!
Death in vain forbids Him rise;
    Alleluia!
Christ has opened Paradise.
    Alleluia!

4 Soar we now where Christ has led,
    Alleluia!
Following our exalted Head;
    Alleluia!
Made like Him, like Him we rise;
    Alleluia!
Ours the cross, the grave, the skies.
    Alleluia!

Charles Wesley, 1739

357

Low in the Grave He Lay

CHRIST AROSE 11 10, with Refrain

Robert Lowry, 1826-1899

1 Low in the grave He lay— Je - sus, my Sav - ior;
2 Vain - ly they watch His bed— Je - sus, my Sav - ior;
3 Death can - not keep his prey— Je - sus, my Sav - ior;

Wait - ing the com - ing day— Je - sus, my Lord.
Vain - ly they seal the dead— Je - sus, my Lord.
He tore the bars a - way— Je - sus, my Lord.

REFRAIN

Up from the grave He a - rose, With a

He a - rose!

might - y tri - umph o'er His foes. He a

He a - rose!

418

Low in the Grave He Lay

rose a Vic - tor from the dark do - main, And He

lives for - ev - er with His saints to reign. He a - rose! He a - rose!

He a - rose! Hal - le - lu - jah! Christ a - rose! He a - rose!

Robert Lowry, 1874

358   The Strife Is O'er, the Battle Done

PALESTRINA (VICTORY) 8 8 8, with Alleluia

Arranged from Palestrina, 1591
by William H. Monk, 1861

Before first stanza only

Al - le - lu - ia! Al - le - lu - ia! Al - le - lu - ia!

Org.

1 The strife is o'er, the bat - tle done;
2 The powers of death have done their worst,
3 The three sad days are quick - ly sped;

The vic - to - ry of life is won; The song of
But Christ their le - gions has dis-persed; Let shouts of
He ris - es glo - rious from the dead; All glo - ry

tri - umph has be - gun. Al - le - lu - ia!
ho - ly joy out - burst. Al - le - lu - ia!
to our ris - en Head. Al - le - lu - ia!

4 He closed the yawning gates of hell;
  The bars from heaven's high portals
    fell;
  Let hymns of praise His triumph tell.
    Alleluia!

5 Lord, by the stripes which wounded Thee,
  From death's dread sting Thy servants
    free,
  That we may live and sing to Thee.
    Alleluia!

Latin, Cologne, 1695
Tr. Francis Pott, 1861

359   Angels, Roll the Rock Away

HENDON 7 7 7 7 7

H. A. Cesar Malan, 1787-1864

1 An - gels, roll the rock a - way; Death, yield up thy
2 Saints on earth, lift up your eyes; Now to glo - ry
3 Heaven un - folds its por - tals wide; Might - y Con - queror,

might - y prey; See, the Sav - ior leaves the tomb, Glow - ing
see Him rise In long tri - umph through the sky, Up to
through them ride; King of Glo - ry, **mount** Thy throne, Bound-less

with im - mor - tal bloom, Glow-ing with im - mor - tal bloom.
wait - ing worlds on high, Up to wait - ing worlds on high.
em - pire is Thine own, Bound-less em - pire is Thine own.

4 Powers of heaven, seraphic choirs,
   Sing, and sweep your golden lyres;
   Sons of men, in humbler strain
   Sing your mighty Savior's reign.

Thomas Scott, 1769

360

Alleluia! Alleluia!

TON-Y-BOTEL 8 7 8 7 D.

Welsh Hymn Melody

May be sung in unison

1 Al - le - lu - ia! Al - le - lu - ia! Hearts to
2 Christ is ris - en, Christ the first-fruits Of the
3 Al - le - lu - ia! Al - le - lu - ia! Glo - ry

heaven and voic - es raise; Sing to God a
ho - ly har - vest - field, Which will all its
to the Three in One: To the Fa - ther,

hymn of glad-ness, Sing to God a hymn of praise;
full a - bun-dance At His sec-ond com-ing yield.
and the Sav-ior, Who the vic-to - ry has won;

Alleluia! Alleluia!

He who on the cross a Vic-tim For the
Then the gold-en ears of har-vest Will their
Glo-ry to the Ho-ly Spir-it, Fount of

world's sal-va-tion bled, Je-sus Christ, the
heads be-fore Him wave, Rip-ened by His
love and sanc-ti-ty; Al-le-lu-ia!

King of Glo-ry, Now is ris-en from the dead.
glo-rious sun-shine From the fur-rows of the grave.
Al-le-lu-ia! To the Tri-une Maj-es-ty.

Christopher Wordsworth, 1862

361   Praise the Savior

UPP, MIN TUNGA 4 4 7   4 4 7   4 4 7

Koralbok (Swedish), 1697

1 Praise the Sav-ior Now and ev-er; Praise Him, all be-
2 Man's work fail-eth, Christ's a-vail-eth; He is all our

neath the skies; Pros-trate ly-ing, Suf-fering, dy-ing
right-eous-ness; He, our Sav-ior, Has for-ev-er

On the cross, a sac-ri-fice. Vic-tory gain-ing,
Set us free from dire dis-tress. Through His mer-it

Life ob-tain-ing, Now in glo-ry He doth rise.
We in-her-it Light and peace and hap-pi-ness.

3   Sin's bonds severed,
     We're delivered;
Christ has bruised the serpent's head;
     Death no longer
     Is the stronger;
Hell itself is captive led.
     Christ has risen
     From death's prison;
O'er the tomb He light has shed.

4   For His favor,
     Praise forever
Unto God the Father sing;
     Praise the Savior,
     Praise Him ever,
Son of God, our Lord and King.
     Praise the Spirit;
     Through Christ's merit,
He doth us salvation bring.

V.H.C. Fortunatus, c. 530-609
Tr. Augustus Nelson

362   Come, Ye Faithful, Raise the Strain

ST. KEVIN 7 6 7 6 D.

Arthur S. Sullivan, 1872

1 Come, ye faith-ful, raise the strain Of   tri-um-phant glad-ness;
2 'Tis   the spring of   souls to-day; Christ hath burst His pris-on,
3 "Al - le-lu - ia!" now we cry To   our King im - mor-tal,

God hath brought His peo - ple forth In - to   joy   from   sad-ness.
And from three days' sleep in death As   a   sun   hath   ris - en;
Who, tri - um - phant, burst the bars Of   the tomb's dark   por - tal;

Now   re - joice, Je - ru - sa - lem, And with true af - fec - tion
All   the win - ter   of our sins, Long and dark, is   fly - ing
"Al - le - lu - ia!" with the Son, God the Fa - ther prais-ing;

Wel - come in   un-wea-ried strains Je - sus' res - ur - rec - tion.
From His   light, to whom we give Laud and praise un-dy - ing.
"Al - le - lu - ia!" yet a - gain To   the Spir-it rais-ing. A-men.

John of Damascus, 8th c.
Tr. John M. Neale, 1859

363   Welcome, Happy Morning

Fortunatus 11 11 11 11 with Refrain

Arthur S. Sullivan, 1872

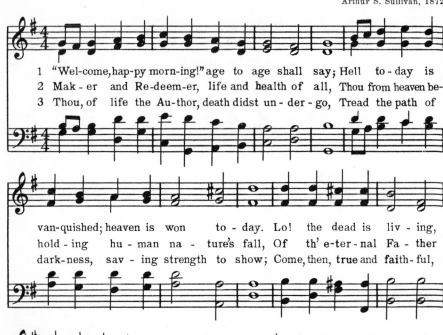

1 "Wel-come, hap-py morn-ing!" age to age shall say; Hell to-day is
2 Mak-er and Re-deem-er, life and health of all, Thou from heaven be-
3 Thou, of life the Au-thor, death didst un-der-go, Tread the path of

van-quished; heaven is won to-day. Lo! the dead is liv-ing,
hold-ing hu-man na-ture's fall, Of th' e-ter-nal Fa-ther
dark-ness, sav-ing strength to show; Come, then, true and faith-ful,

God for-ev-er-more! Him their true Cre-a-tor, all His works a-dore.
true and on-ly Son, Man-hood to de-liv-er, man-hood didst put on.
now ful-fill Thy Word, 'Tis Thine own third morn-ing; rise, O bur-ied Lord.

"Wel-come, hap-py morn-ing!" age to age shall say.

Hell to-day is van-quished; heaven is won to-day.
"Wel-come, hap-py morn-ing!" age to age shall say. A-men.

V.H.C. Fortunatus, c. 530-609
Tr. John Ellerton, 1868

364 The Day of Resurrection

LANCASHIRE 7 6 7 6 D.

Henry Smart, 1836

1 The day of res - ur - rec - tion! Earth, tell it out a - broad;
2 Our hearts be pure from e - vil, That we may see a - right
3 Now let the heavens be joy - ful, Let earth her song be - gin;

The Pass - o - ver of glad - ness, The Pass - o - ver of God.
The Lord in rays e - ter - nal Of res - ur - rec - tion light;
Let all the world keep tri - umph, And all that is there - in;

From death to life e - ter - nal, From earth un - to the sky,
And lis - tening to His ac - cents, May hear, so calm and plain,
In grate - ful ex - ul - ta - tion Their notes let all things blend,

Our Christ hath brought us o - ver With hymns of vic - to - ry.
His own "All hail!" and hear - ing, May raise the vic - tor strain.
For Christ the Lord hath ris - en, Our Joy that hath no end.

St. John of Damascus, 8th c.
Tr. John Mason Neale, 1853

427

365   See, the Conqueror Mounts in Triumph

REX GLORIAE 8 7 8 7 D.

Henry Smart, 1868

1 See, the Con-queror mounts in tri-umph; See the King in roy-al state,
2 Who is this that comes in glo-ry, With the trump of ju-bi-lee?
3 Thou hast raised our hu-man na-ture On the clouds to God's right hand;

Rid-ing on the clouds, His char-iot, To His heaven-ly pal-ace gate.
Lord of bat-tles, God of ar-mies, He has gained the vic-to-ry.
There we sit in heaven-ly plac-es, There with Thee in glo-ry stand.

Hark! the choirs of an-gel-voic-es Joy-ful al-le-lu-ias sing,
He who on the cross did suf-fer, He who from the grave a-rose,
Je-sus reigns, a-dored by an-gels, Man with God is on the throne;

And the por-tals high are lift-ed To re-ceive their heaven-ly King.
He has van-quished sin and Sa-tan, He by death has spoiled His foes.
Might-y Lord, in Thine as-cen-sion We by faith be-hold our own.

Christopher Wordsworth, 1862

366 Alleluia! Sing to Jesus!

LOWELL. 8 7 8 7 D.

H. E. Nichol, 1905

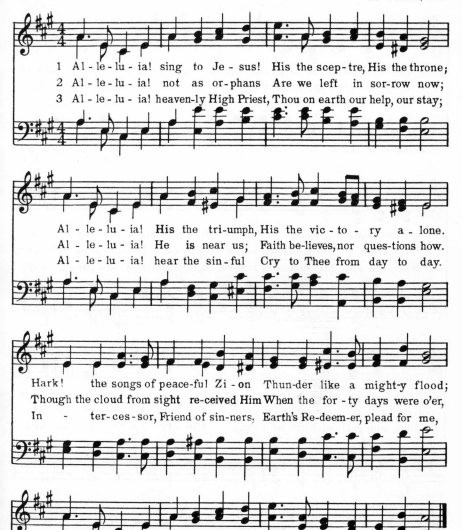

1 Al - le - lu - ia! sing to Je - sus! His the scep-tre, His the throne;
2 Al - le - lu - ia! not as or-phans Are we left in sor-row now;
3 Al - le - lu - ia! heaven-ly High Priest, Thou on earth our help, our stay;

Al - le - lu - ia! His the tri-umph, His the vic - to - ry a - lone.
Al - le - lu - ia! He is near us; Faith be-lieves, nor ques-tions how.
Al - le - lu - ia! hear the sin - ful Cry to Thee from day to day.

Hark! the songs of peace-ful Zi - on Thun-der like a might-y flood;
Though the cloud from sight re-ceived Him When the for - ty days were o'er,
In - ter-ces-sor, Friend of sin-ners, Earth's Re-deem-er, plead for me,

Je - sus, out of ev - ery na-tion, Has re-deemed us by His blood.
Shall our hearts for-get His prom-ise, "I am with you ev - er - more"?
Where the songs of all the sin - less Sweep a-cross the crys-tal sea.

William C. Dix, 1866

367 Hark! Ten Thousand Harps and Voices

HARWELL 8 7 8 7 7 7, with Refrain

Lowell Mason, 1840

1 Hark! ten thou-sand harps and voic-es Sound the note of praise a-bove;
2 King of glo - ry, reign for - ev - er, Thine an ev - er-last-ing crown;
3 Sav - ior, has-ten Thine ap-pear-ing, Bring, O bring the glo-rious day

Je - sus reigns and heaven re - joic-es, Je - sus reigns, the God of love;
Noth-ing from Thy love shall sev-er Those whom Thou hast made Thine own,
When, the aw - ful sum-mons hear-ing, Heaven and earth shall pass a - way;

See, He sits while an - gels stand, Je - sus rules at God's right hand.
Hap - py ob - jects of Thy grace, Des-tined to be-hold Thy face.
Then with gold - en harps we'll sing, Glo - ry, glo-ry to our King!

REFRAIN

Al - le - lu - ia! Al - le - lu - ia! Al - le - lu - ia! A - men.

Thomas Kelly, 1806

430

368   Rejoice, the Lord Is King

ARTHUR'S SEAT 6 6 6 6 8 8

John Goss, 1874

1 Re - joice, the Lord is King; Your Lord and King a -
2 His king-dom can - not fail; He rules o'er earth and

dore; Re - joice, give thanks, and sing, And tri - umph
heaven; The keys of death and hell Are to our

ev - er - more. Lift up your heart, lift up your voice;
Je - sus given. Lift up your heart, lift up your voice;

Re - joice! a - gain I say, Re - joice!
Re - joice! a - gain I say, Re - joice!

3 He all His foes shall quell,
   Shall all our sins destroy,
And every bosom swell
   With pure seraphic joy.
Lift up your heart, lift up your voice;
Rejoice! again I say, Rejoice!

4 Rejoice in glorious hope;
   Jesus, the Judge, shall come,
And take His servants up
   To their eternal home.
We soon shall hear th' archangel's voice,
The trump of God shall sound, Rejoice!

Charles Wesley, 1748

369 Hail, Thou Once Despised Jesus!

NOBLE 8 7 8 7 D.

Noble Cain
Harmonized by Seymour Swets, 1957

1 Hail, Thou once de - spis - ed Je - sus! Hail, Thou Gal - i - le - an King!
2 Pas - chal Lamb, by God ap-point-ed, All our sins on Thee were laid;
3 Je - sus, hail! en-throned in glo - ry, There for-ev - er to a - bide;
4 Wor - ship, hon - or, power, and bless-ing, Thou art wor-thy to re-ceive;

Thou didst suf - fer to re-lease us, Thou didst free sal - va - tion bring.
By al-might-y love a-noint-ed, Thou hast full a-tone-ment made.
All the heaven-ly hosts a-dore Thee, Seat - ed at Thy Fa-ther's side.
Loud-est prais - es, with-out ceas - ing, Meet it is for us to give.

Hail, Thou ag - o - niz - ing Sav-ior, Bear-er of our sin and shame!
All Thy peo-ple are for - giv - en, Through the vir-tue of Thy blood;
There for sin-ners Thou art plead-ing, There Thou dost our place pre-pare;
Help, ye bright an - gel - ic spir-its, Bring your sweet-est, no-blest lays;

By Thy mer-its we find fa - vor, Life is giv - en through Thy Name.
O - pened is the gate of heav - en, Peace is made 'twixt man and God.
Ev - er for us in - ter-ced - ing, Till in glo - ry we ap - pear.
Help to sing our Sav-ior's mer-its, Help to chant Em - man-uel's praise.

John Bakewell, 1757

370 Day of Judgment! Day of Wonders!

CORONAE 8 7 8 7 4 7

William H. Monk, 1871

1 Day of judg-ment! day of won-ders! Hark! the trum-pet's
2 See the Judge, our na-ture wear-ing, Clothed in maj-es-

aw - ful sound, Loud - er than a thou-sand thun-ders,
ty di - vine; You who long for His ap - pear - ing

Shakes the vast cre - a - tion round. How the
Then shall say, This God is mine! Gra - cious

sum - mons Will the sin - ner's heart con - found!
Sav - ior, Own me in that day as Thine.

3 At His call the dead awaken,
  Rise to life from earth and sea;
All the powers of nature, shaken
  By His looks, prepare to flee.
    Careless sinner,
  What will then become of thee?

4 But to those who have confessed,
  Loved and served the Lord below,
He will say, Come near, ye blessed,
  See the kingdom I bestow;
    You forever
  Shall my love and glory know.

John Newton, 1774

433

371 Wake, Awake, for Night Is Flying

SLEEPERS, WAKE 8 9 8 D. 6 6 4 8 8

Philipp Nicolai, 1599

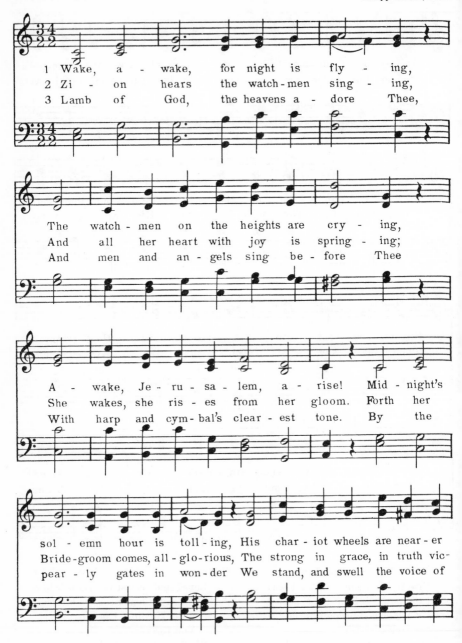

1 Wake, a - wake, for night is fly - ing,
2 Zi - on hears the watch - men sing - ing,
3 Lamb of God, the heavens a - dore Thee,

The watch - men on the heights are cry - ing,
And all her heart with joy is spring - ing;
And men and an - gels sing be - fore Thee

A - wake, Je - ru - sa - lem, a - rise! Mid - night's
She wakes, she ris - es from her gloom. Forth her
With harp and cym - bal's clear - est tone. By the

sol - emn hour is toll - ing, His char - iot wheels are near - er
Bride - groom comes, all - glo - rious, The strong in grace, in truth vic-
pear - ly gates in won - der We stand, and swell the voice of

Wake, Awake, for Night Is Flying

roll - ing; He comes; pre-pare, ye vir - gins wise;
to - rious; Her star is risen, her light is come.
thun - der In bursts of cho - ral mel - o - dy.

Rise up with will - ing feet; Go forth, the Bride-groom meet;
All hail, Thou pre-cious One, Lord Je - sus, God's dear Son!
To mor - tal eyes and ears What glo - ry now ap - pears!

Al - le - lu - ia! Bear through the night your
Al - le - lu - ia! The joy - ful call we
Al - le - lu - ia! We raise the song, we

well-trimmed light, Speed forth to join the mar - riage rite.
an - swer all, And fol - low to the nup - tial hall.
swell the throng, To praise Thee a - ges all a - long.

Philipp Nicolai, 1599
Tr. Catherine Winkworth, 1858

372 At the Name of Jesus

KING OF GLORY 6 5 6 5 D.

Albert Piersma, 1933

1 At the Name of Je - sus Ev - ery knee shall bow,
2 At His voice cre - a - tion Sprang at once to sight:

Ev - ery tongue con - fess Him King of Glo - ry now.
All the an - gel - fac - es, All the hosts of light,

'Tis the Fa-ther's pleas - ure We should call Him Lord,
Thrones and dom - i - na - tions, Stars up - on their way,

Who from the be - gin - ning Was the might - y Word.
All the heaven - ly or - ders In their great ar - ray.

3 In your hearts enthrone Him,
   There let Him subdue
All that is not holy,
   All that is not true.
Look to Him, your Captain,
   In temptation's hour,
Let His will enfold you
   In its light and power.

4 Brothers, this Lord Jesus
   Shall return again
With His Father's glory,
   With His angel-train;
For all wreaths of empire
   Meet upon His brow,
And our hearts confess Him
   King of Glory now.

Caroline M. Noel, 1870

436

Beautiful Savior

CRUSADERS' HYMN 5 5 7 5 5 8

Silesian Folk-song, 1842

1 Beau - ti - ful Sav - ior! King of cre - a - tion!
2 Fair are the mead - ows, Fair are the wood - lands,
3 Fair is the sun - shine, Fair is the moon - light,

Son of God and Son of Man! Tru - ly I'd love Thee,
Robed in flowers of bloom-ing spring; Je - sus is fair - er,
Bright the spark - ling stars on high; Je - sus shines bright-er,

Tru - ly I'd serve Thee, Light of my soul, my joy, my crown.
Je - sus is pur - er; He makes our sor-rowing spir - it sing.
Je - sus shines pur - er Than all the an - gels in the sky.

4 Beautiful Savior!
   Lord of the nations!
   Son of God and Son of Man!
   Glory and honor,
   Praise, adoration,
   Now and forevermore be Thine!

Münster *Gesangbuch,* 1677
Tr. J. A. Seiss, 1873

374 This Is My Father's World

TERRA BEATA S.M.D.

Franklin L. Sheppard, 1852-1930

1 This is my Fa-ther's world, And to my lis-tening ears All
2 This is my Fa-ther's world: The birds their car-ols raise, The
3 This is my Fa-ther's world: O let me ne'er for-get That

na - ture sings, and round me rings The mu-sic of the spheres.
morn - ing light, the lil - y white, De-clare their Mak-er's praise.
though the wrong seems oft so strong, God is the Rul-er yet.

This is my Fa-ther's world; I rest me in the thought Of
This is my Fa-ther's world: He shines in all that's fair; In the
This is my Fa-ther's world: Why should my heart be sad? The

rocks and trees, of skies and seas—His hand the won - ders wrought.
rus-tling grass I hear Him pass; He speaks to me ev-ery-where.
Lord is King, let the heav-ens ring! God reigns; let the earth be glad.

Words from *Thoughts for Every Day Living*
Copyright, 1901, by Charles Scribner's Sons, 1929, by Katherine T. Babcock
Reprinted by permission of the publishers
Maltbie D. Babcock, 1858-1901

375   # Jesus, the Very Thought of Thee

ST. AGNES C.M.

John B. Dykes, 1866

1 Je - sus, the ver - y thought of Thee
2 Nor voice can sing, nor heart can frame,
3 O hope of ev - ery con - trite heart,

With sweet-ness fills my breast; But sweet - er far Thy
Nor can the mem - ory find A sweet - er sound than
O joy of all the meek, To those who fall, how

face to see, And in Thy pres - ence rest.
Thy blest Name, O Sav - ior of man - kind!
kind Thou art! How good to those who seek!

4 But what to those who find? Ah, this
   Nor tongue nor pen can show!
   The love of Jesus, what it is
   None but His loved ones know.

Latin Hymn, 11th Cent.
Tr. Edward Caswall, 1849

376   O Christ, Our Hope, Our Heart's Desire

MANOAH C.M.

Henry W. Greatorex's
Collection, 1851

1 O Christ, our hope, our heart's de - sire, Re-
2 How vast the mer - cy and the love Which
3 But now the bands of death are burst, The

demp-tion's on - ly spring! Cre - a - tor of the
laid our sins on Thee, And led Thee to a
ran - som has been paid; And Thou art on Thy

world art Thou, Its Sav - ior and its King.
cru - el death, To set Thy peo - ple free.
Fa - ther's throne, In glo-rious robes ar - rayed. A - men.

4 O Christ, be Thou our lasting joy,
   Our ever great reward!
   Our only glory may it be
   To glory in the Lord.

Latin Hymn, 7th Cent.
Tr. J. Chandler, 1837

377   We Have Heard the Joyful Sound

JESUS SAVES 7 6 7 6 7 7 7 6

William J. Kirkpatrick, 1838-1921

Majestically

1 We have heard the joy-ful sound: Je-sus saves! Je-sus saves!
2 Waft it on the roll-ing tide: Je-sus saves! Je-sus saves!

Spread the ti - dings all a - round: Je-sus saves! Je-sus saves!
Tell to sin - ners far and wide: Je-sus saves! Je-sus saves!

Bear the news to ev - ery land, Climb the steeps and cross the waves;
Sing, ye is - lands of the sea! Ech - o back, ye o - cean caves!

On - ward! 'tis our Lord's com-mand; Je-sus saves! Je-sus saves!
Earth shall keep her ju - bi - lee; Je-sus saves! Je-sus saves!

3 Sing above the battle strife:
   Jesus saves! Jesus saves!
By His death and endless life
   Jesus saves! Jesus saves!
Sing it softly through the gloom,
   When the heart for mercy craves;
Sing in triumph o'er the tomb:
   Jesus saves! Jesus saves!

4 Give the winds a mighty voice:
   Jesus saves! Jesus saves!
Let the nations now rejoice;
   Jesus saves! Jesus saves!
Shout salvation full and free,
   Highest hills and deepest caves;
This our song of victory:
   Jesus saves! Jesus saves!

Priscilla J. Owens, 1829-1899

378   I Know Not Why God's Wondrous Grace

EL NATHAN C.M., with Refrain

James McGranahan, 1840-1907

Moderato

1 I know not why God's won-drous grace To me He hath made known,
2 I know not how this sav-ing faith To me He did im - part,
3 I know not how the Spir - it moves, Con-vinc-ing men of sin,
4 I know not what of good or ill May be re-served for me,

Nor why, un-wor-thy, Christ in love Re - deemed me for His own.
Nor how be-liev-ing in His Word Wrought peace with-in my heart.
Re - veal-ing Je - sus through the Word, Cre - at - ing faith in Him.
Of wea-ry ways or gold - en days, Be - fore His face I see.

REFRAIN

But "I know whom I have be-liev - ed, and am per-suad-ed that He is

a-ble To keep that which I've com-mit-ted Un-to Him a-gainst that day."

Daniel W. Whittle, 1840-1901

379 ## Lord Jesus, I Long to Be Perfectly Whole

FISCHER 11 11 11 11, with Refrain

William G. Fischer, 1872

1 Lord Je-sus, I long to be per-fect-ly whole; I want Thee for-ev - er to
2 Lord Je-sus, look down from Thy throne in the skies, And help me to make a com-
3 Lord Je-sus, for this I most hum-bly en-treat; I wait, bless-ed Lord, at Thy
4 Lord Je-sus, Thou see-est I pa-tient-ly wait; Come now, and with-in me a

live in my soul; Break down ev-ery i - dol, cast out ev-ery foe;
plete sac - ri - fice; I give up my - self and what - ev - er I know;
cru - ci - fied feet; By faith, for my cleans-ing, I see Thy blood flow;
new heart cre-ate; To those who have sought Thee, Thou nev-er saidst "No;"

REFRAIN

Now wash me, and I shall be whit-er than snow. Whit-er than snow, yes,

whit-er than snow; Now wash me, and I shall be whit-er than snow. A - men.

James L. Nicholson

380   Amazing Grace! How Sweet the Sound

ARLINGTON C.M.

Arranged from Thomas A. Arne, 1762

1 A - maz - ing grace! how sweet the sound, That
2 'Twas grace that taught my heart to fear And
3 Through man - y dan - gers, toils, and snares I

saved a wretch like me! I once was lost, but
grace my fears re - lieved; How pre - cious did that
have al - read - y come; 'Tis grace hath brought me

now am found, Was blind, but now I see.
grace ap - pear The hour I first be - lieved!
safe thus far And grace will lead me home. A - men.

4 When we've been there ten thousand years,
    Bright shining as the sun,
We've no less days to sing God's praise
    Than when we first begun.   Amen.

John Newton, 1725-1807

444

381   "Man of Sorrows," What a Name

HALLELUJAH! WHAT A SAVIOR 7 7 7 8

Philip P. Bliss, 1838-1876

1 "Man of sor - rows," what a name For the
2 Bear - ing shame and scoff - ing rude, In my
3 Lift - ed up was He to die, "It is

Son of God who came Ru - ined sin - ners
place con - demned He stood, Sealed my par - don
fin - ished," was His cry, Now in heaven ex -

to re-claim! Hal-le - lu - jah! what a Sav - ior!
with His blood; Hal-le - lu - jah! what a Sav - ior!
alt - ed high, Hal-le - lu - jah! what a Sav - ior! A - men.

4 When He comes, our glorious King,
  All His ransomed home to bring,
  Then anew this song we'll sing,
  Hallelujah! what a Savior!   Amen.

Philip P. Bliss, 1838-1876

382   Majestic Sweetness Sits Enthroned

ORTONVILLE C.M., 5 Lines

Thomas Hastings, 1837

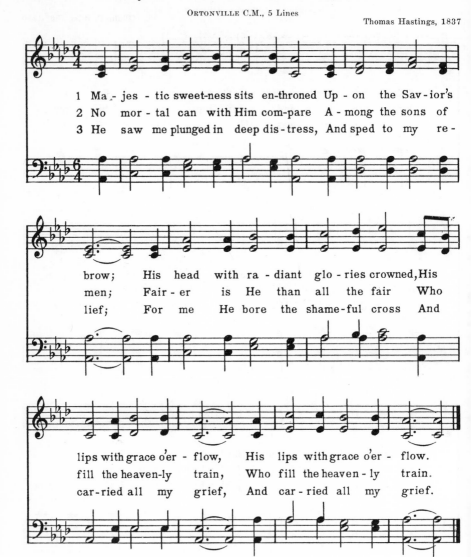

1 Ma - jes - tic sweet-ness sits en-throned Up - on the Sav - ior's
2 No mor - tal can with Him com-pare A - mong the sons of
3 He saw me plunged in deep dis - tress, And sped to my re -

brow; His head with ra - diant glo - ries crowned, His
men; Fair - er is He than all the fair Who
lief; For me He bore the shame-ful cross And

lips with grace o'er - flow, His lips with grace o'er - flow.
fill the heaven-ly train, Who fill the heaven - ly train.
car-ried all my grief, And car - ried all my grief.

4 To Him I owe my life and breath,
   And all the joys I have;
He makes me triumph over death,
   And saves me from the grave.

Samuel Stennett, 1787

383   O For a Thousand Tongues

AZMON C.M.

Carl G. Gläser, 1792-1872
Arranged by Lowell Mason, 1837

1 O for a thou - sand tongues to sing My
2 My gra - cious Mas - ter and my God, O
3 Je - sus! the Name that charms our fears, That

great Re - deem - er's praise, The glo - ries of my
help me to pro - claim, To spread through all the
bids our sor - rows cease; 'Tis mu - sic in the

God and King, The tri - umphs of His grace.
earth a - broad The hon - ors of Thy Name.
sin - ner's ears, 'Tis life and health and peace. A - men.

4 He breaks the power of canceled sin,
   He sets the prisoner free;
His blood can make the foulest clean;
   His blood availed for me.

5 Hear Him, ye deaf; His praise, ye
   dumb,
   Your loosened tongues employ;
Ye blind, behold your Savior come;
   And leap, ye lame, for joy. Amen.

Charles Wesley, 1707-1788

384 How Sweet the Name of Jesus Sounds

St. Peter C.M.

Alexander R. Reinagle, 1836

1 How sweet the Name of Je-sus sounds
2 It makes the wound-ed spir-it whole,
3 Je-sus, my Shep-herd, Guard-ian, Friend!

In a be-liev-er's ear! It soothes his sor-rows,
And calms the trou-bled breast; 'Tis man-na to the
My Proph-et, Priest, and King! My Lord, my Life, my

heals his wounds, And drives a-way his fear.
hun-gry soul, And to the wea-ry, rest.
Way, my End! Ac-cept the praise I bring.

4 Weak is the effort of my heart,
And cold my warmest thought;
But when I see Thee as Thou art,
I'll praise Thee as I ought.

5 Till then I would Thy love proclaim
With every fleeting breath;
And may the music of Thy Name
Refresh my soul in death.

John Newton, 1779

385 'Tis Not That I Did Choose Thee

CRUCIFIX 7 6 7 6 D.

Greek Melody

1 'Tis not that I did choose Thee, For, Lord, that could not be;
2 'Twas sov-ereign mer-cy called me And taught my o-pening mind;

This heart would still re-fuse Thee, Hadst Thou not cho-sen me.
The world had else en-thralled me, To heaven-ly glo-ries blind.

Thou from the sin that stained me Hast cleansed and set me free;
My heart owns none be-fore Thee, For Thy rich grace I thirst;

Of old Thou hast or-dained me, That I should live to Thee.
This know-ing, if I love Thee, Thou must have loved me first.

Josiah Conder, 1836

386 How Vast the Benefits Divine

SERAPH C.M.D.

Gottfried Wilhelm Fink, 1842

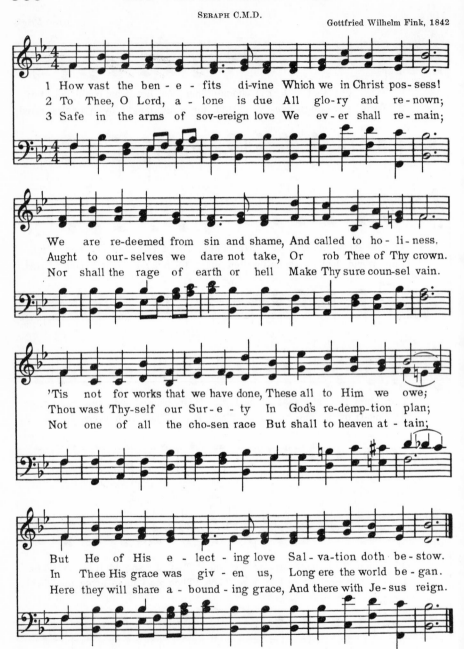

1 How vast the ben - e - fits di-vine Which we in Christ pos-sess!
2 To Thee, O Lord, a - lone is due All glo-ry and re-nown;
3 Safe in the arms of sov-ereign love We ev-er shall re-main;

We are re-deemed from sin and shame, And called to ho - li-ness.
Aught to our-selves we dare not take, Or rob Thee of Thy crown.
Nor shall the rage of earth or hell Make Thy sure coun-sel vain.

'Tis not for works that we have done, These all to Him we owe;
Thou wast Thy-self our Sur-e - ty In God's re-demp-tion plan;
Not one of all the cho-sen race But shall to heaven at - tain;

But He of His e - lect - ing love Sal - va-tion doth be-stow.
In Thee His grace was giv - en us, Long ere the world be-gan.
Here they will share a - bound - ing grace, And there with Je-sus reign.

Augustus M. Toplady, 1774
Revised, Dewey Westra, 1931

450

387   I Sought the Lord, and Afterward I Knew

Finlandia 10 10 10 8 10 8

Jean Silbelius, 1865-1957
Arranged by Seymour Swets, 1934

1 I sought the Lord, and af-ter-ward I knew   He moved my soul to
2 Thou didst reach forth Thy hand and mine en - fold;   I walked and sank not
3 I find, I walk, I love; but O, the whole   Of love is but my

seek Him, seek-ing me; It was not I that found, O Sav-ior true;
on the storm-vexed sea; 'Twas not so much that I on Thee took hold,
an-swer, Lord, to Thee! For Thou wert long be-fore-hand with my soul;

No, I was found, was found of Thee. It was not
As Thou, dear Lord, on me, on me. 'Twas not so
Al - ways, al-ways Thou lov - edst me. For Thou wert

I that found, O Sav-ior true; No, I was found, was found of Thee.
much that I on Thee took hold, As Thou, dear Lord, on me, on me.
long be-fore-hand with my soul; Al-ways, al-ways Thou lov - edst me.

Anonymous, about 1887.

451

388   Rock of Ages, Cleft for Me

TOPLADY 7 7 7 7 7 7

Thomas Hastings, 1830

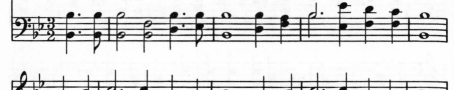

1 Rock of A - ges, cleft for me, Let me hide my-self in Thee;
2 Not the la-bors of my hands Can ful - fil Thy law's de-mands;
3 Noth-ing in my hand I bring, Sim-ply to Thy cross I cling;

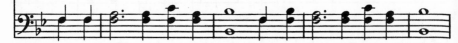

Let the wa - ter and the blood, From Thy wound-ed side which flowed,
Could my zeal no lan-guor know, Could my tears for- ev - er flow,
Na - ked, come to Thee for dress; Help-less, look to Thee for grace;

Be of sin the dou - ble cure: Save from guilt and make me pure.
All for sin could not a - tone; Thou must save, and Thou a - lone.
Foul, I to the foun-tain fly; Wash me, Sav-ior, or I die.

4 While I draw this fleeting breath,
When mine eyelids close in death,
When I rise to worlds unknown,
See Thee on Thy judgment-throne,
Rock of Ages, cleft for me,
Let me hide myself in Thee.

Augustus M. Toplady, 1776

389   Not What My Hands Have Done

LEOMINSTER S.M.D.

George William Martin, 1862
Harmonized by Arthur S. Sullivan, 1874

1 Not what my hands have done Can save my guilt-y soul;
2 Thy grace a-lone, O God, To me can par-don speak;
3 I bless the Christ of God; I rest on love di-vine;

Not what my toil-ing flesh has borne Can make my spir-it whole.
Thy power a-lone, O Son of God, Can this sore bond-age break.
And with un-fal-tering lip and heart I call this Sav-ior mine.

Not what I feel or do Can give me peace with God;
No oth-er work save Thine, No oth-er blood will do;
'Tis He that sav-eth me And free-ly par-don gives;

Not all my prayers and sighs and tears Can bear my aw-ful load.
No strength save that which is di-vine Can bear me safe-ly through.
I love be-cause He lov-eth me; I live be-cause He lives.

Horatius Bonar, 1864

390   Eternal Spirit, God of Truth

SARAH C.M.

Charles H. Gabriel, 1901

1 E - ter - nal Spir - it, God of truth,
2 'Tis Thine tó soothe the sor - rowing mind,
3 Sub - due the power of ev - ery sin,

Our con - trite hearts in - spire; Kin - dle a
With guilt and fear op - pressed; 'Tis Thine to
What - e'er that sin may be, That we, in

flame of heaven-ly love, And feed the pure de - sire.
bid the dy - ing live, And give the wea - ry rest.
sin - gle - ness of heart, May wor - ship on - ly Thee.

4 Then with our spirit witness bear
   That we are sons of God,
Redeemed from sin and death and hell
   Through Christ's atoning blood.

T. Cotterill, 1810

391   Breathe on Me, Breath of God

TRENTHAM S.M.

Robert Jackson, 1842-1914

1 Breathe on me, Breath of God, Fill me with life a - new, That I may love what Thou dost love, And do what Thou wouldst do.

2 Breathe on me, Breath of God, Un - til my heart is pure, Un - til with Thee I will Thy will, To do and to en - dure.

3 Breathe on me, Breath of God, Till I am whol - ly Thine, Till all this earth - ly part of me Glows with Thy fire di - vine. A - men.

4 Breathe on me, Breath of God,
So shall I never die,
But live with Thee the perfect life
Of Thine eternity.   Amen.

Edwin Hatch, 1835-1889

Spirit Divine, Attend Our Prayer

GRÄFENBERG C.M.

Johann Crüger's
Praxis Pietatis Melica, 1653

1 Spir - it di - vine, at - tend our prayer
2 Come as the light; to wait - ing minds
3 Come as the fire; en - kin - dle now

And make our hearts Thy home; De - scend with all Thy
That long the truth to know Re - veal the nar - row
The sac - ri - fi - cial flame, That all our souls an

gra - cious power; Come, Ho - ly Spir - it, come.
path of right, The way of du - ty show.
of - fering be To our Re - deem - er's name.

4. Come as the dew; on hearts that pine
Descend in this still hour,
Till every barren place shall own
With joy Thy quickening power.

Andrew Reed, 1829
Samuel Longfellow, 1864

393   ## Creator Spirit, by Whose Aid

Melita 8 8 8 8 8 8

John B. Dykes, 1823-1876

1 Cre - a - tor Spir - it, by whose aid The world's foun-da-tions
2 O source of un - cre - at - ed light, The Fa-ther's prom-ised
3 Plen - teous of grace, de-scend from high, Rich in Thy seven-fold

first were laid, Come, vis - it ev - ery pi - ous mind;
Par - a - clete, Thrice ho - ly fount, thrice ho - ly fire,
en - er - gy; Make us e - ter - nal truths re - ceive

Come, pour Thy joys on hu - man kind; From sin and sor - row
Our hearts with heaven-ly love in-spire; Come and Thy sa - cred
And prac - tise all that we be - lieve; Give us Thy-self, that

set us free, And make Thy tem - ples wor - thy Thee.
unc - tion bring To sanc - ti - fy us while we sing.
we may see The Fa - ther and the Son by Thee. A - men.

9th Century Latin hymn
Tr. John Dryden, 1693

394   Spirit of God, Dwell Thou Within My Heart

MORECAMBE 10 10 10 10

Frederick C. Atkinson, 1880

1 Spir - it of God, dwell Thou with - in my heart; Wean it from
2 I ask no dream, no proph - et ec - sta - sies, No sud - den
3 Didst Thou not bid us love Thee, God and King? All, all Thine

earth, through all its puls - es move; Stoop to my weak - ness,
rend - ing of the veil of clay, No an - gel vis - it -
own: soul, heart, and strength, and mind. I see the cross—there

might-y as Thou art, And make me love Thee as I ought to love.
ant, no o-pening skies; But take the dim-ness of my soul a - way.
teach my heart to cling; O let me seek Thee and O let me find!

4 Teach me to feel that Thou art always nigh;
   Teach me the struggles of the soul to bear;
  To check the rising doubt, the rebel sigh;
   Teach me the patience of unanswered prayer.

5 Teach me to love Thee as Thine angels love,
   One holy passion filling all my frame—
  The baptism of the heaven-descended Dove;
   My heart an altar, and Thy love the flame.

George Croly, 1854

395 Holy Spirit, Light Divine

MERCY (GOTTSCHALK) 7 7 7 7

Arranged from
Louis M. Gottschalk, 1854

1 Ho - ly Spir - it, light di - vine, Shine with-
2 Ho - ly Spir - it, power di - vine, Cleanse this
3 Ho - ly Spir - it, joy di - vine, Cheer this

in this heart of mine; Chase the shades of
guilt - y heart of mine; Long has sin, with-
sad - dened heart of mine; Bid my man - y

night a - way, Turn my dark - ness in - to day.
out con - trol, Held do - min - ion o'er my soul.
woes de - part, Heal my wound - ed, bleed - ing heart.

4 Holy Spirit, all divine,
Dwell within this heart of mine;
Cast down every idol-throne,
Reign supreme, and reign alone.

Andrew Reed, 1817, *alt.*

396 Come, Holy Spirit, Heavenly Dove

ST. AGNES C.M.

John B. Dykes, 1866

1 Come, Ho - ly Spir - it, heaven - ly Dove,
2 Look how we grov - el here be - low,
3 In vain we tune our for - mal songs,

With all Thy quick - ening powers; Kin - dle a flame of
Fond of these tri - fling toys; Our souls can nei - ther
In vain we strive to rise; Ho - san - nas lan - guish

sa - cred love In these cold hearts of ours.
fly nor go To reach e - ter - nal joys.
on our tongues, And our de - vo - tion dies.

4 Come, Holy Spirit, heavenly Dove,
   With all Thy quickening powers;
   Come, shed abroad a Savior's love,
   And that shall kindle ours.

Isaac Watts, 1707

460

397   Dwell in Me, O Blessed Spirit

DWELL IN ME 8 7 8 7, with Refrain

Georgia Guiney Berky

1 Dwell in me, O bless-ed Spir-it! How I need Thy help di - vine!
2 Round the cross where Thou hast led me, Let my pur-est feel-ings twine.
3 Let me feel Thy sa-cred pres-ence; Then my faith will ne'er de-cline.

In the way of life e - ter - nal, Keep, O keep this heart of mine!
With the blood from sin that cleansed me, Seal a-new this heart of mine.
Com-fort Thou and help me on - ward; Fill with love this heart of mine.

REFRAIN

Dwell in me, O bless-ed Spir - it! Gra-cious Teach-er, Friend di-vine!

For the home of bliss that waits me O pre-pare this heart of mine!

Martha J. Lankton

461

398 The Church's One Foundation

AURELIA 7 6 7 6 D.

Samuel S. Wesley's setting of *Jerusalem the Golden*, 1864

1 The Church's one foun-da-tion Is Je-sus Christ, her Lord;
2 E-lect from ev-ery na-tion, Yet one o'er all the earth,

She is His new cre-a-tion By wa-ter and the Word;
Her char-ter of sal-va-tion, One Lord, one faith, one birth;

From heaven He came and sought her To be His ho-ly bride;
One ho-ly Name she bless-es, Par-takes one ho-ly food,

With His own blood He bought her, And for her life He died.
And to one hope she press-es, With ev-ery grace en-dued.

3 Though with a scornful wonder
Men see her sore oppressed,
By schisms rent asunder,
By heresies distressed,
Yet saints their watch are keeping,
Their cry goes up, "How long?"
And soon the night of weeping
Shall be the morn of song.

4 'Mid toil and tribulation
And tumult of her war,
She waits the consummation
Of peace forevermore,
Till with the vision glorious
Her longing eyes are blest,
And the great Church victorious
Shall be the Church at rest.

Samuel J. Stone, 1866

399 Jesus Shall Reign Where'er the Sun

DUKE STREET L.M.

John Hatton, died 1793

1 Je - sus shall reign wher - e'er the sun Does his suc-
2 To Him shall end - less prayer be made, And prais - es
3 Peo - ple and realms of ev - ery tongue Dwell on His

ces - sive jour - neys run; His king - dom stretch from
throng to crown His head; His Name, like sweet per -
love with sweet - est song, And in - fant voic - es

shore to shore, Till moons shall wax and wane no more.
fume, shall rise With ev - ery morn - ing sac - ri - fice.
shall pro - claim Their ear - ly bless - ings on His Name.

4 Blessings abound where'er He reigns;
The prisoner leaps to lose his chains,
The weary find eternal rest,
And all the sons of want are blest.

5 Let every creature rise and bring
Peculiar honors to our King,
Angels descend with songs again
And earth repeat the loud Amen.

Isaac Watts, 1719

463

400   Shout, for the Blessed Jesus Reigns

TRURO L.M.

Charles Burney, 1726-1814

1 Shout, for the bless-ed Je-sus reigns; Through dis-tant
lands His tri-umphs spread; And sin-ners, freed from
end-less pains, Own Him their Sav-ior and their Head.

2 He calls His cho-sen from a-far, They all at
Zi-on's gates ar-rive; Those who were dead in
sin be-fore By sov-ereign grace are made a-live.

3 Gen-tiles and Jews His laws o-bey; Na-tions re-
mote their of-ferings bring And un-con-strained their
hom-age pay To their ex-alt-ed God and King.

4 O may His holy Church increase,
   His Word and Spirit still prevail,
While angels celebrate His praise
   And saints His growing glories hail.

5 Loud hallelujahs to the Lamb,
   From all below and all above!
In lofty songs exalt His name,
   In songs as lasting as His love.

Benjamin Beddome, 1769

401   ## From Greenland's Icy Mountains

MISSIONARY HYMN 7 6 7 6 D.

Lowell Mason, 1823

1 From Green-land's i - cy moun-tains, From In - dia's cor - al strand,
2 What though the spic - y breez-es Blow soft o'er Cey-lon's isle,

Where Af-ric's sun - ny foun-tains Roll down their gold-en sand,
Though ev - ery pros-pect pleas - es, And on - ly man is vile?

From man-y an an-cient riv - er, From man-y a palm-y plain
In vain with lav-ish kind-ness The gifts of God are strown;

Christ calls us to de - liv - er His lands from er - ror's chain.
The hea-then in his blind-ness Bows down to wood and stone.

3 Shall we, whose souls are lighted
   With wisdom from on high,
Shall we to men benighted
   The lamp of life deny?
Salvation! O salvation!
   The joyful sound proclaim,
Till earth's remotest nation
   Has learned Messiah's Name.

4 Waft, waft, ye winds, His story,
   And you, ye waters, roll,
Till like a sea of glory
   It spreads from pole to pole;
Till o'er our ransomed nature
   The Lamb for sinners slain,
Redeemer, King, Creator,
   In bliss returns to reign.

Reginald Heber, 1819

402 Glorious Things of Thee Are Spoken

AUSTRIAN HYMN 8 7 8 7 D.

Franz Joseph Haydn, 1797

1 Glo-rious things of thee are spo-ken, Zi - on, cit - y of our God;
2 See, the streams of liv - ing wa-ters, Spring-ing from e - ter - nal love,
3 Sav - ior, if of Zi-on's cit - y I, through grace, a mem-ber am,

He whose word can-not be bro - ken Formed thee for His own a - bode;
Well sup - ply thy sons and daugh-ters And all fear of want re-move:
Let the world de-ride or pit - y, I will glo-ry in Thy Name.

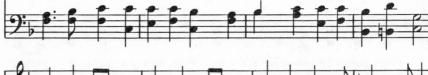

On the Rock of A - ges found-ed, What can shake thy sure re-pose?
Who can faint, while such a riv - er Ev - er flows their thirst t'as-suage?
Fad - ing is the world-ling's pleas-ure, All His boast-ed pomp and show;

With sal-va-tion's walls sur-round-ed Thou may'st smile at all thy foes.
Grace which, like the Lord, the Giv-er, Nev-er fails from age to age.
Sol - id joys and last-ing treas-ure None but Zi-on's chil-dren know. A-men.

John Newton 1779, alt.

403   Speed Thy Servants, Savior, Speed Them

Zion 8 7 8 7 4 7

Thomas Hastings, 1830

1 Speed Thy ser-vants, Sav-ior, speed them, Thou art Lord of winds and waves.
2 Friends and home and all for-sak - ing, Lord, they go at Thy com-mand;
3 When no fruit ap-pears to cheer them And they seem to toil in vain,

They were bound, but Thou hast freed them; Now they go to free the slaves.
As their stay Thy prom-ise tak - ing, While they trav-erse sea and land;
Then in mer-cy, Lord, draw near them, Then their sink-ing hopes sus - tain;

Be Thou with them: 'Tis Thine arm a - lone that saves.
O be with them: Lead them safe - ly by the hand.
Thus sup - port - ed, Let their zeal re - vive a - gain.

Be Thou with them: 'Tis Thine arm a - lone that saves.
O be with them: Lead them safe - ly by the hand.
Thus sup - port - ed, Let their zeal re - vive a - gain.

4 In the midst of opposition,
   Let them trust, O Lord, in Thee;
When success attends their mission,
   Let Thy servants humblest be.
     Never leave them
   Till Thy face in heaven they see.

Thomas Kelly, 1820

404   Lord, Speak to Me, That I May Speak

CANONBURY L.M.   Arranged from Robert A. Schumann's
Nachtstücke, No. 4, 1839

1 Lord, speak to me, that I may speak In
2 O teach me, Lord, that I may teach The
3 O lead me, Lord, that I may lead The

liv - ing ech - oes of Thy tone; As Thou hast sought, so
pre - cious things Thou dost im - part; And wing my words that
wan-dering and the wa-vering feet; O feed me, Lord, that

let me seek Thine err - ing chil - dren lost and lone.
they may reach The hid - den depths of man - y a heart.
I may feed The hun-gering ones with man - na sweet.

4 O strengthen me, that while I stand
     Firm on the Rock and strong in Thee,
I may stretch out a loving hand
     To wrestlers with the troubled sea.

5 O use me, Lord, use even me,
     Just as Thou wilt, and when, and where;
Until Thy blessed face I see,
     Thy rest, Thy joy, Thy glory share.

Frances R. Havergal, 1872

405 Far and Near the Fields Are Teeming

CLEMM 8 7 8 7, with Refrain

J. B. O. Clemm

1 Far and near the fields are teem-ing With the waves of rip-ened grain;
2 Send them forth with morn's first beam-ing, Send them in the noon-tide's glare;
3 Thou whom Christ the Lord is send-ing, Gath-er now the sheaves of gold;

Far and near their gold is gleam-ing O'er the sun-ny slope and plain.
When the sun's last rays are gleam-ing, Bid them gath-er ev-ery-where
Heaven-ward then at eve-ning wend-ing, Thou shalt come with joy un-told.

REFRAIN

Lord of har-vest, send forth reap-ers; Hear us, Lord, to Thee we cry;

Send them now the sheaves to gath-er, Ere the har-vest-time pass by.

J. O. Thompson

406 Comfort, Comfort Ye My People

THIRSTING 8 7 8 7 7 7 8 8

Louis Bourgeois, 1551
Harmony from DeVries *Koraalboek*
Adapted by Henry Bruinsma, 1946

1 Com-fort, com-fort ye My peo-ple, Speak ye peace, thus saith our God;
2 For the her-ald's voice is cry-ing In the des-ert far and near,
3 Make ye straight what long was crook-ed, Make the rough-er plac-es plain;

Com-fort those who sit in dark-ness, Mourn-ing 'neath their sor-row's load.
Bid-ding all men to re-pent-ance, Since the king-dom now is here.
Let your hearts be true and hum-ble, As be-fits His ho-ly reign.

Speak ye to Je-ru-sa-lem Of the peace that waits for them;
O that warn-ing cry o-bey! Now pre-pare for God a way;
For the glo-ry of the Lord Now o'er earth is shed a-broad;

Tell her that her sins I cov-er, And her war-fare now is o-ver.
Let the val-leys rise to meet Him And the hills bow down to greet Him.
And all flesh shall see the to-ken That His Word is nev-er bro-ken.

Johannes Olearius, 1671
Tr. Catherine Winkworth, 1863

407 Guide Me, O Thou Great Jehovah

CWM RHONDDA 8 7 8 7 8 7 7

Welsh hymn melody

1 Guide me, O Thou great Je - ho - vah, Pil-grim through this bar-ren land;
2 O - pen now Thy crys - tal foun-tain, Whence the heal-ing stream doth flow.
3 When I tread the verge of Jor-dan, Bid my anx - ious fears sub-side;

I am weak, but Thou art might-y, Hold me with Thy power-ful hand.
Let the fire and cloud-y pil - lar Lead me all my jour-ney through.
Death of death, and hell's de-struc-tion, Land me safe on Ca-naan's side.

Bread of heav - en, Bread of heav - en, Feed me till I want no
Strong De-liv - er-er, strong De-liv - er-er, Be Thou still my strength and
Songs of prais - es, songs of prais-es I will ev - er give to

more, Feed me till I want no more.
shield, Be Thou still my strength and shield.
Thee, I will ev - er give to Thee. A - men.

William Williams, **1745**
Tr. Peter Williams, *alt.*, **1771**

408 Great Is Thy Faithfulness

FAITHFULNESS 11 10 11 10, with Refrain

William M. Runyan

1 Great is Thy faith - ful-ness, O God my Fa - ther,
2 Sum - mer and win - ter and spring-time and har - vest,
3 Par - don for sin and a peace that en - dur - eth,

There is no shad - ow of turn - ing with Thee;
Sun, moon and stars in their cours - es a - bove
Thine own dear pres - ence to cheer and to guide,

Thou chang-est not, Thy com - pas - sions, they fail not;
Join with all na - ture in man - i - fold wit - ness
Strength for to - day and bright hope for to - mor - row,

As Thou hast been Thou for - ev - er wilt be.
To Thy great faith - ful - ness, mer - cy and love.
Bless - ings all mine, with ten thou - sand be - side!

Great Is Thy Faithfulness

REFRAIN

Great is Thy faith-ful-ness! Great is Thy faith-ful-ness!

Morn - ing by morn - ing new mer - cies I see;

All I have need - ed Thy hand hath pro - vid - ed,

Great is Thy faith - ful - ness, Lord, un - to me!

Rejoice, Ye Pure in Heart

MARION S.M., with Refrain

Arthur H. Messiter, 1834-1916

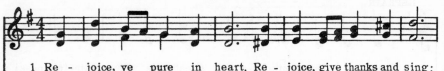

1 Re - joice, ye pure in heart, Re - joice, give thanks and sing;
2 Bright youth and snow-crowned age, Strong men and maid-ens fair,
3 Yes, on through life's long path, Still chant-ing as ye go;

Your fes - tal ban - ner wave on high, The cross of Christ your King.
Raise high your free, ex - ult - ing song, God's won-drous praise de-clare.
From youth to age, by night and day, In glad-ness and in woe.

REFRAIN

Re-joice, re-joice, Re-joice, give thanks and sing. A - men.
Re-joice, re-joice,

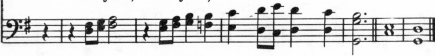

4 Still lift your standard high,
Still march in firm array,
As warriors through the darkness toil
Till dawns the golden day.

Edward Hayes Plumptre, 1865

410

Come to the Savior Now

INVITATION 6 6 6 6 D.

Frederick C. Maker, 1844-1927

1 Come to the Sav-ior now, He gen-tly call-eth thee;
2 Come to the Sav-ior now, Ye who have wan-dered far;
3 Come to the Sav-ior now! He of-fers all to thee,

In true re-pent-ance bow, Be-fore Him bend the knee;
Re-new your sol-emn vow, For His by right you are;
And in His mer-its thou Hast an un-fail-ing plea.

He wait-eth to be-stow Sal-va-tion, peace and love,
Come like poor wan-dering sheep, Re-turn-ing to His fold;
No vain ex-cus-es frame, For feel-ings do not stay;

True joy on earth be-low, A home in heaven a-bove.
His arm will safe-ly keep, His love will ne'er grow cold.
None who to Je-sus came Were ev-er sent a-way.

4 Come to the Savior, all,
    Whate'er your burdens be;
Hear now His loving call,
    "Cast all your care on Me."

Come, and for every grief
    In Jesus you will find
A sure and safe relief,
    A loving friend and kind.

John M. Wigner, 1844-1911

411　How Firm a Foundation

Adeste Fideles 11 11 11 11

In J. F. Wade's
Cantus Diversi, 1751

1 How firm a foun - da - tion, ye saints of the Lord,
2 "Fear not, I am with thee, O be not dis - mayed;

Is laid for your faith in His ex - cel - lent Word!
For I am thy God, I will still give thee aid;

What more can He say than to you He has said,
I'll strength-en thee, help thee, and cause thee to stand,

To you who for ref - uge to Je - sus have fled?
Up - held by My gra-cious, om - nip - o - tent hand,

How Firm a Foundation

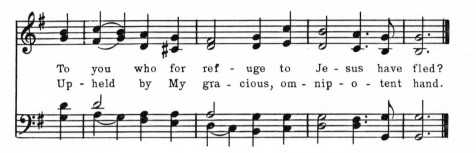

To you who for ref - uge to Je - sus have fled?
Up - held by My gra - cious, om - nip - o - tent hand.

3 "When through the deep waters I call thee to go,
The rivers of sorrow shall not overflow;
For I will be with thee thy trials to bless,
And sanctify to thee thy deepest distress.

4 "When through fiery trials thy pathway shall lie,
My grace all-sufficient shall be thy supply;
The flame shall not hurt thee; I only design
Thy dross to consume, and thy gold to refine.

5 "The soul that on Jesus has leaned for repose,
I will not, I will not desert to his foes;
That soul, though all hell should endeavor to shake,
I'll never, no never, no never forsake!"

"K" in John Rippon's *Selection of.Hymns*, 1787

412 I Love to Tell the Story

HANKEY 7 6 7 6 D., with Refrain
William G. Fischer, 1869
Harmonized by Herbert P. Main, 1870

1 I love to tell the sto - ry Of un - seen things a - bove,
2 I love to tell the sto - ry; More won-der - ful it seems

Of Je - sus and His glo - ry, Of Je - sus and His love.
Than all the gold - en fan - cies Of all our gold - en dreams.

I love to tell the sto - ry Be-cause I know 'tis true;
I love to tell the sto - ry, It did so much for me;

It sat - is-fies my long-ings As noth - ing else could do.
And that is just the rea - son I tell it now to thee.

I Love to Tell the Story

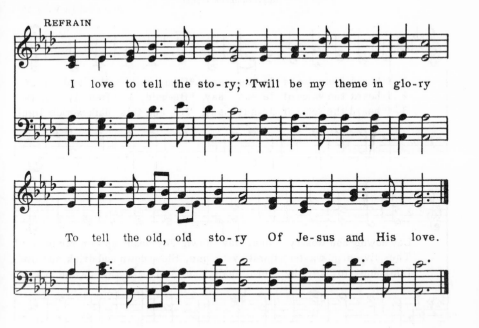

I love to tell the sto-ry; 'Twill be my theme in glo-ry

To tell the old, old sto-ry Of Je-sus and His love.

3 I love to tell the story;
　　'Tis pleasant to repeat
　What seems, each time I tell it,
　　More wonderfully sweet.
　I love to tell the story,
　　For some have never heard
　The message of salvation
　　From God's own holy Word.

4 I love to tell the story,
　　For those who know it best
　Seem hungering and thirsting
　　To hear it like the rest.
　And when in scenes of glory
　　I sing the new, new song,
　'Twill be the old, old story
　　That I have loved so long.

Catherine Hankey, 1866

413　I Heard the Voice of Jesus Say

RESTING-PLACE C.M.D.

Henry Vander Werp, 1911

1 I heard the voice of Jesus say, "Come un-to Me and rest,
2 I heard the voice of Jesus say, "Be-hold, I free-ly give
3 I heard the voice of Jesus say, "I am this dark world's light;

Lay down, thou wea-ry one, lay down Thy head up-on My breast."
The liv-ing wa-ter; thirst-y one, Stoop down and drink, and live!"
Look un-to Me; thy morn shall rise, And all thy day be bright."

I came to Je-sus as I was, Wea-ry and worn and sad;
I came to Je-sus and I drank Of that life-giv-ing stream;
I looked to Je-sus and I found In Him my star, my sun;

I found in Him a rest-ing place, And He has made me glad.
My thirst was quenched, my soul re-vived, And now I live in Him.
And in that light of life I'll walk, Till trav-eling days are done.

Horatius Bonar, 1846

414   ## Shepherd of Tender Youth

CUTTING 6 6 4 6 6 6 4

William F. Sherwin, 1826-1888

1 Shep-herd of ten - der youth, Guid - ing in love and truth
2 Thou art the great High Priest, Thou hast pre-pared the feast
3 Ev - er be Thou our Guide, Our Shep-herd and our Pride,

Through de-vious ways, Christ, our tri - um-phant King, We come Thy
Of heaven-ly love. In all our mor - tal pain None calls on
Our Staff and Song. Je - sus, Thou Christ of God, By Thine en -

Name to sing; Hith - er our chil - dren bring To shout Thy praise.
Thee in vain; Help Thou didst not dis-dain, Help from a - bove.
dur - ing Word Lead us where Thou hast trod; Make our faith strong.

4 So now, and till we die,
   Sound we Thy praises high,
     And joyful sing.
  Let youth, yea, all the throng
  Who to Thy Church belong,
   Unite to swell the song
     To Christ our King.

Clement of Alexandria, 220 A.D.
Tr. Henry M. Dexter, 1846

415 O God, Great Father

Melcombe L. M.

Samuel Webbe, 1782

1 O God, great Fa - ther, Lord and King! Our chil - dren
2 Thy cov - enant kind-ness did of old Our fa - thers
3 Look down up - on us while we pray And vis - it

un - to Thee we bring; And strong in faith and
and their seed en - fold; That an - cient prom - ise
us in grace to - day; These lit - tle ones Thou

hope and love, We dare Thy sted - fast Word to prove.
stand - eth sure, And shall while heaven and earth en - dure.
didst re - ceive, Thy pre - cious prom-ise we be - lieve.

4 They now the outward sign receive;
  Wilt Thou Thy Holy Spirit give,
  And keep and help them by Thy power
  In every hard and trying hour.

5 Guide Thou their feet in holy ways,
  Shine on them through the darkest days;
  Uphold them till their life be past
  And bring them all to heaven at last.

E. Embree Hoss

416 Our Children, Lord, in Faith and Prayer

NAOMI C.M.

Arranged by Lowell Mason, 1836

1 Our chil - dren, Lord, in faith and prayer, We now de - vote to Thee; Let them Thy cov - enant mer - cies share And Thy sal - va - tion see.

2 Such help - less babes Thou didst em - brace While dwell - ing here be - low; To us and ours, O God of grace, The same com - pas - sion show.

3 In ear - ly days their hearts se - cure From world - ly snares, we pray; O let them to the end en - dure In ev - ery right - eous way.

Thomas Haweis, 1732-1820

417   Savior, Like a Shepherd Lead Us

BRADBURY 8 7 8 7 D.

William B. Bradbury, 1859

1 Sav - ior, like a shep-herd lead us, Much we need Thy ten-der care;
2 We are Thine, do Thou be-friend us, Be the Guard-ian of our way;
3 Thou hast prom-ised to re - ceive us, Poor and sin-ful though we be;

In Thy pleas-ant pas-tures feed us, For our use Thy folds pre-pare.
Keep Thy flock, from sin de - fend us, Seek us when we go a-stray.
Thou hast mer-cy to re - lieve us, Grace to cleanse, and power to free.

Bless-ed Je-sus, bless-ed Je-sus, Thou hast bought us, Thine we are;
Bless-ed Je-sus, bless-ed Je-sus, Hear Thy chil-dren when they pray;
Bless-ed Je-sus, bless-ed Je-sus, Ear - ly let us turn to Thee;

Bless-ed Je-sus, bless-ed Je-sus, Thou hast bought us, Thine we are.
Bless-ed Je-sus, bless-ed Je-sus, Hear Thy chil-dren when they pray.
Bless-ed Je-sus, bless-ed Je-sus, Ear - ly let us turn to Thee.

4 Early let us seek Thy favor,
Early let us do Thy will;
Blessed Lord and only Savior,
With Thy love our bosoms fill.
Blessed Jesus, blessed Jesus,
Thou hast loved us; love us still.

Dorothy Bradbury Thrupp, 1779-1847

418 ## Savior, Who Thy Flock Art Feeding

BROCKLESBURY 8 7 8 7

Charlotte A. Barnard, 1868

1 Sav - ior, who Thy flock art feed - ing
2 Now, these lit - tle ones re - ceiv - ing,
3 Nev - er, from Thy pas - ture rov - ing,

With the shep-herd's kind - est care, All the fee - ble
Fold them in Thy gra - cious arm; There, we know, Thy
Let them be the li - on's prey; Let Thy ten - der -

gen - tly lead - ing, While the lambs Thy bos - om share;
Word be - liev - ing, On - ly there se - cure from harm.
ness, so lov - ing, Keep them through life's dan - gerous way.

4 Then, within Thy fold eternal,
   Let them find a resting-place,
   Feed in pastures ever vernal,
   Drink the rivers of Thy grace.

William A. Mühlenberg, 1826

419 Thus Saith the Mercy of the Lord

BELIEF C.M.

English Melody

Smoothly

1 Thus saith the mer - cy of the Lord:
2 A - bram be - lieved the prom - ised grace
3 Je - sus the an - cient faith con - firms,

"I'll be a God to thee; I'll bless thy nu - merous
And gave his child to God, But wa - ter seals the
To our fore - fa - thers given; He takes young chil - dren

race, and they Shall be a seed to Me."
bless - ing now That once was sealed with blood.
to His arms, And calls them heirs of heaven.

4 Our God, how faithful are His ways!
   His love endures the same;
   Nor from the promise of His grace
   Blots out His children's name.

5 Thus to the parents and their seed
   Shall Thy salvation come;
   And numerous households meet at last
   In one eternal home.

Isaac Watts, 1707

420 Come, for the Feast Is Spread

Something for Jesus 6 4 6 4 6 6 6 4

Robert Lowry, 1872

1 Come, for the feast is spread, Hark to the call;
Come to the Living Bread, Of - fered to all.
Come to His house of wine, Low on His breast re - cline,
All that He has is thine; Come, sin - ner, come.

2 Come where the foun - tain flows, Riv - er of life,
Heal - ing for all thy woes, Doubt - ing and strife.
Mil - lions have been sup-plied, No one was e'er de - nied,
Come to the crim - son tide; Come, sin - ner, come.

3 Come to the throne of grace, Bold - ly draw near;
He who would win the race Must tar - ry here.
What - e'er thy want may be, Here is the grace for thee,
Je - sus thine on - ly plea; Come, Chris - tian, come.

4 Come to the better land,
   Pilgrim, make haste;
Earth is a foreign strand,
   Wilderness waste.
Here are the harps of gold,
Here are the joys untold,
Crowns for the young and old;
   Come, pilgrim, come.

5 Jesus, we come to Thee,
   O take us in!
Set Thou our spirits free,
   Cleanse us from sin.
Then, in yon land of light,
Clothed in our robes of white,
Resting not day nor night,
   Thee will we sing.

Henry Burton, 1840-1930

421 According to Thy Gracious Word

HARVEY'S CHANT C.M.

William B. Bradbury, 1853

1 Ac - cord - ing to Thy gra - cious word, In
2 Thy bod - y, bro - ken for my sake, My
3 Geth - sem - a - ne can I for - get? Or

meek hu - mil - i - ty, This will I do, my dy - ing Lord:
bread from heaven shall be; Thy tes - ta - men - tal cup I take,
there Thy con - flict see, Thine ag - o - ny and blood - y sweat,

I will re - mem - ber Thee, I will re - mem - ber Thee.
And thus re - mem - ber Thee, And thus re - mem - ber Thee.
And not re - mem - ber Thee, And not re - mem - ber Thee?

4 When to the cross I turn mine eyes
  And rest on Calvary,
O Lamb of God, my sacrifice,
  I must remember Thee.

5 And when these failing lips grow dumb
  And mind and memory flee,
When Thou shalt in Thy kingdom come,
  Then, Lord, remember me.

James Montgomery, 1825

422 O Jesus, Joy of Loving Hearts

BACA L.M., 5 Lines

William B. Bradbury, 1816-1868

1 O Je-sus, joy of lov-ing hearts, Thou fount of life, Thou
2 Thy truth un-changed has ev - er stood, Thou sav-est those that
3 We taste Thee, O Thou liv-ing bread, And long to feast up -

light of men, From full-est bliss that earth im-parts We turn un-
on Thee call; To them that seek Thee, Thou art good, To them that
on Thee still; We drink of Thee, the foun-tain-head, And thirst our

filled to Thee a-gain, We turn un-filled to Thee a - gain.
find Thee, all in all, To them that find Thee, all in all.
souls from Thee to fill, And thirst our souls from Thee to fill.

4 Our restless spirits yearn for Thee,
   Where'er our changeful lot is cast,
Glad, that Thy gracious smile we see,
   Blest, that our faith can hold Thee fast.

5 O Jesus, ever with us stay,
   Make all our moments calm and bright;
Chase the dark night of sin away,
   Shed o'er the world Thy holy light.

Latin, 11th cent.
Tr. Ray Palmer, 1858

423   Deck Thyself, My Soul, with Gladness

SCHMÜCKE DICH, O LIEBE SEELE L.M.D.

Johann Crüger, 1649
Rhythm by Seymour Swets, 1934

1 Deck thy-self, my soul, with glad-ness, Leave the
2 Has-ten as a bride to meet Him, And with

gloom-y haunts of sad-ness, Come in-to the day-light's
lov-ing rev-erence greet Him; For with words of life im-

splen-dor, There with joy thy prais-es ren-der
mor-tal Now He knock-eth at thy por-tal;

Un-to Him whose grace un-bound-ed Has this
O-pen wide the gates be-fore Him, Say-ing,

Deck Thyself, My Soul, with Gladness

won - drous ban-quet found - ed. High o'er all the earth He
while thou dost a - dore Him, Suf - fer, Lord, that I re -

reign - eth, Yet to dwell with thee He deign - eth.
ceive Thee, And I nev - er - more will leave Thee.

3 Ah! how hungers all my spirit
   For the love I do not merit!
   Oft have I, with sighs fast thronging,
   Thought upon this food with longing;
   In the battle, well-nigh worsted,
   For this cup of life have thirsted,
   For the Friend who here invites us,
   And to God Himself unites us.

4 Jesus, bread of life, I pray Thee,
   Let me gladly here obey Thee;
   I am by Thy grace invited,
   Be Thy love with love requited.
   From this banquet let me measure,
   Lord, how vast and deep its treasure;
   Through the gifts Thou here dost give me
   As Thy guest in heaven receive me.

Johann Franck, 1649
Tr. Catherine Winkworth, 1863

424 Just As I Am, Without One Plea

WOODWORTH L.M.

William B. Bradbury, 1849

1 Just as I am, with-out one plea, But that Thy
2 Just as I am, and wait-ing not To rid my
3 Just as I am, though tossed a-bout With man-y a

blood was shed for me, And that Thou bidd'st me
soul of one dark blot, To Thee, whose blood can
con - flict, man-y a doubt, Fight-ings and fears with-

come to Thee, O Lamb of God, I come, I come!
cleanse each spot, O Lamb of God, I come, I come!
in, with-out, O Lamb of God, I come, I come!

4 Just as I am, poor, wretched, blind;
Sight, riches, healing of the mind,
Yea, all I need, in Thee to find,
O Lamb of God, I come, I come!

5 Just as I am! Thou wilt receive,
Wilt welcome, pardon, cleanse, relieve;
Because Thy promise I believe,
O Lamb of God, I come, I come!

Charlotte Elliott, 1836

425

Jesus, Lover of My Soul

MARTYN 7 7 7 7 D.

Simeon B. Marsh, 1834

1 Je-sus, Lov-er of my soul, Let me to Thy bos-om fly,
2 Oth-er ref-uge have I none; Hangs my help-less soul on Thee;

While the near-er wa-ters roll, While the tem-pest still is high.
Leave, O leave me not a-lone, Still sup-port and com-fort me.

Hide me, O my Sav-ior, hide, Till the storm of life is past;
All my trust on Thee is stayed, All my help from Thee I bring;

Safe in-to the ha-ven guide; O re-ceive my soul at last!
Cov-er my de-fense-less head With the shad-ow of Thy wing.

3 Thou, O Christ, art all I want;
   More than all in Thee I find.
Raise the fallen, cheer the faint,
   Heal the sick, and lead the blind.
Just and holy is Thy Name,
   I am all unrighteousness;
False and full of sin I am,
   Thou art full of truth and grace.

4 Plenteous grace with Thee is found,
   Grace to cover all my sin;
Let the healing streams abound,
   Make me, keep me pure within.
Thou of life the fountain art,
   Freely let me take of Thee;
Spring Thou up within my heart,
   Rise to all eternity.

Charles Wesley, 1740

426   Jesus, with Thy Church Abide

GOWER'S LITANY 7 7 7 6

John H. Gower, 1891

Slowly and with feeling

1 Je - sus, with Thy Church a - bide; Be her
2 May she guide the poor and blind, Seek the
3 May her lamp of truth be bright; Bid her

Sav - ior, Lord and Guide, While on earth her
lost un - til she find And the bro - ken -
bear a - loft its light Through the realms of

rit.

faith is tried: We be - seech. Thee, hear us.
heart - ed bind: We be - seech Thee, hear us.
pa - gan night: We be - seech Thee, hear us.

4 Judge her not for work undone,
Judge her not for fields unwon,
Bless her works in Thee begun:
We beseech Thee, hear us.

5 May she holy triumphs win,
Overthrow the hosts of sin,
Gather all the nations in:
We beseech Thee, hear us.

Thomas Benson Pollock, 1871, *alt.*

494

427   I Need Thee Every Hour

NEED 6 4 6 4, with Refrain

Robert Lowry, 1872

1 I need Thee ev-ery hour, Most gra - cious Lord;
2 I need Thee ev-ery hour, Stay Thou near by;
3 I need Thee ev-ery hour, In joy or pain;

No ten - der voice like Thine Can peace af - ford.
Temp - ta - tions lose their power When Thou art nigh.
Come quick - ly and a - bide, Or life is vain.

REFRAIN

I need Thee, O I need Thee, Ev - ery hour I need Thee;

O bless me now, my Sav - ior, I come to Thee.

4 I need Thee every hour,
   Teach me Thy will;
And Thy rich promises
   In me fulfill.

5 I need Thee every hour,
   Most Holy One;
O make me Thine indeed,
   Thou blessed Son!

Annie S. Hawks, 1872
Refrain, Robert Lowry, 1872

495

428   Out of My Bondage, Sorrow, and Night

JESUS, I COME   Irregular

George C. Stebbins, 1846-1945

1 Out of my bond-age, sor-row and night, Je-sus, I come,
2 Out of my shame-ful fail-ure and loss, Je-sus, I come,

Je-sus, I come; In-to Thy free-dom, glad-ness and light,
Je-sus, I come; In-to the glo-rious gain of Thy cross,

Je-sus, I come to Thee. Out of my sick-ness in-to Thy health,
Je-sus, I come to Thee. Out of earth's sor-rows in-to Thy balm,

Out of my want and in-to Thy wealth, Out of my
Out of life's storms and in-to Thy calm, Out of dis-

Out of My Bondage, Sorrow, and Night

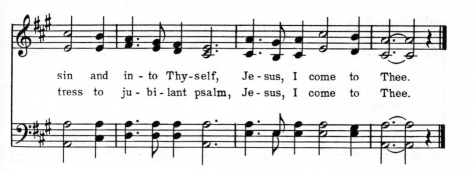

sin and in - to Thy-self, Je - sus, I come to Thee.
tress to ju - bi - lant psalm, Je - sus, I come to Thee.

3 Out of unrest and arrogant pride,
　　Jesus, I come, Jesus, I come;
　Into Thy blessed will to abide,
　　Jesus, I come to Thee.
　Out of myself to dwell in Thy love,
　Out of despair into raptures above,
　Upward for aye on wings like a dove,
　　Jesus, I come to Thee.

4 Out of the fear and dread of the tomb,
　　Jesus, I come, Jesus, I come;
　Into the joy and light of Thy home,
　　Jesus, I come to Thee.
　Out of the depths of ruin untold,
　Into the peace of Thy sheltering fold,
　Ever Thy glorious face to behold,
　　Jesus, I come to Thee.

William T. Sleeper, 1819-1904

429 In the Cross of Christ I Glory

RATHBUN 8 7 8 7

Ithamar Conkey, 1851

1 In the cross of Christ I glo - ry, Tow - ering
2 When the woes of life o'er - take me, Hopes de -
3 When the sun of bliss is beam - ing Light and

o'er the wrecks of time; All the light of sa - cred
ceive and fears an - noy, Nev - er shall the cross for -
love up - on my way, From the cross the ra - diance,

sto - ry Gath - ers round its head sub - lime.
sake me; Lo! it glows with peace and joy.
stream - ing, Adds more lus - ter to the day. A - men.

4 Bane and blessing, pain and pleasure,
   By the cross are sanctified;
   Peace is there, that knows no measure,
   Joys that through all time abide. Amen.

John Bowring, 1825

498

430   Lord, Like the Publican I Stand

AVONDALE C.M.

Charles H. Gabriel, 1856-1932

1 Lord, like the pub - li - can I stand
2 I smite up - on my anx - ious breast,
3 My guilt, my shame, I all con - fess,

And lift my heart to Thee; Thy par - doning grace,
O'er - whelmed with ag - o - ny; O save my soul
I have no hope nor plea But Je - sus' blood

O God, com - mand, Be mer - ci - ful to me.
by sin op-pressed, Be mer - ci - ful to me.
and right-eous - ness, Be mer - ci - ful to me.

4 Here at Thy cross I still would wait,
   Nor from its shelter flee,
Till Thou, O God, in mercy great,
   Art merciful to me.

T. Raffles, 1831

431 Our Father, Clothed with Majesty

The Lord's Prayer (Vater unser) L.M., 6 Lines
Schumann's *Gesangbuch*, 1539

1 Our Fa-ther, clothed with maj-es-ty, Who, dwell-ing in e-ter-ni-ty, Hast set Thy glo-rious throne on high, In Christ, Thy Son, do we draw nigh, In hum-ble prayer to seek Thy face For Thy pa-ter-nal love and grace.

2 Thy Name be hal-lowed ev-er-more, Till all that live on earth a-dore And bless Thee, and with glad ac-claim Ex-tol Thy vir-tues and Thy fame. May we, Thy chil-dren here be-low, In all our deeds Thine im-age show.

Our Father, Clothed with Majesty

3 Lord, may Thy Kingdom come with haste;
Lay Satan's dark domain to waste;
And rule us by Thy precious Word,
Till everywhere Thy praise be heard.
Let all the earth Thy Name revere,
For Thou in glory shalt appear.

4 Thy will be done, Thy will alone,
On earth below as round Thy throne.
Thy precepts all are wise and true;
Thy holy will we pray to do.
May all, then, humbly stand in awe
And gladly keep Thy perfect law.

5 Give us our needful bread this day
And show Thy faithful care, we pray.
Our earthly needs Thou, Lord, dost know;
Then let on us Thy blessings flow.
Save us from want and poverty
And make our spirits rich in Thee.

6 Do not our trespasses record,
But freely pardon them, dear Lord,
As we, who by Thy grace must live,
Our debtors' trespasses forgive.
Yea, cleanse our hearts from every stain,
In Him who on the cross was slain.

7 Into temptation bring us not,
But guard us lest we stray, O God;
Thou knowest that our strength is mean,
Our passions foul, our hearts unclean.
How helpless, Father, we should be
If in this state cast off by Thee!

8 O fount of power, life, and light,
Deliver us from Satan's might;
His strength is great and we are frail,
Our sinful flesh is prone to fail.
Against all lust and vanity
O help us, then, and make us free.

9 For all the kingdom, Lord, is Thine,
All power and majesty divine.
Thou who wilt be our Helper near,
Who in Thy Son our pleas wilt hear,
Who hast unbarred salvation's door,
Thine be all praise forevermore.

10 Dear Father, do not hide Thy face,
For we rely upon Thy grace.
Our hearts, O Lord, who seest all,
Condemn us not whene'er we call,
But say, since Thou dost hear our plea,
"Amen, Amen, so shall it be!"

Dewey Westra, 1931

501

432   I Greet Thee, Who My Sure Redeemer Art

RESOLUTION 10 10 10 10   Louis Bourgeois, 1505-1561
Harmonized by Claude Goudimel, 1505-1572

Joyfully; with one broad beat to each measure

1 I greet Thee, who my sure Re -
2 Thou art the King of mer - cy
3 Thou art the life by which a -

deem - er art, My on - ly
and of grace, Reign - ing om -
lone we live, And all our

Trust and Sav - ior of my heart,
ni - po - tent in ev - ery place:
sub - stance and our strength re - ceive;

Who pain didst un - der - go for
So come, O King, and our whole
Com - fort us by Thy faith and

I Greet Thee, Who My Sure Redeemer Art

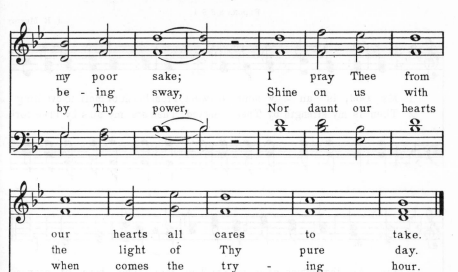

my poor sake; I pray Thee from
be - ing sway, Shine on us with
by Thy power, Nor daunt our hearts

our hearts all cares to take.
the light of Thy pure day.
when comes the try - ing hour.

4 Thou hast the true and perfect gentleness,
No harshness hast Thou and no bitterness;
Make us to taste the sweet grace found in Thee
And ever stay in Thy sweet unity.

5 Our hope is in no other save in Thee,
Our faith is built upon Thy promise free;
Come, give us peace, make us so strong and sure,
That we may conquerors be and ills endure.

John Calvin, 1509-1564

433 My God, Is Any Hour So Sweet

EUDORA 8 8 8 4

J. R. Murray

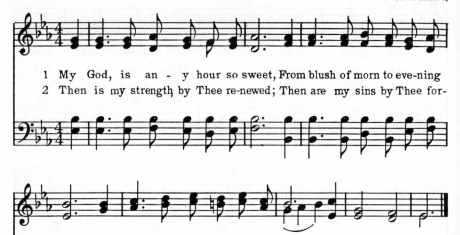

1 My God, is an - y hour so sweet, From blush of morn to eve-ning
2 Then is my strength by Thee re-newed; Then are my sins by Thee for-

star, As that which calls me to Thy feet, The hour of prayer?
given; Then dost Thou cheer my sol - i - tude With hopes of heaven.

3 No words can tell what sweet relief
   There for my every want I find,
What strength for warfare, balm for grief,
   What peace of mind.

4 Hushed is each doubt, gone every fear;
   My spirit seems in heaven to stay;
And e'en the penitential tear
   Is wiped away.

5 Lord, till I reach yon blissful shore,
   No privilege so dear shall be
As thus my inmost soul to pour
   In prayer to Thee.

Charlotte Elliott, 1834

504

434   # Prayer Is the Soul's Sincere Desire

EVAN C.M.

William H. Havergal, 1846

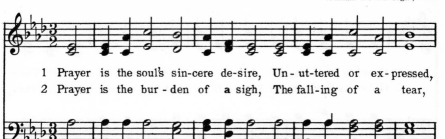

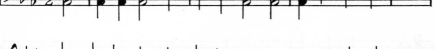

1 Prayer is the soul's sin-cere de-sire, Un - ut-tered or ex-pressed,
2 Prayer is the bur - den of **a** sigh, The fall-ing of a tear,

The mo-tion of a hid-den fire That trem-bles in the breast.
The up-ward glanc-ing of the eye, When none but God is near.

3 Prayer is the Christian's vital breath,
    The Christian's native air,
His watchword at the gates of death;
    He enters heaven with prayer.

4 Prayer is the contrite sinner's voice,
    Returning from his ways,
While angels in their songs rejoice
    And cry, "Behold, he prays!"

5 O Thou by whom we come to God,
    The life, the truth, the way,
The path of prayer Thyself hast trod:
    Lord, teach us how to pray.

James Montgomery, 1819

435   Humble Praises, Holy Jesus

VESPER HYMN 8 7 8 7, with Refrain

Dimitri Bortniansky, 1752-1828

1 Hum-ble prais-es, ho - ly Je-sus, In-fant voic-es raise to Thee;
2 Gra-cious Sav-ior, be Thou with us, Let Thy mer-cy rich - ly flow;

In Thy mer-cy, O re-ceive us! Suf - fer us Thy lambs to be.
Give Thy Spir-it, bless-ed Je - sus, Light and life on us be-stow.

REFRAIN

Hal - le - lu - jah, sweet-ly sing-ing, Joy-ful trib-ute now we bring.

Hal - le - lu - jah, Hal - le - lu - jah! Hal - le - lu - jah to our King!

436   What a Friend We Have in Jesus

CONVERSE (ERIE) 8 7 8 7 D.

Charles D. Converse, 1868

1 What a Friend we have in Je-sus, All our sins and griefs to bear!
2 Have we tri-als and temp-ta-tions? Is there trou-ble an-y-where?
3 Are we weak and heav-y la-den, Cum-bered with a load of care?—

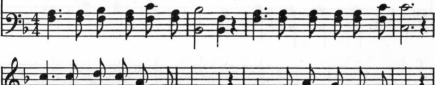

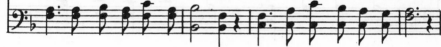

What a priv-i-lege to car-ry Ev-ery-thing to God in prayer!
We should nev-er be dis-cour-aged; Take it to the Lord in prayer!
Pre-cious Sav-ior, still our ref-uge!— Take it to the Lord in prayer!

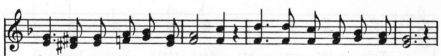

O what peace we of-ten for-feit, O what need-less pain we bear,
Can we find a friend so faith-ful, Who will all our sor-rows share?
Do thy friends de-spise, for-sake thee? Take it to the Lord in prayer!

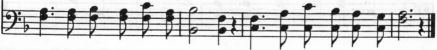

All be-cause we do not car-ry Ev-ery-thing to God in prayer!
Je-sus knows our ev-ery weak-ness; Take it to the Lord in prayer!
In His arms He'll take and shield thee; Thou wilt find a sol-ace there.

Joseph Scriven, 1820-1866

437 More Love to Thee, O Christ

MORE LOVE TO THEE 6 4 6 4 6 6 4 4

William H. Doane, 1868

1 More love to Thee, O Christ, More love to Thee!
2 Once earth-ly joy I craved, Sought peace and rest;
3 Then shall my lat-est breath Whis-per Thy praise;

Hear Thou the prayer I make On bend-ed knee.
Now Thee a-lone I seek; Give what is best.
This be the part-ing cry My heart shall raise;

This is my ear-nest plea: More love, O
This all my prayer shall be: More love, O
This still its prayer shall be: More love, O

Christ, to Thee, More love to Thee, More love to Thee!
Christ, to Thee, More love to Thee, More love to Thee!
Christ, to Thee, More love to Thee, More love to Thee!

Elizabeth P. Prentiss, 1869

508

438   Thy Love to Me, O Christ

To tune of *More Love to Thee*, No. 437

1 Thy love to me, O Christ,
    Thy love to me,
Not mine to Thee, I plead,
    Not mine to Thee.
This is my comfort strong,
This is my joyful song,
    Thy love to me,
    Thy love to me.

2 Thy record I believe,
    Thy Word to me;
Thy love I now receive,
    Full, changeless, free—
Love from the sinless Son,
Love to the sinful one,
    Thy love to me,
    Thy love to me.

3 Immortal love of Thine,
    Thy sacrifice,
Infinite need of mine
    Fully supplies.
Streams of Thy heavenly power
Flow to me, hour by hour,
    Thy love to me,
    Thy love to me.

4 Let me more clearly trace
    Thy love to me,
See in the Father's face
    His love to Thee,
Know as He loves the Son,
So dost Thou love Thine own,
    Thy love to me,
    Thy love to me.

Mrs. Merrill E. Gates, 1886

439   I Will Sing of My Redeemer

MY REDEEMER 8 7 8 7, with Refrain

James McGranahan, 1840-1907
Revised 1956

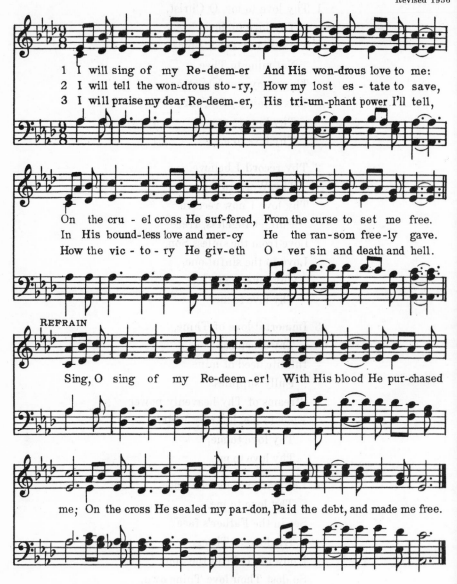

1 I will sing of my Re-deem-er And His won-drous love to me:
2 I will tell the won-drous sto-ry, How my lost es-tate to save,
3 I will praise my dear Re-deem-er, His tri-um-phant power I'll tell,

On the cru-el cross He suf-fered, From the curse to set me free.
In His bound-less love and mer-cy He the ran-som free-ly gave.
How the vic-to-ry He giv-eth O-ver sin and death and hell.

REFRAIN

Sing, O sing of my Re-deem-er! With His blood He pur-chased

me; On the cross He sealed my par-don, Paid the debt, and made me free.

4 I will sing of my Redeemer
And His heavenly love to me;
He from death to life has brought me,
Son of God, with Him to be.

Philip P. Bliss, 1878

510

440   My Jesus, I Love Thee

CARITAS 11 11 11 11

Adoniram J. Gordon, 1836-1895

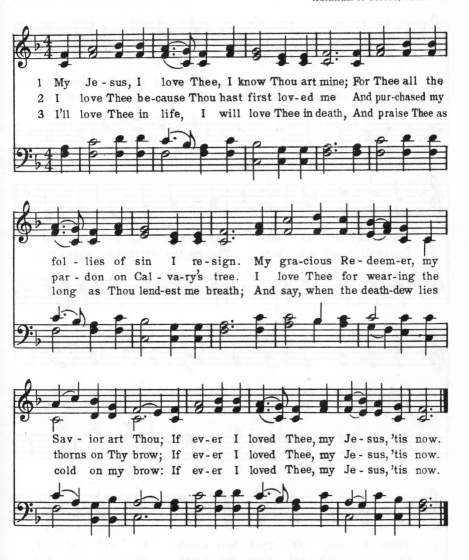

1 My Je-sus, I love Thee, I know Thou art mine; For Thee all the
2 I love Thee be-cause Thou hast first lov-ed me And pur-chased my
3 I'll love Thee in life, I will love Thee in death, And praise Thee as

fol-lies of sin I re-sign. My gra-cious Re-deem-er, my
par-don on Cal-va-ry's tree. I love Thee for wear-ing the
long as Thou lend-est me breath; And say, when the death-dew lies

Sav-ior art Thou; If ev-er I loved Thee, my Je-sus, 'tis now.
thorns on Thy brow; If ev-er I loved Thee, my Je-sus, 'tis now.
cold on my brow: If ev-er I loved Thee, my Je-sus, 'tis now.

4 In mansions of glory and endless delight,
I'll ever adore Thee in heaven so bright;
I'll sing with the glittering crown on my brow:
If ever I loved Thee, my Jesus, 'tis now.

William R. Featherstone, 1842-1878

441   Jesus, Priceless Treasure

LINDEMAN 6 6 5 6 6 5 7 8 6

Ludvig M. Lindeman, 1812-1887

1 Je - sus, price-less treas-ure, Source of pur - est pleas-ure,
2 In Thine arms I rest me; Foes who would mo - lest me

Tru - est Friend to me: Ah, how long I've pant - ed
Can-not reach me here. Though the earth be shak - ing,

And my heart has faint - ed, Thirst-ing, Lord, for Thee.
Ev - ery heart be quak - ing, Je - sus calms my fear.

Thine I am, O spot - less Lamb! I will suf - fer
Fires may flash and thun - der crash, Yea, and sin and

Jesus, Priceless Treasure

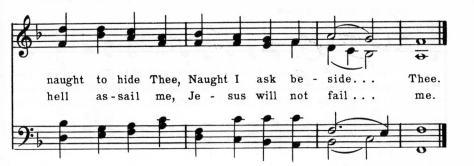

naught to hide Thee, Naught I ask be - side... Thee.
hell as-sail me, Je - sus will not fail... me.

3 Hence with earthly treasure!
   Thou art all my pleasure,
      Jesus, all my choice.
   Hence, thou empty glory!
   Naught to me thy story,
      Told with tempting voice.
   Pain or loss or shame or cross
      Shall not from my Savior move me,
      Since He deigns to love me.

4 Fare thee well that errest,
   Thou that earth preferrest,
      Thou wilt tempt in vain.
   Fare thee well, transgression!
   Hence, abhorred possession!
      Come not forth again.
   Past your hour, O pride and power!
      Worldly life, thy bonds I sever;
      Fare thee well forever!

5 Hence, all fear and sadness!
   For the Lord of gladness,
      Jesus, enters in.
   Those who love the Father,
   Though the storms may gather,
      Still have peace within.
   Yea, whate'er I here must bear,
      Thou art still my purest pleasure,
      Jesus, priceless treasure.

Johann Franck, 1653
Tr. Catherine Winkworth, 1863

442 For All the Saints

SINE NOMINE 10 10 10 8

R. Vaughan Williams, 1906

May be sung in unison

1 For all the saints who from their la-bors rest, Who Thee by faith be-
2 Thou wast their Rock, their For-tress and their Might; Thou, Lord, their Cap-tain
3 O may Thy sol-diers, faith-ful, true and bold, Fight as the saints who

fore the world con-fessed, Thy Name, O Je - sus, be for - ev - er
in the well-fought fight. Thou, in the dark-ness drear, their one true
no - bly fought of old, And win with them the vic-tor's crown of

blest: Al - - le - lu - ia, Al - le - lu - ia.
Light: Al - - le - lu - ia, Al - le - lu - ia.
gold: Al - - le - lu - ia, Al - le - lu - ia.

4 O blest communion, fellowship divine!
We feebly struggle, they in glory shine;
Yet all are one in Thee, for all are Thine:
Alleluia, Alleluia!

5 And when the fight is fierce, the warfare long,
Steals on the ear the distant triumph song,
And hearts are brave again, and arms are strong:
Alleluia, Alleluia!

6 From earth's wide bounds, from ocean's farthest coast,
Through gates of pearl streams in the countless host,
Singing to Father, Son, and Holy Ghost:
Alleluia, Alleluia!

William Walsham How, 1864

443   Faith of Our Fathers

ST. CATHERINE L. M., 6 Lines

Henri F. Hemy, 1864
Arranged by James G. Walton, 1874

1 Faith of our fa - thers! liv - ing still In spite of dun - geon,
2 Our fa-thers, chained in pris-ons dark, Were still in heart and
3 Faith of our fa - thers! we will love Both friend and foe in

fire and sword; O how our hearts beat high with joy
con - science free; How sure will be their chil - dren's peace
all our strife, And preach thee, too, as love knows how,

When-e'er we hear that glo-rious Word! Faith of our fa - thers,
If they, like them, con - tend for thee! Faith of our fa - thers,
By kind - ly words and vir - tuous life. Faith of our fa - thers,

ho - ly faith! We will be true to thee till death.
ho - ly faith! We will be true to thee till death.
ho - ly faith! We will be true to thee till death.

Frederick W. Faber, 1849

444　A Mighty Fortress Is Our God

EIN' FESTE BURG 8 7 8 7 6 6 6 6 7

Martin Luther, 1483-1546

1 A might-y for-tress is our God, A bul-wark
2 Did we in our own strength con-fide, Our striv-ing

nev-er fail - ing; Our Help-er He, a-
would be los - ing; Were not the right Man

mid the flood Of mor-tal ills pre-vail - ing.
on our side, The Man of God's own choos - ing.

For still our an-cient foe Doth seek to work us
Dost ask who that may be? Christ Je-sus, it is

A Mighty Fortress Is Our God

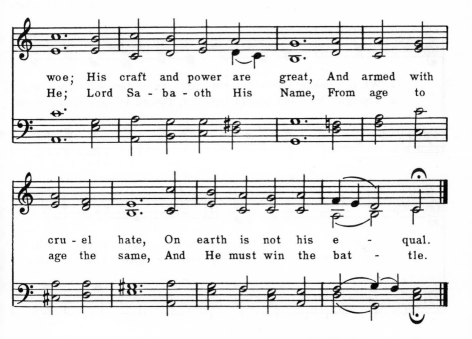

woe; His craft and power are great, And armed with
He; Lord Sa - ba - oth His Name, From age to

cru - el hate, On earth is not his e - qual.
age the same, And He must win the bat - tle.

3 And though this world, with devils filled,
   Should threaten to undo us,
   We will not fear, for God has willed
   His truth to triumph through us.
   The prince of darkness grim,
   We tremble not for him;
   His rage we can endure,
   For lo! his doom is sure,
   One little Word shall fell him.

4 That Word above all earthly powers—
   No thanks to them—abideth;
   The Spirit and the gifts are ours
   Through Him who with us sideth.
   Let goods and kindred go,
   This mortal life also;
   The body they may kill,
   God's truth abideth still,
   His kingdom is forever.

Martin Luther, 1529
Tr. Frederick H. Hedge, 1853

517

445 When Peace, Like a River

It Is Well 11 8 11 9, with Refrain

Philip P. Bliss, 1876

1 When peace, like a riv-er, at-tend-eth my way,
2 Though Sa-tan should buf-fet, though tri-als should come,

When sor-rows like sea-bil-lows roll,
Let this blest as-sur-ance con-trol,

What-ev-er my lot, Thou hast taught me to say:
That Christ has re-gard-ed my help-less es-tate,

It is well, it is well with my soul.
And has shed His own blood for my soul.

When Peace, Like a River

REFRAIN

It is well . . . . with my soul . . . . ;
It is well with my soul;
It is well, it is well with my soul.

3 My sin—O the bliss of this glorious thought!—
   My sin, not in part, but the whole,
  Is nailed to the cross and I bear it no more;
   Praise the Lord, praise the Lord, O my soul!

4 O Lord, haste the day when my faith shall be sight,
   The clouds be rolled back as a scroll,
  The trump shall resound and the Lord shall descend;
   Even so—it is well with my soul.

Horatio G. Spafford, 1828-1888

446   My Faith Looks Up to Thee

Olivet 6 6 4 6 6 6 4

Lowell Mason, 1832

1 My faith looks up to Thee, Thou Lamb of Cal - va - ry,
2 May Thy rich grace im-part Strength to my faint - ing heart,
3 While life's dark maze I tread And griefs a - round me spread,

Sav - ior di - vine. Now hear me when I pray, Take all my
My zeal in - spire. As Thou hast died for me, O may my
Be Thou my Guide. Bid dark-ness turn to day, Wipe sor - row's

guilt a - way, O let me from this day Be whol - ly Thine!
love to Thee Pure, warm and change-less be, A liv - ing fire!
tears a - way, Nor let me ev - er stray From Thee a - side.

4 When ends life's transient dream,
   When death's cold, sullen stream
      Would o'er me roll,
   Blest Savior, then, in love,
   Fear and distrust remove;
      O bear me safe above,
       A ransomed soul!

Ray Palmer, 1830

447   Blest Be the Tie That Binds

DENNIS S. M.

Hans G. Nägeli, 1773-1836
Arr. by Lowell Mason, 1845

1 Blest be the tie that binds Our
2 Be - fore our Fa - ther's throne We
3 We share our mu - tual woes, Our

hearts in Chris - tian love; The fel - low - ship of
pour our ar - dent prayers; Our fears, our hopes, our
mu - tual bur - dens bear, And of - ten for each

kin - dred minds Is like to that a - bove.
aims, are one, Our com - forts and our cares.
oth - er flows The sym - pa - thiz - ing tear.

4 When we are called to part,
   It gives us inward pain;
But we shall still be joined in heart
   And hope to meet again.

5 This glorious hope revives
   Our courage by the way;
While each in expectation lives
   And waits to see the day.

6 From sorrow, toil and pain
   And sin, we shall be free;
And perfect love and friendship reign
   Through all eternity.

John Fawcett, 1782

448   Christ, Whose Glory Fills the Skies

LUX PRIMA (GOUNOD) 7 7 7 7 7 7

Charles F. Gounod, 1872

1 Christ, whose glo-ry fills the skies, Christ, the true and
2 Dark and dis-mal is the morn Un-ac-com-pa-
3 Vis-it, then, this soul of mine, Pierce the gloom of

on-ly Light, Sun of Right-eous-ness, a - rise,
nied by Thee; Joy-less is the day's re - turn,
sin and grief; Fill me, Ra-dian-cy di - vine,

Tri-umph o'er the shades of night; Day-spring from on
Till Thy mer-cy's beams I see, Till they in - ward
Scat-ter all my un-be-lief; More and more Thy-

high, be near; Day-star, in my heart ap-pear.
light im-part, Till Thou cheer and warm my heart.
self dis-play, Shin-ing to the per-fect day.

Charles Wesley, 1740

449   # Fill Thou My Life

ELLACOMBE C. M. D.   From *Gesangbuch der Herzogl*
Würtemberg, 1784

1 Fill Thou my life, O Lord, my God, In ev - ery part with praise,
2 Praise in the com-mon words I speak, Life's com-mon looks and tones,
3 So shall each fear, each fret, each care, Be turned in-to a song,

That my whole be-ing may pro-claim Thy be - ing and Thy ways.
In in - ter-course at hearth or board With my be - lov - ed ones,
And ev - ery wind-ing of the way The ech - o shall pro - long;

Not for the lip of praise a - lone, Nor e'en the prais-ing heart
En - dur-ing wrong, re-proach, or loss, With sweet and sted-fast will,
So shall no part of day or night From sa-cred-ness be free,

I ask, but for a life made up Of praise in ev - ery part.
Lov-ing and bless-ing those who hate, Re - turn - ing good for ill.
But all my life, in ev - ery step, Be fel - low-ship with Thee.

Horatius Bonar, 1866

450 O Master, Let Me Walk with Thee

MARYTON L. M.

H. Percy Smith, 1825-1898

1 O Mas-ter, let me walk with Thee In low-ly
2 Help me the slow of heart to move By some clear
3 Teach me Thy pa-tience; still with Thee In clos-er,

paths of ser-vice free; Tell me Thy se-cret, help me
win-ning word of love; Teach me the way-ward feet to
dear-er com-pa-ny, In work that keeps faith sweet and

bear The strain of toil, the fret of care.
stay, And guide them in the home-ward way.
strong, In trust that tri-umphs o-ver wrong.

4 In hope that sends a shining ray
   Far down the future's broadening way,
   In peace that only Thou canst give,
   With Thee, O Master, let me live.

Washington Gladden, 1879

451

Take Time to Be Holy

HOLINESS 6 5 6 5 D.

George C. Stebbins, 1846-1945

1 Take time to be ho-ly, Speak oft with thy Lord;
2 Take time to be ho-ly, The world rush-es on;
3 Take time to be ho-ly, Let Him be thy Guide,
4 Take time to be ho-ly, Be calm in thy soul;

A - bide in Him al-ways, And feed on His Word;
Spend much time in se-cret With Je-sus a - lone;
And run not be-fore Him, What-ev-er be-tide;
Each thought and each mo-tive Be-neath His con-trol;

Make friends of God's chil-dren, Help those who are weak,
By look-ing to Je-sus, Like Him thou shalt be;
In joy or in sor-row Still fol-low thy Lord,
Thus led by His Spir-it To foun-tains of love,

For - get-ting in noth-ing His bless-ing to seek.
Thy friends in thy con-duct His like-ness shall see.
And look-ing to Je-sus, Still trust in His Word.
Thou soon shalt be fit-ted For ser-vice a - bove.

William D. Longstaff, 1822-1894

452   Have Thine Own Way, Lord

HOLY DESIRE 9 9 9 9

George C. Stebbins, 1907

1 Have Thine own way, Lord! Have Thine own way! Thou art the
2 Have Thine own way, Lord! Have Thine own way! Search me and
3 Have Thine own way, Lord! Have Thine own way! Wound-ed and

Pot - ter, I am the clay. Mold me and make me
try me, Mas-ter, to - day. O - pen mine eyes, my
wea - ry, help me, I pray. Pow - er, all pow - er,

af - ter Thy will, While I am wait-ing, yield-ed and still.
sin show me now, As in Thy pres-ence hum-bly I bow.
sure-ly is Thine; Touch me and heal me, Sav-ior di - vine.

4 Have Thine own way, Lord! Have Thine own way!
   Hold o'er my being absolute sway.
   Fill with Thy Spirit; then all shall see
   Christ only, always, living in me.

Adelaide A. Pollard, 1906

453   O For a Closer Walk with God

BEATITUDO C. M.

John B. Dykes, 1875

1 O for a clos - er walk with God,
2 Where is the bless - ed - ness I knew
3 What peace - ful hours I once en - joyed!

A calm and heaven - ly frame, A light to shine up -
When first I sought the Lord? Where is the soul - re -
How sweet their mem - ory still! But they have left an

on the road That leads me to the Lamb!
fresh - ing view Of Je - sus and His Word?
ach - ing void The world can nev - er fill.

4 The dearest idol I have known,
   Whate'er that idol be,
   Help me to tear it from Thy throne
   And worship only Thee.

5 So shall my walk be close with God,
   Calm and serene my frame;
   So purer light shall mark the road
   That leads me to the Lamb.

William Cowper, 1772

454 Nearer, Still Nearer

STILL NEARER 9 10 9 10 10

Mrs. C. H. Morris, 1862-1929

1 Near-er, still near-er, close to Thy heart, Draw me, my
2 Near-er, still near-er, noth-ing I bring, Naught as an
3 Near-er, still near-er, Lord, to be Thine, Sin with its
4 Near-er, still near-er, while life shall last, Till safe in

Sav-ior, so pre-cious Thou art. Fold me, O fold me
of-fering to Je-sus my King— On-ly my sin-ful,
fol-lies I glad-ly re-sign, All of its pleas-ures,
glo-ry my an-chor is cast; Through end-less a-ges,

close to Thy breast; Shel-ter me safe in that ha-ven of
now con-trite heart; Grant me the cleans-ing Thy blood doth im-
pomp and its pride; Give me but Je-sus, my Lord cru-ci-
ev-er to be Near-er, my Sav-ior, still near-er to

rest, Shel-ter me safe in that ha-ven of rest.
part, Grant me the cleans-ing Thy blood doth im-part.
fied, Give me but Je-sus, my Lord cru-ci-fied.
Thee, Near-er, my Sav-ior, still near-er to Thee.

Mrs. C. H. Morris, 1862-1929

455 In the Hour of Trial

PENITENCE 6 5 6 5 D.

Spencer Lane, 1879

1 In the hour of tri - al, Je - sus, plead for me;
2 With for - bid - den pleas-ures Would this vain world charm,
3 Should Thy mer - cy send me Sor - row, toil and woe,
4 When in dust and ash - es To the grave I sink,

Lest by base de - ni - al I de-part from Thee;
Or its sor - did treas-ures Spread to work me harm,
Or should pain at - tend me On my path be - low,
When heaven's glo-ry flash - es O'er the shelv-ing brink,

When Thou seest me wa - ver, With a look re - call,
Bring to my re - mem-brance Sad Geth-sem - a - ne,
Grant that I may nev - er Fail Thy hand to see;
On Thy truth re - ly - ing Through that mor-tal strife,

Nor for fear or fa - vor Suf - fer me to fall.
Or, in dark - er sem-blance, Cross-crowned Cal-va - ry.
Grant that I may ev - er Cast my care on Thee.
Lord, re - ceive me, dy - ing, To e - ter - nal life.

James Montgomery, 1834, *alt.*

456 Jesus, I My Cross Have Taken

ELLESDIE 8 7 8 7 D.

Wolfgang A. Mozart, 1756-1791
Arranged by Hubert P. Main, 1839-1925

1 Je - sus, I my cross have tak - en,
2 Let the world de - spise and leave me,

All to leave, and fol - low Thee; Des - ti - tute, de -
They have left my Sav - ior, too; Hu - man hearts and

spised, for - sak - en, Thou, from hence, my all shalt be;
looks de - ceive me, Thou art not, like man, un - true;

Per - ish ev - ery fond am - bi - tion,
And while Thou shalt smile up - on me,

Jesus, I My Cross Have Taken

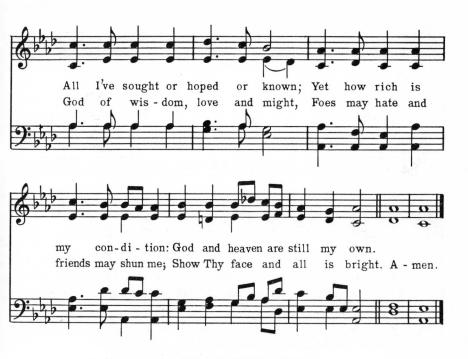

All I've sought or hoped or known; Yet how rich is
God of wis-dom, love and might, Foes may hate and

my con-di-tion: God and heaven are still my own.
friends may shun me; Show Thy face and all is bright. A - men.

3 Man may trouble and distress me,
    'Twill but drive me to Thy breast;
Life with trials hard may press me,
    Heaven will bring me sweeter rest;
O 'tis not in grief to harm me
    While Thy love is left to me;
O 'twere not in joy to charm me,
    Were that joy unmixed with Thee.

4 Haste thee on from grace to glory,
    Armed by faith, and winged by prayer;
Heaven's eternal day's before thee,
    God's own hand shall guide thee there;
Soon shall close thine earthly mission,
    Swift shall pass thy pilgrim days;
Hope shall change to glad fruition,
    Faith to sight, and prayer to praise. Amen.

Henry F. Lyte, 1825

457 Lord Jesus, Can It Ever Be?

FEDERAL STREET L. M.

Henry K. Oliver, 1832

1 Lord Je - sus, can it ev - er be, A mor - tal
2 A - shamed of Je - sus! soon - er far Let eve - ning
3 A - shamed of Je - sus! just as soon Let mid-night

man a - shamed of Thee? A - shamed of Thee, whom
blush to own a star; He sheds the beams of
be a - shamed of noon; 'Tis mid - night with my

an - gels praise, Whose glo-ries shine through end - less days?
light di - vine O'er this be - night - ed soul of mine.
soul till He, Bright Morn-ing Star, bid dark - ness flee.

4 Ashamed of Jesus! that dear Friend
  On whom my hopes of heaven depend!
  No; when I blush, be this my shame,
  That I no more revere His Name.

Joseph Grigg, 1765, *alt.*

458 Come, Ye Disconsolate

ALMA (CONSOLATION) 11 10 11 10

Arranged from Samuel Webbe, 1792

1 Come, ye dis - con - so - late, wher - e'er ye lan - guish,
2 Joy of the des - o - late, light of the stray - ing,
3 Here see the bread of life; see wa - ters flow - ing

Come to the mer - cy-seat, fer - vent - ly kneel;
Hope of the pen - i - tent, fade - less and pure!
Forth from the throne of God, pure from a - bove.

Here bring your wound-ed hearts, here tell your an - guish;
Here speaks the Com-fort-er, in mer - cy say - ing,
Come to the feast pre-pared; come, ev - er know - ing

Earth has no sor - rows that heaven can - not heal.
"Earth has no sor - rows that heaven can - not cure."
Earth has no sor - rows but heaven can re - move.

Thomas Moore, 1816
Stanza 3, Thomas Hastings, 1832

533

459 Jesus Calls Us; O'er the Tumult

GALILEE (JUDE) 8 7 8 7

William H. Jude, 1887

1 Je - sus calls us; o'er the tu - mult Of our
2 As, of old, a - pos - tles heard it By the
3 In our joys and in our sor - rows, Days of

life's wild, rest - less sea, Day by day His sweet voice
Gal - i - le - an lake, Turned from home and toil and
toil and hours of ease, Still He calls, in cares and

sound - eth, Say - ing, "Chris - tian, fol - low Me."
kin - dred, Leav - ing all for His dear sake,
pleas - ures, "Chris-tian, love Me more than these."

4 Jesus calls us; by Thy mercies,

Savior, may we hear Thy call,

Give our hearts to Thine obedience,

Serve and love Thee best of all.

Mrs. Cecil F. Alexander, 1852

460 Jesus, Savior, Pilot Me

PILOT 7 7 7 7 7 7

John E. Gould, 1871

1 Je - sus, Sav-ior, pi - lot me   O - ver life's tem-pes-tuous sea;
2 As   a moth-er stills her child, Thou canst hush the o-cean wild;
3 When at last I   near the shore And the fear - ful break-ers roar

Un - known waves be-fore me roll, Hid - ing rocks and treach-erous shoal;
Bois-terous waves o-bey Thy will, When Thou say'st to them, "Be still!"
'Twixt me and the peace-ful rest, Then, while lean-ing on Thy breast,

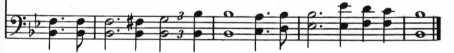

Chart and com-pass come from Thee; Je - sus, Sav - ior, pi - lot me.
Won-drous Sov-ereign of   the   sea, Je - sus, Sav - ior, pi - lot me.
May   I   hear Thee say to me, "Fear not, I   will pi - lot thee."

Edward Hopper, 1871

461   # God Moves in a Mysterious Way

DUNDEE C. M.

Arranged from Christopher Tye, 1553
In the *Scottish Psalter* of 1615

1 God moves in a mys - te - rious way His
2 Deep in un - fath - om - a - ble mines Of
3 Ye fear - ful saints, fresh cour - age take; The

won - ders to per - form; He plants His foot - steps
nev - er - fail - ing skill, He treas - ures up His
clouds ye so much dread Are big with mer - cy

in the sea And rides up - on the storm.
bright de - signs And works His sov - ereign will.
and shall break In bless - ings on your head.

4 His purposes will ripen fast,
   Unfolding every hour;
The bud may have a bitter taste,
   But sweet will be the flower.

5 Blind unbelief is sure to err
   And scan His work in vain;
God is His own Interpreter
   And He will make it plain.

William Cowper, 1772

462   # Take My Life, and Let It Be

HENDON 7 7 7 7 7

H. A. Cesar Malan, 1787-1864

1 Take my life and let it be Con-se-crat-ed,
2 Take my hands and let them move At the im-pulse
3 Take my voice and let me sing Al-ways, on-ly,

Lord, to Thee. Take my mo-ments and my days; Let them
of Thy love. Take my feet, and let them be Swift and
for my King. Take my lips, and let them be Filled with

flow in end-less praise, Let them flow in end-less praise.
beau-ti-ful for Thee, Swift and beau-ti-ful for Thee.
mes-sag-es from Thee, Filled with mes-sa-ges from Thee.

4 Take my silver and my gold;
Not a mite would I withhold.
Take my intellect, and use
Every power as Thou shalt choose.

5 Take my will and make it Thine;
It shall be no longer mine.
Take my heart, it is Thine own;
It shall be Thy royal throne.

6 Take my love; my Lord, I pour
At Thy feet its treasure store.
Take myself, and I will be
Ever, only, all for Thee.

Frances R. Havergal, 1874

463 He Leadeth Me

HE LEADETH ME L. M., with Refrain

William B. Bradbury, 1864

1 He lead - eth me: O bless - ed thought! O
2 Some - times 'mid scenes of deep - est gloom, Some -

words with heaven-ly com-fort fraught! What-e'er I do, wher-
times where E - den's bow-ers bloom, By wa - ters still, o'er

e'er I be, Still 'tis God's hand that lead - eth me.
trou - bled sea, Still 'tis God's hand that lead - eth me.

REFRAIN

He lead - eth me, He lead - eth me; By

He Leadeth Me

His own hand He lead-eth me. His faith-ful fol-lower I would be, For by His hand He lead-eth me.

3 Lord, I would clasp Thy hand in mine,
   Nor ever murmur nor repine,
   Content, whatever lot I see,
   Since 'tis my God that leadeth me.

4 And when at last my race is run,
   The Savior's work in me is done,
   E'en death's cold wave I will not flee,
   Since God through Jordan leadeth me.

Joseph H. Gilmore, 1862

464   Christian, Dost Thou See Them?

ST. ANDREW OF CRETE 6 5 6 5 D.

John B. Dykes, 1868

1 Chris-tian, dost thou see them On the ho - ly ground,
2 Chris-tian, dost thou feel them, How they work with - in,
3 Chris-tian, dost thou hear them, How they speak thee fair:

How the powers of dark - ness Com-pass thee a - round?
Striv-ing, tempt-ing, lur - ing, Goad-ing in - to sin?
"Al - ways fast and vig - il? Al-ways watch and prayer?"

Chris-tian, up and smite them, Count-ing gain but loss;
Chris-tian, nev - er trem - ble; Nev - er be down - cast;
Chris-tian, an - swer bold - ly: "While I breathe I pray!"

Smite them; Christ is with thee, Sol - dier of the cross.
Gird thee for the bat - tle, Watch and pray and fast.
Peace shall fol - low bat - tle, Night shall end in day.

St. Andrew of Crete, 660-732
Tr. John M. Neale, 1862

465   Am I a Soldier of the Cross?

ARLINGTON C. M.

Thomas A. Arne, 1762

1 Am I a sol - dier of the cross, A fol - lower of the Lamb, And shall I fear to own His cause, Or blush to speak His Name?

2 Must I be car - ried to the skies On flow-ery beds of ease, While oth - ers fought to win the prize And sailed through blood - y seas?

3 Are there no foes for me to face? Must I not stem the flood? Is this vile world a friend to grace, To help me on to God?

4 Since I must fight if I would reign,
Increase my courage, Lord;
I'll bear the toil, endure the pain,
Supported by Thy Word.

Isaac Watts, 1724

466   Onward, Christian Soldiers

St. Gertrude 6 5 6 5 D., with Refrain

Arthur S. Sullivan, 1871

1 On-ward, Chris-tian sol - diers, March-ing as to war,
2 Like a might-y ar - my Moves the Church of God;

With the cross of Je - sus Go - ing on be - fore;
Broth-ers, we are tread - ing Where the saints have trod;

Christ, the roy - al Mas - ter, Leads a-gainst the foe;
We are not di - vid - ed, All one bod - y we,

For - ward in - to bat - tle See His ban-ners go.
One in hope and doc - trine, One in char - i - ty.

Onward, Christian Soldiers

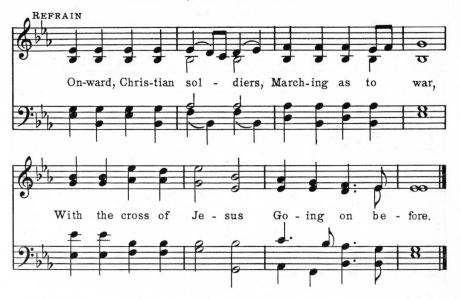

REFRAIN

On-ward, Chris-tian sol - diers, March-ing as to war,

With the cross of Je - sus Go - ing on be - fore.

3 Crowns and thrones may perish,
　　Kingdoms rise and wane,
But the Church of Jesus
　　Constant will remain;
Gates of hell can never
　　'Gainst that Church prevail;
We have Christ's own promise,
　　And that cannot fail.

4 Onward, then, ye people,
　　Join our happy throng,
Blend with ours your voices
　　In the triumph-song:
Glory, laud and honor
　　Unto Christ the King;
This through countless ages
　　Men and angels sing.

Sabine Baring-Gould, 1865

467 Stand Up, Stand Up for Jesus

WEBB 7 6 7 6 D.

George J. Webb, 1837

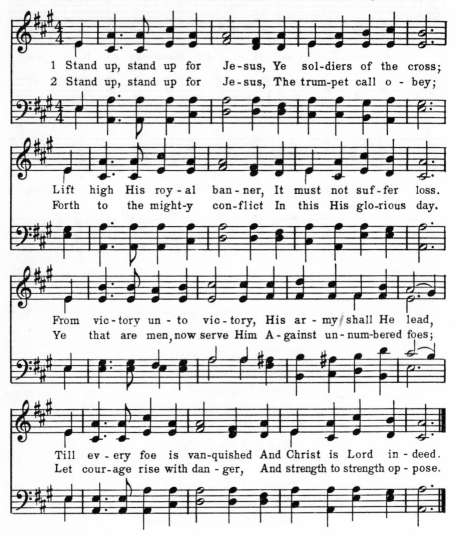

1 Stand up, stand up for Je-sus, Ye sol-diers of the cross;
2 Stand up, stand up for Je-sus, The trum-pet call o-bey;

Lift high His roy-al ban-ner, It must not suf-fer loss.
Forth to the might-y con-flict In this His glo-rious day.

From vic-tory un-to vic-tory, His ar-my shall He lead,
Ye that are men, now serve Him A-gainst un-num-bered foes;

Till ev-ery foe is van-quished And Christ is Lord in-deed.
Let cour-age rise with dan-ger, And strength to strength op-pose.

3 Stand up, stand up for Jesus,
   Stand in His strength alone:
The arm of flesh will fail you,
   Ye dare not trust your own.
Put on the gospel armor,
   Each piece put on with prayer;
Where duty calls, or danger,
   Be never wanting there.

4 Stand up, stand up for Jesus,
   The strife will not be long;
This day the noise of battle,
   The next the victor's song.
To him that overcometh
   A crown of life shall be;
He with the King of Glory
   Shall reign eternally.

George Duffield, 1858

468   # God of the Prophets

TOULON 10 10 10 10

Arranged from Louis Bourgeois, 1551

1 God of the proph - ets! Bless the proph - ets' sons;
2 A - noint them proph - ets! Make their ears at - tent
3 A - noint them priests! Strong in - ter - ces - sors, Lord!

E - li - jah's man - tle o'er E - li - sha cast;
To Thy di - vin - est speech, their hearts a - wake
A - noint them with the Spir - it of Thy Son;

Each age its sol - emn task may claim but once;
To hu - man need; their lips make el - o - quent
Theirs not a jew - eled crown, a blood-stained sword;

Make each one no - bler, strong - er than the last.
To gird the right and ev - ery e - vil break.
Theirs, by sweet love, for Christ a king - dom won.

4 Make them apostles! Heralds of Thy cross.
    Forth may they go to tell all realms Thy grace,
    Inspired of Thee, may they count all but loss,
    And stand at last with joy before Thy face.

Denis Wortman, 1884, *alt.*

469 By the Sea of Crystal

CRYSTAL 6 5 6 5 D.

John Vanderhoven, 1933

1 By the sea of crys - tal, Saints in glo - ry stand,
2 Out of trib - u - la - tion, Death and Sa - tan's hand,
3 "Un - to God Al - might - y, Sit - ting on the throne,

Myr - i - ads in num - ber, Drawn from ev - er - y land.
They have been trans - lat - ed At the Lord's com - mand.
And the Lamb, vic - to - rious, Be the praise a - lone.

Robed in white ap - par - el, Washed in Je - sus' blood,
In their hands they're hold - ing Palms of vic - to - ry;
God has wrought sal - va - tion, He did won-drous things;

They now reign in heav - en With the Lamb of God.
Hark! the ju - bilant cho - rus Shouts tri - um - phant - ly:
Who shall not ex - tol Thee, Ho - ly King of Kings?"

William Kuipers, 1933

546

470   Abide with Me

Eventide 10 10 10 10

William H. Monk, 1861

1 A - bide with me; fast falls the e - ven - tide; The dark-ness
2 Swift to its close ebbs out life's lit - tle day; Earth's joys grow
3 I need Thy pres - ence ev - ery pass-ing hour; What but Thy

deep - ens; Lord, with me a - bide. When oth - er help - ers
dim, its glo-ries pass a - way; Change and de - cay in
grace can foil the temp-ter's power? Who like Thy-self my

fail and com-forts flee, Help of the help-less, O a - bide with me.
all a-round I see; O Thou who chang-est not, a - bide with me.
guide and stay can be? Through cloud and sun-shine, O a - bide with me.

4 I fear no foe, with Thee at hand to bless;
   Ills have no weight and tears no bitterness.
   Where is death's sting? Where, grave, thy victory?
   I triumph still, if Thou abide with me.

5 Hold Thou Thy cross before my closing eyes,
   Shine through the gloom, and point me to the skies;
   Heaven's morning breaks and earth's vain shadows flee;
   In life, in death, O Lord, abide with me.

Henry F. Lyte, 1793-1847

471 Jerusalem the Golden

EWING 7 6 7 6 D.

Alexander Ewing, 1853

1 Je - ru - sa - lem the gold-en, With milk and hon - ey blest,
2 They stand, those halls of Zi - on, All ju - bi - lant with song

Be - neath thy con - tem - pla - tion Sink heart and voice op - pressed.
And bright with many an an - gel And all the mar - tyr throng.

I know not, O I know not What joys a - wait us there,
The Prince is ev - er in them, The day-light is se - rene;

What ra - dian - cy of glo - ry, What bliss be - yond com - pare!
The pas - tures of the bless - ed Are decked in glo - rious sheen.

3 There is the throne of David;
   And there, from care released,
The song of them that triumph,
   The shout of them that feast;
And they who with their Leader
   Have conquered in the fight,
Forever and forever
   Are clad in robes of white.

4 O sweet and blessed country,
   The home of God's elect!
O sweet and blessed country
   That eager hearts expect!
Jesus, in mercy bring us
   To that dear land of rest,
Who art, with God the Father
   And Spirit, ever blest.

Bernard of Cluny, 12th Cent.
Tr. John M. Neale, 1851

548

472

Sun of My Soul

<small>Hursley L. M.</small>

Arranged by William H. Monk, 1861

1 Sun of my soul, Thou Sav - ior dear, It is not
2 When the soft dews of kind - ly sleep My wea - ry
3 A - bide with me from morn till eve, For with - out

night if Thou be near; O may no earth - born
eye - lids gen - tly steep, Be my last thought, how
Thee I can - not live; A - bide with me when

cloud a - rise To hide Thee from Thy ser - vant's eyes!
sweet to rest For - ev - er on my Sav - ior's breast!
night is nigh, For with - out Thee I dare not die.

4 If some poor wandering child of Thine
Have spurned today the voice divine,
Now, Lord, the gracious work begin;
Let him no more lie down in sin.

5 Forgive me, Lord, for Thy dear Son,
The ill that I this day have done,
That with the world, myself, and Thee,
I, ere I sleep, at peace may be.

6 O may my soul on Thee repose
And with sweet sleep mine eyelids close,
Sleep that may me more vigorous make
To serve my God when I awake.

7 Praise God, from whom all blessings flow;
Praise Him, all creatures here below;
Praise Him above, ye heavenly host;
Praise Father, Son, and Holy Ghost.

<small>John Keble, 1820
Stanzas 5-7, Bishop Ken, 1674</small>

473　God Be with You Till We Meet Again

FAREWELL 9 8.8 9, with Refrain

William G. Tomer, 1880

1 God be with you till we meet a-gain, By His coun-sels
2 God be with you till we meet a-gain, 'Neath His wings pro-

guide, up-hold you, With His sheep se-cure-ly fold you;
tect - ing hide you, Dai - ly man-na still pro - vide you;

REFRAIN

God be with you till we meet a-gain. Till we meet,......
God be with you till we meet a-gain. Till we meet,

till we meet,....... Till we meet at Je - sus'
till we meet, till we meet,

God Be with You Till We Meet Again

feet;   Till   we   meet, ...   till   we

till   we   meet,   Till we meet,   till   we

meet,

God be with you till we meet a - gain.

meet, till   we   meet,

3 God be with you till we meet again;

   When life's perils thick confound you,

   Put His arms unfailing 'round you;

God be with you till we meet again.

4 God be with you till we meet again,

   Keep love's banner floating o'er you,

   Smite death's threatening wave before you;

God be with you till we meet again.

Jeremiah E. Rankin, 1880

474 Hours and Days and Years and Ages

O LIEBE MEINER LIEBE 8 7 8 7 D.

Manuscript *Herrnhut Choralbuch*, 1735

1 Hours and days and years and a - ges
2 But from sin Thy mer - cy drew us,

Swift as mov - ing shad - ows flee; As we scan life's
Would not leave our souls a - lone; Gra - cious Lord, Thou

fleet - ing pag - es, Naught en - dur - ing do we see;
didst re - new us, All our guilt Thou didst a - tone;

On the paths our feet are wend - ing
Yea, the plan of Thy sal - va - tion,

Hours and Days and Years and Ages

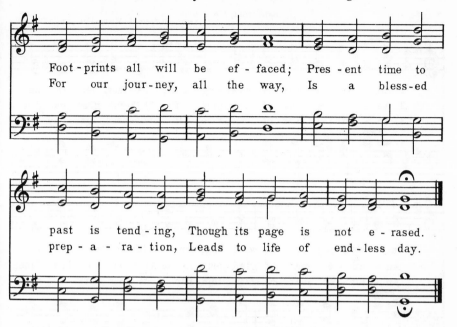

Foot - prints all will be ef - faced; Pres - ent time to
For our jour - ney, all the way, Is a bless - ed

past is tend - ing, Though its page is not e - rased.
prep - a - ra - tion, Leads to life of end - less day.

3 And though time will all things conquer,
    It shall not our lot decide;
 Thou alone, eternal Father,
    Wilt for aye our Lord abide;
 And when dangers round us gather,
    They cannot our souls molest;
 In Thy Son Thou art our Father,
    In Thy love our hearts e'er rest.

4 Speed along, then, years and ages,
    With your gladness and your pain;
 E'en when deepest sorrow rages,
    Faithful will our God remain;
 Though all earthly friends forsake us,
    Guided by His loving hand
 To His heart we'll aye betake us,
    Looking toward our fatherland.

Tr. L. P. Brink, 1929

553

475 Another Year Is Dawning

SALVATORI 7 6 7 6 D.

Arranged from J. Michael Haydn, 1737-1806

1 An - oth-er year is dawn-ing! Dear Fa-ther, let it be,
2 An - oth-er year of mer-cies, Of faith-ful-ness and grace;
3 An - oth-er year of ser-vice, Of wit-ness for Thy love;

In work-ing or in wait-ing, An - oth-er year with Thee;
An - oth-er year of glad-ness In the shin-ing of Thy face;
An - oth-er year of train-ing For ho-lier work a-bove.

An - oth-er year of lean-ing Up-on Thy lov-ing breast,
An - oth-er year of prog-ress, An-oth-er year of praise,
An - oth-er year is dawn-ing! Dear Fa-ther, let it be

An - oth-er year of trust-ing, Of qui-et, hap-py rest.
An - oth-er year of prov-ing Thy pres-ence all the days.
On earth, or else in heav-en, An - oth-er year for Thee.

Frances R. Havergal, 1874

554

476 God of Our Fathers

NATIONAL HYMN 10 10 10 10

George W. Warren, 1892

Trumpets, before each stanza

ff

1 God of our fa-thers, whose al-might-y hand
Leads forth in beau-ty all the star-ry band
Of shin-ing worlds in splen-dor through the skies,
Our grate-ful songs be-fore Thy throne a-rise.

2 Thy love di-vine has led us in the past;
In this free land by Thee our lot is cast;
Be Thou our Rul-er, Guard-ian, Guide and Stay;
Thy Word our law, Thy paths our cho-sen way.

3 From war's alarms, from deadly pestilence,
Be Thy strong arm our ever sure defense;
May true religion in our hearts increase;
May bounteous goodness nourish us in peace.

4 Refresh Thy people on their toilsome way,
Lead us from night to never-ending day;
Fill all our lives with love and grace divine;
And glory, laud, and praise be ever Thine.

Daniel C. Roberts, 1876

O God, Beneath Thy Guiding Hand

WAREHAM L. M.

William Knapp, 1738

1 O God, be - neath Thy guid - ing hand
2 Thou heard'st, well - pleased, the song, the prayer;
3 Laws, free - dom, truth and faith in God
4 And here Thy Name, O God of love,

Our ex - iled fa - thers crossed the sea;
Thy bless - ing came; and still its power
Came with those ex - iles o'er the waves;
Their chil - dren's chil - dren shall a - dore,

And when they trod the win - try strand,
Shall on - ward, through all a - ges, bear
And where their pil - grim feet have trod,
Till these e - ter - nal hills re - move

With prayer and psalm they wor - shipped Thee.
The mem - ory of that ho - ly hour.
The God they trust - ed guards their graves.
And spring a - dorns the earth no more.

Leonard Bacon, 1833

478

From Ocean unto Ocean

LANCASHIRE 7 6 7 6 D.

Henry Smart, 1813-1879

1 From o-cean un-to o-cean Our land shall own Thee Lord,
2 O Christ, for Thine own glo-ry And for our coun-try's weal,
3 Where er-ror smites with blind-ness, En-slaves and leads a-stray,
4 Our Sav-ior King, de-fend us And guide where we should go;

And, filled with true de-vo-tion, O-bey Thy sov-ereign Word.
We hum-bly plead be-fore Thee: Thy-self in us re-veal;
Do Thou in lov-ing-kind-ness Pro-claim Thy gos-pel day,
Forth with Thy mes-sage send us, Thy love and light to show,

Our prai-ries and our moun-tains, For-est and fer-tile field,
And may we know, Lord Je-sus, The touch of Thy dear hand;
Till all the tribes and rac-es That dwell in this fair land,
Till, fired with true de-vo-tion, En-kin-dled by Thy Word,

Our riv-ers, lakes and foun-tains To Thee shall trib-ute yield.
And, healed of our dis-eas-es, The tempt-er's power with-stand.
A-dorned with Chris-tian grac-es, With-in Thy courts shall stand.
From o-cean un-to o-cean Our land shall own Thee Lord.

Robert Murray, 1832-1910

479   I Love Thy Kingdom, Lord

St. Thomas S.M.

Aaron Williams, 1731-1776

1 I love Thy king - dom, Lord, The house of Thine a - bode, The Church our blest Re - deem - er saved With His own pre - cious blood.

2 I love Thy Church, O God! Her walls be - fore Thee stand, Dear as the ap - ple of Thine eye, And grav - en on Thy hand.

3 For her my tears shall fall; For her my prayers as - cend; To her my cares and toils be given, Till toils and cares shall end. A - men.

4 Beyond my highest joy
I prize her heavenly ways,
Her sweet communion, solemn vows,
Her hymns of love and praise.

5 Sure as Thy truth shall last,
To Zion shall be given
The brightest glories earth can yield,
And brighter bliss of heaven. Amen.

Timothy Dwight, 1800, *alt.*

480   O Jesus, I Have Promised

ANGEL'S STORY 7 6 7 6 D.

Arthur H. Mann, 1850-1929

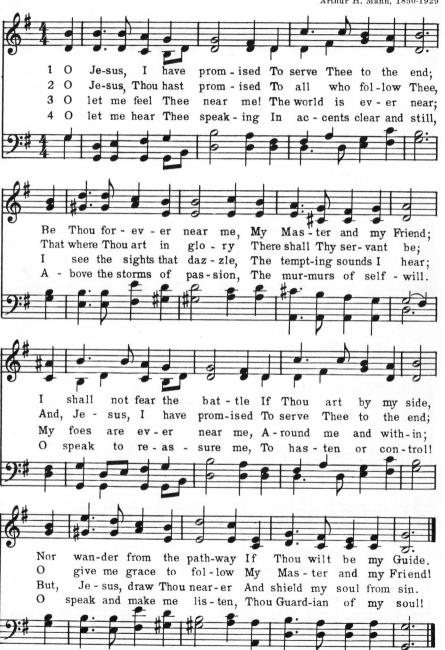

1 O Je-sus, I have prom-ised To serve Thee to the end;
2 O Je-sus, Thou hast prom-ised To all who fol-low Thee,
3 O let me feel Thee near me! The world is ev-er near;
4 O let me hear Thee speak-ing In ac-cents clear and still,

Be Thou for-ev-er near me, My Mas-ter and my Friend;
That where Thou art in glo-ry There shall Thy ser-vant be;
I see the sights that daz-zle, The tempt-ing sounds I hear;
A-bove the storms of pas-sion, The mur-murs of self-will.

I shall not fear the bat-tle If Thou art by my side,
And, Je-sus, I have prom-ised To serve Thee to the end;
My foes are ev-er near me, A-round me and with-in;
O speak to re-as-sure me, To has-ten or con-trol!

Nor wan-der from the path-way If Thou wilt be my Guide.
O give me grace to fol-low My Mas-ter and my Friend!
But, Je-sus, draw Thou near-er And shield my soul from sin.
O speak and make me lis-ten, Thou Guard-ian of my soul!

Used by permission. E. Ramsey Goodliffe

John Ernest Bode, 1869, *alt.*

481   O Perfect Love

O PERFECT LOVE 11 10 11 10

Joseph Barnby, 1838-1896

1 O   per - fect Love, all   hu - man thought tran-scend - ing,
2 O   per - fect Life, be   Thou their full   as - sur - ance
3 Grant them the   joy which bright-ens earth - ly   sor - row;

Low - ly   we   kneel   in   prayer be - fore Thy   throne,
Of   ten - der   char - i - ty   and sted - fast   faith,
Grant them the   peace which calms all earth - ly   strife,

That theirs may be   the   love which knows no   end - ing,
Of   pa - tient hope and   qui - et, brave en - dur - ance,
And   to   life's day the   glo-rious un - known mor - row

Whom Thou in   sa - cred vow dost join   in   one.
With   child-like trust that fears no   pain   nor   death.
That dawns up - on   e - ter - nal   love   and   life. A - men.

Dorothy F. Gurney, 1883, *alt*

560

482   We Give Thee But Thine Own

SCHUMANN S. M.   Mason and Webb's *Cantica Laudis*
Boston, 1850

1 We give Thee but Thine own, What - e'er the
2 May we Thy boun - ties thus As stew - ards
3 To com - fort and to bless, To find a

gift may be; All that we have is Thine a -
true re - ceive, And glad - ly, as Thou bless - est
balm for woe, To tend the lone and fa - ther -

lone, A trust, O Lord, from Thee.
us, To Thee our first - fruits give.
less Is an - gels' work be - low.

4 The captive to release,
   To God the lost to bring,
   To teach the way of life and peace—
   It is a Christ-like thing.

5 And we believe Thy Word,
   Though dim our faith may be;
   Whate'er for Thine we do, O Lord,
   We do it unto Thee.

William Walsham How, 1823-1897

483 Come, Ye That Fear Jehovah

TOURS 7 6 7 6 D.

Berthold Tours, 1872

1 Come, ye that fear Je - ho-vah, Ye saints, your voic-es raise;
2 All kin-dreds of the na-tions To Christ the Lord shall turn,
3 Both high and low shall wor-ship, Both strong and weak shall bend,

Come, stand in awe be - fore Him And sing His glo-rious praise.
Through earth's re-mot - est re-gions His al - tar-fires shall burn.
A faith-ful Church shall serve Him Till gen - er - a - tions end.

Ye low - ly and af - flict - ed Who on His Word re - ly,
All king-dom, power and glo - ry Be - long to Him a - lone;
His praise shall be re - count - ed To na - tions yet to be,

Your heart shall live for - ev - er, The Lord will sat - is - fy.
He rul - eth o'er the na-tions, Kings bow be-fore His throne.
The tri - umphs of His jus - tice A new-born world shall see.

Adapted from Psalm 22

484 Lead On, O King Eternal

LANCASHIRE 7 6 7 6 D.

Henry Smart, 1813-1879

1 Lead on, O King E - ter - nal, The day of march has come;
2 Lead on, O King E - ter - nal, Till sin's fierce war shall cease,
3 Lead on, O King E - ter - nal, We fol - low, not with fears;

Hence-forth in fields of con - quest Thy tents shall be our home.
And ho - li - ness shall whis - per The sweet a - men of peace;
For glad-ness breaks like morn-ing Wher-e'er Thy face ap - pears;

Through days of prep - a - ra - tion Thy grace has made us strong,
For not with swords' loud clash-ing, Or roll of stir-ring drums,
Thy cross is lift - ed o'er us, We jour-ney in its light;

And now, O King E - ter - nal, We lift our bat - tle song.
With deeds of love and mer - cy The heaven-ly king-dom comes.
The crown a - waits the con-quest; Lead on, O God of might.

Ernest W. Shurtleff, 1887

Blest Be That Sacred Covenant Love

NOMINA C.M.

Henry Smart, 1813-1879

1 Blest be that sa - cred cov - enant love, U -
niting, though we part; We may be called far
off to move, We still are one in heart.

2 Joined in one spir - it to our Head, Where
He ap - points, we go; And while we in His
foot - steps tread, Show forth His praise be - low.

3 O may we ev - er walk with Him, And
noth - ing know be - side; Naught else de - sire, naught
else es - teem But Je - sus Cru - ci - fied.

4 Nor joy nor grief, nor time nor place,
    Nor life nor death can part
Those who, enjoying Jesus' grace,
    In Him are one in heart.

Charles Wesley, 1742

486 O Lord, Beneath Thy Guiding Hand

CENTENNIAL HYMN (MAMIE) L. M.

Adrian Hartog, 1957

1 O Lord, be-neath Thy guid-ing hand Our fa-thers'
2 Be-lief in Thy sus-tain-ing power Re-stored their
3 In ev-ery part of life the light Of knowl-edge

fa - thers formed our creed, Brought prayer and psalm to
hearts in days of fear; Thy grace and glo - ry,
shines, at home, a - broad. May cov-enant chil - dren,

this fair land And were sup - plied in ev - ery need.
hour by hour, Gave hope and bless-ing through each year.
taught the right, Tell oth - ers of their sov-ereign God.

4 Thy Name, O Lord, still leads, still draws;

That Name we sing with ardent voice,

That thousands more may know Thy laws

And in Thy saving cross rejoice.

Marie J. Post, 1957

487 May the Grace of Christ Our Savior

STOCKWELL 8 7 8 7

Darius E. Jones, 1851

1 May the grace of Christ our Sav - ior And the
2 Thus may we a - bide in un - ion With each

Fa - ther's bound-less love, With the Ho - ly Spir - it's
oth - er and the Lord, And pos - sess, in sweet com -

fa - vor, Rest up - on us from a - bove.
mun - ion, Joys which earth can-not af - ford. A - men.

(Alternate Tune: CONVERSE, No. 436)

John Newton, 1779

Now Blessed Be Jehovah God

CORONATION, C. M., 6 Lines

Oliver Holden, 1793

1 Now bless-ed be Je-ho-vah God, The God of Is-ra-el, Who on-ly do-eth won-drous works, In glo-ry that ex-cel; Who on-ly do-eth won-drous works, In glo-ry that..... ex-cel.

2 And bless-ed be His glo-rious Name To all e-ter-ni-ty; The whole earth let His glo-ry fill; A-men: So let it be; The whole earth let His glo-ry fill; A-men: So let..... it be.

Adapted from *Psalm 72*

489   Hear Our Prayer, O Lord

WHELPTON 5 5 6 5

George Whelpton

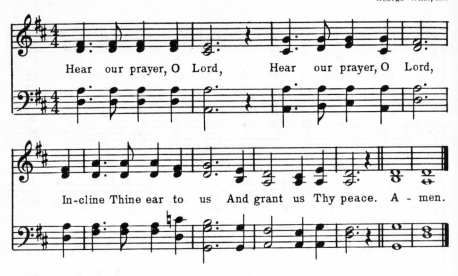

Hear our prayer, O Lord,   Hear our prayer, O Lord,

In-cline Thine ear to us And grant us Thy peace. A - men.

490   Praise Ye the Lord, Ye Hosts Above

WINCHESTER OLD C. M.

Arranged from Christopher Tye, 1553

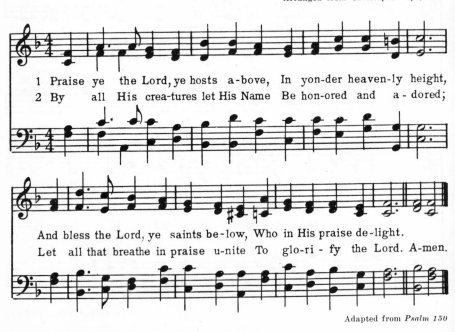

1 Praise ye the Lord, ye hosts a-bove, In yon-der heaven-ly height,
2 By all His crea-tures let His Name Be hon-ored and a - dored;

And bless the Lord, ye saints be-low, Who in His praise de-light.
Let all that breathe in praise u-nite To glo-ri - fy the Lord. A-men.

Adapted from *Psalm 150*

491 Glory Be to the Father

GLORIA PATRI

From Henry W. Greatorex'
Collection, 1851

Glo - ry be to the Fa - ther and to the
Son and to the Ho - ly Ghost; As it
was in the be - gin - ning, is now and ev - er
shall be, world with - out end. A - men, A - men.

Anonymous, 2nd Cent.

492 Glory Be to the Father

GLORIA PATRI

Charles Meineke, 1782-1850

Glo - ry be to the Fa - ther and to the Son and to the Ho - ly Ghost; As it was in the be - gin - ning, is now and ev - er shall be, world with - out end. A - men, A - men.

493   Praise God, from Whom All Blessings Flow

OLD HUNDREDTH L. M.

Louis Bourgeois, 1551

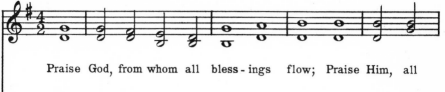

Praise God, from whom all bless - ings flow; Praise Him, all

crea - tures here be - low; Praise Him a - bove, ye

heaven-ly host; Praise Fa-ther, Son and Ho - ly Ghost. A-men.

Bishop Thomas Ken, 1693

DOCTRINAL STANDARDS

OF THE

CHRISTIAN REFORMED CHURCH

CONSISTING OF

THE BELGIC CONFESSION

THE HEIDELBERG CATECHISM

AND

THE CANONS OF DORT

TO WHICH ARE APPENDED

THE ECUMENICAL CREEDS

PUBLICATION COMMITTEE OF THE CHRISTIAN REFORMED CHURCH
PUBLISHERS
GRAND RAPIDS, MICHIGAN

CONFESSION OF FAITH

The first of the Doctrinal Standards of the Christian Reformed Church is the Confession of Faith. It is usually called the *Belgic Confession* because it originated in the Southern Netherlands, now known as Belgium. Its chief author was *Guido de Brès,* a preacher of the Reformed Churches of the Netherlands, who died a martyr to the faith in the year 1567. During the sixteenth century the churches in this country were exposed to the most terrible persecution by the Roman Catholic government. To protest against this cruel oppression, and to prove to the persecutors that the adherents of the Reformed faith were no rebels, as was laid to their charge, but law-abiding citizens who professed the true Christian doctrine according to the Holy Scriptures, de Brès prepared this Confession in the year 1561. In the following year a copy was sent to king Philip II, together with an address in which the petitioners declared that they were ready to obey the government in all lawful things, but that they would ''offer their backs to stripes, their tongues to knives, their mouths to gags, and their whole bodies to the fire,'' rather than deny the truth expressed in this Confession.

Although the immediate purpose of securing freedom from persecution was not attained, and de Brès himself fell as one of the many thousands who sealed their faith with their lives, his work has endured and will continue to endure for ages. In its composition the author availed himself to some extent of a Confession of the Reformed Churches in France, written chiefly by John Calvin and published two years earlier. The work of de Brès, however, is not a mere revision of Calvin's work, but an independent composition. In the Netherlands it was at once gladly received by the churches, and adopted by the National Synods, held during the last three decades of the sixteenth century. After a careful revision, not of the contents but of the text, the great Synod of Dort in 1618-19 adopted this Confession as one of the Doctrinal Standards of the Reformed Churches, to which all office-bearers of the churches were required to subscribe. Its excellence as one of the best symbolical statements of Reformed doctrine has been generally recognized.

ARTICLE I

THERE IS ONLY ONE GOD

We all believe with the heart and confess with the mouth that there is one only simple and spiritual Being, which we call God; and that He is eternal, incomprehensible, invisible, immutable, infinite, almighty, perfectly wise, just, good, and the overflowing fountain of all good.

ARTICLE II

BY WHAT MEANS GOD IS MADE KNOWN UNTO US

We know Him by two means: First, by the creation, preservation, and government of the universe; which is before our eyes as a most elegant book, wherein all creatures, great and small, are as so many characters leading us to *see clearly the invisible things of God,* even *his everlasting power and divinity,* as the apostle Paul says (Rom. 1: 20). All which things are sufficient to convince men and leave them without excuse. Second, He makes Himself more clearly and fully known to us by His holy and divine Word, that is to say, as far as is necessary for us to know in this life, to His glory and our salvation.

ARTICLE III

THE WRITTEN WORD OF GOD

We confess that this Word of God was not sent nor delivered by the will of man, but that *men spake from God, being moved by the Holy Spirit,* as the apostle Peter says; and that afterwards God, from a special care which He has for us and our salvation, commanded His servants, the prophets and apostles, to commit His revealed word to writing; and He Himself wrote with His own finger the two tables of the law. Therefore we call such writings holy and divine Scriptures.

ARTICLE IV

CANONICAL BOOKS OF THE HOLY SCRIPTURE

We believe that the Holy Scriptures are contained in two books, namely, the Old and the New Testament, which are canonical, against which nothing can be alleged. These are thus named in the Church of God.

The books of the Old Testament are the five books of Moses, to wit: Genesis, Exodus, Leviticus, Numbers, Deuteronomy; the book of Joshua, Judges, Ruth, the two books of Samuel, the two of the Kings, two books of the Chronicles, commonly called Paralipomenon, the first of Ezra, Nehemiah, Esther; Job, the Psalms of David, the three books of Solomon, namely, the Proverbs, Ecclesiastes, and the Song of Songs; the four great prophets, Isaiah, Jeremiah, Ezekiel, and Daniel; and the twelve lesser prophets, namely, Hosea, Joel, Amos, Obadiah, Jonah, Micah, Nahum, Habakkuk, Zephaniah, Haggai, Zechariah, and Malachi.

Those of the New Testament are the four evangelists, to wit: Matthew, Mark, Luke, and John; the Acts of the Apostles; the fourteen epistles of the apostle Paul, namely, one to the Romans, two to the Corinthians, one to the Galatians, one to the Ephesians, one to the Philippians, one to the Colossians, two to the Thessalonians, two to Timothy, one to Titus, one to Philemon, and one to the Hebrews; the seven epistles of the other apostles, namely, one of James, two of Peter, three of John, one of Jude; and the Revelation of the apostle John.

ARTICLE V

WHENCE THE HOLY SCRIPTURES DERIVE THEIR DIGNITY AND AUTHORITY

We receive all these books, and these only, as holy and canonical, for the regulation, foundation, and confirmation of our faith; believing without any doubt all things contained in them, not so much because the Church receives and approves them as such, but more especially because the Holy Spirit witnesses in our hearts that they are from God, and also because they carry the evidence thereof in themselves. For the very blind are able to perceive that the things foretold in them are being fulfilled.

ARTICLE VI

THE DIFFERENCE BETWEEN THE CANONICAL AND APOCRYPHAL BOOKS

We distinguish those sacred books from the apocryphal, viz.: the third and fourth books of Esdras, the books of Tobit, Judith, Wisdom, Jesus Sirach, Baruch, the Appendix to the book of Esther, the Song of the Three Children in the Furnace, the History of Susannah, of Bell and the Dragon, the Prayer of Manasseh, and the two books of the Maccabees. All of which the Church may read and take instruction from, so far as they agree with the canonical books; but they are far from having such power and efficacy that we may from their testimony confirm any point of faith or of the Christian religion; much less may they be used to detract from the authority of the other, that is, the sacred books

ARTICLE VII

THE SUFFICIENCY OF THE HOLY SCRIPTURES TO BE THE ONLY RULE OF FAITH

We believe that those Holy Scriptures fully contain the will of God, and that whatsoever man ought to believe unto salvation is sufficiently taught therein. For since the whole manner of worship which God requires of us is written in them at large, it is unlawful for any one, though an apostle, to teach otherwise than we are now taught in the Holy Scriptures: *nay, though it were an angel from heaven,* as the apostle Paul says. For since it is forbidden to *add unto or take away anything from the Word of God*, it does thereby evidently appear that the doctrine thereof is most perfect and complete in all respects.

Neither may we consider any writings of men, however holy these men may have been, of equal value with those divine Scriptures, nor ought we to consider custom, or the great multitude, or antiquity, or succession of times and persons, or councils, decrees or statutes, as of equal value with the truth of God, since the truth is above all; *for all men are of themselves liars, and more vain than vanity itself.* Therefore we reject with all our hearts whatsoever does not agree with this infallible rule, which the apostles have taught us, saying, *Prove the spirits, whether they are of God.* Likewise: *If any one cometh unto you, and bringeth not this teaching, receive him not into your house.*

ARTICLE VIII

GOD IS ONE IN ESSENCE, YET DISTINGUISHED IN THREE PERSONS

According to this truth and this Word of God, we believe in one only God, who is the one single essence, in which are three persons, really, truly, and eternally distinct according to their incommunicable properties; namely, the Father, and the Son, and the Holy Spirit. The Father is the cause, origin, and beginning of all things visible and invisible; the Son is the word, wisdom, and image of the Father; the Holy Spirit is the eternal power and might, proceeding from the Father and the Son. Nevertheless, God is not by this distinction divided into three, since the Holy Scriptures teach us that the Father, and the Son, and the Holy Spirit have each His personality, distinguished by Their properties; but in such wise that these three persons are but one only God.

Hence, then, it is evident that the Father is not the Son, nor the Son the Father, and likewise the Holy Spirit is neither the Father nor the Son. Nevertheless, these persons thus distinguished are not divided, nor intermixed; for the Father has not assumed the flesh, nor has the Holy Spirit, but the Son only. The Father has never been without His Son, or without His Holy Spirit. For They are all three co-eternal and co-essential. There is neither first nor last; for They are all three one, in truth, in power, in goodness, and in mercy.

ARTICLE IX

THE PROOF OF THE FOREGOING ARTICLE OF THE TRINITY OF PERSONS IN ONE GOD

All this we know as well from the testimonies of Holy Writ as from their operations, and chiefly by those we feel in ourselves. The testimonies of the Holy Scriptures that teach us to believe this Holy Trinity are written in many places of the Old Testament, which are not so necessary to enumerate as to choose them out with discretion and judgment.

In Genesis, chap. 1: 26, 27, God says: *Let us make man in our image, after our likeness,* etc. *And God created man in his own image, male and female created he them.* And Gen. 3: 22, *Behold, the man is become as one of us.* From this saying, Let *us* make man in *our* image, it appears that there are more persons than one in the Godhead; and when He says, *God* created, He signifies the unity.

It is true, He does not say how many persons there are, but that which appears to us somewhat obscure in the Old Testament is very plain in the New. For when our Lord was baptized in Jordan, the voice of the Father was heard, saying, *This is my beloved Son;* the Son was seen in the water, and the Holy Spirit appeared in the shape of a dove. This form is also instituted by Christ in the baptism of all believers: *Make disciples of all the nations, baptizing them into the name of the Father and of the Son and of the Holy Spirit.* In the Gospel of Luke the angel Gabriel thus addressed Mary, the mother of our Lord: *The Holy Spirit shall come upon thee, and the power of the Most High shall overshadow thee; wherefore also the holy thing which is begotten shall be called the Son of God.* Likewise: *The grace of the Lord Jesus Christ, and the love of God, and the communion of the Holy Spirit, be with you all.* And (A.V.): *There are three that bear record in heaven, the Father, the Word, and the Holy Ghost: and these three are one.*

In all these places we are fully taught that there are three persons in one only divine essence. And although this doctrine far surpasses all human understanding, nevertheless we now believe it by means of the Word of God, but expect hereafter to enjoy the perfect knowledge and benefit thereof in heaven.

Moreover, we must observe the particular offices and operations of these three persons towards us. The Father is called our Creator, by His power; the Son is our Savior and Redeemer, by His blood; the Holy Spirit is our Sanctifier, by His dwelling in our hearts.

This doctrine of the Holy Trinity has always been affirmed and maintained by the true Church since the time of the apostles to this very day against the Jews, Mohammedans, and some false Christians and heretics, as Marcion, Manes, Praxeas, Sabellius, Samosatenus, Arius, and such like, who have been justly condemned by the orthodox fathers. Therefore, in this point, we do willingly receive the three creeds, namely, that of the Apostles, of Nicea, and of Athanasius; likewise that which, conformable thereunto, is agreed upon by the ancient fathers

ARTICLE X

JESUS CHRIST IS TRUE AND ETERNAL GOD

We believe that Jesus Christ according to His divine nature is the only begotten Son of God, begotten from eternity, not made, nor created (for then He would be a creature), but co-essential and co-eternal with the Father, *the very image of his substance and the effulgence of his glory,* equal unto Him in all things. He is the Son of God, not only from the time that He assumed our nature but from all eternity, as these testimonies, when compared together, teach us. Moses says that God created the world; and St. John says that all things were made by that Word which he calls God. The apostle says that God made the world by His Son; likewise, that God created all things by Jesus Christ. Therefore it must needs follow that He who is called God, the Word, the Son, and Jesus Christ, did exist at that time when all things were created by Him. Therefore the prophet Micah says: *His goings forth are from of old, from everlasting.* And the apostle: *He hath neither beginning of days nor end of life.* He therefore is that true, eternal, and almighty God whom we invoke, worship, and serve.

ARTICLE XI

THE HOLY SPIRIT IS TRUE AND ETERNAL GOD

We believe and confess also that the Holy Spirit from eternity proceeds from the Father and the Son; and therefore neither is made, created, nor begotten, but only proceeds from both; who in order is the third person of the Holy Trinity; of one and the same essence, majesty, and glory with the Father and the Son; and therefore is the true and eternal God, as the Holy Scriptures teach us.

ARTICLE XII

THE CREATION OF ALL THINGS, ESPECIALLY THE ANGELS

We believe that the Father by the Word, that is, by His Son, has created of nothing the heaven, the earth, and all creatures, when it seemed good unto Him, giving unto every creature its being, shape, form, and several offices to serve its Creator; that He also still upholds and governs them by His eternal providence and infinite power for the service of mankind, to the end that man may serve his God.

He also created the angels good, to be His messengers and to serve His elect; some of whom are fallen from that excellency in which God created them into everlasting perdition, and the others have by the grace of God remained stedfast and continued in their first state. The devils and evil spirits are so depraved that they are enemies of God and every good thing; to the utmost of their power as murderers watching to ruin the Church and every member thereof, and by their wicked stratagems to destroy all; and are, therefore, by their own wickedness adjudged to eternal damnation, daily expecting their horrible torments.

Therefore we reject and abhor the error of the Sadducees, who deny the existence of spirits and angels; and also that of the Manichees, who assert that the devils have their origin of themselves, and that they are wicked of their own nature, without having been corrupted.

ARTICLE XIII

THE PROVIDENCE OF GOD AND HIS GOVERNMENT OF ALL THINGS

We believe that the same good God, after He had created all things, did not forsake them or give them up to fortune or chance, but that He rules and governs them according to His holy will, so that nothing happens in this world without His appointment; nevertheless, God neither is the Author of nor can be charged with the sins which are committed. For His power and goodness are so great and incomprehensible that He orders and executes His work in the most excellent and just manner, even then when devils and wicked men act unjustly. And as to what He does surpassing human understanding, we will not curiously inquire into farther than our capacity will admit of; but with the greatest humility and reverence adore the righteous judgments of God, which are hid from us, contenting ourselves that we are pupils of Christ, to learn only those things which He has revealed to us in His Word, without transgressing these limits.

This doctrine affords us unspeakable consolation, since we are taught thereby that nothing can befall us by chance, but by the direction of our most gracious and heavenly Father; who watches over us with a paternal care, keeping all creatures so under His power that *not a hair of our head (for they are all numbered), nor a sparrow can fall to the ground without the will of our Father,* in whom we do entirely trust; being persuaded that He so restrains the devil and all our enemies that without His will and permission they cannot hurt us.

And therefore we reject that damnable error of the Epicureans, who say that God regards nothing but leaves all things to chance.

ARTICLE XIV

THE CREATION AND FALL OF MAN, AND HIS INCAPACITY TO PERFORM WHAT IS TRULY GOOD

We believe that God created man out of the dust of the earth, and made and formed him after His own image and likeness, good, righteous, and holy, capable in all things to will agreeably to the will of God. But *being in honor, he understood it not,* neither knew his excellency, but wilfully subjected himself to sin and consequently to death and the curse, giving ear to the words of the devil. For the commandment of life, which he had received, he transgressed; and by sin separated himself from God, who was his true life; having corrupted his whole nature; whereby he made himself liable to corporal and spiritual death. And being thus become wicked, perverse, and corrupt in all his ways, he has lost all his excellent gifts which he had received from God, and retained only small remains thereof, which, however, are sufficient to leave man without excuse; for all the light which is in us is changed into darkness, as the Scriptures teach us, saying: *The light shineth in the darkness, and the darkness apprehended it not;* where St. John calls men darkness.

Therefore we reject all that is taught repugnant to this concerning the free will of man, since man is but a slave to sin, and *can receive nothing, except it have been given him from heaven.* For who may presume to boast that he of himself can do any good, since Christ says: *No man can come to me, except the Father that sent me draw him?* Who will glory in his own will, who understands that *the mind of the flesh is enmity against God?* Who can speak of his knowledge, since *the natural man receiveth not the things of the Spirit of God?* In short, who dare suggest any thought, since he knows that *we are not sufficient of ourselves to account anything as of ourselves, but that our sufficiency is of God?* And therefore what the apostle says ought justly to be held sure and firm, that *God worketh in us both to will and to work, for his good pleasure.* For there is no understanding nor will conformable to the divine understanding and will but what Christ has wrought in man; which He teaches us, when He says: *Apart from me ye can do nothing.*

ARTICLE XV

ORIGINAL SIN

We believe that through the disobedience of Adam original sin is extended to all mankind; which is a corruption of the whole nature and a hereditary disease, wherewith even infants in their mother's womb are infected, and which produces in man all sorts of sin, being in him as a root thereof, and therefore is so vile and abominable in the sight of God that it is sufficient to condemn all mankind. Nor is it altogether abolished or wholly eradicated even by baptism; since sin always issues forth from this woeful source, as water from a fountain; notwithstanding it is not imputed to the children of God unto condemnation, but by His grace and mercy is forgiven them. Not that they should rest securely in sin, but that a sense of this corruption should make believers often to sigh, desiring to be delivered from this body of death.

Wherefore we reject the error of the Pelagians, who assert that sin proceeds only from imitation.

ARTICLE XVI

ETERNAL ELECTION

We believe that, all the posterity of Adam being thus fallen into perdition and ruin by the sin of our first parents, God then did manifest Himself such as He is; that is to say, merciful and just: **merciful,** since He delivers and preserves from this perdition all whom He in His eternal and unchangeable counsel of mere goodness has elected in Christ Jesus our Lord, without any respect to their works; **just,** in leaving others in the fall and perdition wherein they have involved themselves.

ARTICLE XVII

THE RECOVERY OF FALLEN MAN

We believe that our most gracious God, in His admirable wisdom and goodness, seeing that man had thus thrown himself into physical and spiritual death and made himself wholly miserable, was pleased to seek and comfort him, when he trembling fled from His presence, promising him that He would give His Son (who would be *born of a woman*) *to bruise the head of the serpent* and to make him blessed.

ARTICLE XVIII

THE INCARNATION OF JESUS CHRIST

We confess, therefore, that God has fulfilled the promise which He made to the fathers by the mouth of His holy prophets, when He sent into the world, at the time appointed by Him, His own only-begotten and eternal Son, who *took upon Him the form of a servant* and *became like unto man,* really assuming the true human nature with all its infirmities, sin excepted; being conceived in the womb of the blessed virgin Mary by the power of the Holy Spirit without the means of man; and did not only assume human nature as to the body, but also a true human soul, that He might be a real man. For since the soul was lost as well as the body, it was necessary that He should take both upon Him, to save both.

Therefore we confess (in opposition to the heresy of the Anabaptists, who deny that Christ assumed human flesh of His mother) that Christ *partook of the flesh and blood of the children;* that He is a *fruit of the loins of David after the flesh; born of the seed of David according to the flesh; a fruit of the womb of Mary; born of a woman; a branch of David; a shoot of the root of Jesse; sprung from the tribe of Judah;* descended from the Jews according to the flesh; of the seed of Abraham, since (A.V.) *he took on him the seed of Abraham,* and *was made like unto his brethren in all things, sin excepted;* so that in truth He is our IMMANUEL, that is to say, *God with us.*

ARTICLE XIX

THE UNION AND DISTINCTION OF THE TWO NATURES IN THE PERSON OF CHRIST

We believe that by this conception the person of the Son is inseparably united and connected with the human nature; so that there are not two Sons of God, nor two persons, but two natures united in one single person; yet each nature retains its own distinct properties. As, then, the divine nature has always remained uncreated, without beginning of days or end of life, filling heaven and earth, so also has the human nature not lost its properties but remained a creature, having beginning of days, being a finite nature, and retaining all the properties of a real body. And though He has by His resurrection given immortality to the same, nevertheless He has not changed the reality of His human nature; forasmuch as our salvation and resurrection also depend on the reality of His body.

But these two natures are so closely united in one person that they were not separated even by His death. Therefore that which He, when dying, commended into the hands of His Father, was a real human spirit, departing from His body. But in the meantime the divine nature always remained united with the human, even when He lay in the grave; and the Godhead did not cease to be in Him, any more than it did when He was an infant, though it did not so clearly manifest itself for a while. Wherefore we confess that He is **very God** and **very man**: very God by His power to conquer death; and very man that He might die for us according to the infirmity of His flesh.

ARTICLE XX

GOD HAS MANIFESTED HIS JUSTICE AND MERCY IN CHRIST

We believe that God, who is perfectly merciful and just, sent His Son to assume that nature in which the disobedience was committed, to make satisfaction in the same, and to bear the punishment of sin by His most bitter passion and death. God therefore manifested His justice against His Son when He laid our iniquities upon Him, and poured forth His mercy and goodness on us, who were guilty and worthy of damnation, out of mere and perfect love, giving His Son unto death for us, and raising Him for our justification, that through Him we might obtain immortality and life eternal.

ARTICLE XXI

THE SATISFACTION OF CHRIST, OUR ONLY HIGH PRIEST, FOR US

We believe that Jesus Christ is ordained with an oath to be an everlasting High Priest, after the order of Melchizedek; and that He has presented Himself in our behalf before the Father, to appease His wrath by His full satisfaction, by offering Himself on the tree of the cross, and pouring out His precious blood to purge away our sins, as the prophets had foretold. For it is written: *He was wounded for our transgressions, he was bruised for our iniquities; the chastisement of our peace was upon him; and with his stripes we are healed. He was led as a lamb to the slaughter, and numbered with the transgressors;* and condemned by Pontius Pilate as a malefactor, though he had first declared Him innocent. Therefore, He *restored that which he took not away,* and *suffered, the righteous for the unrighteous,* as well in His body as in His soul, feeling the terrible punishment which our sins had merited; insomuch that *his sweat became as it were great drops of blood falling down upon the ground.* He called out: *My God, my God, why hast thou forsaken me?* and has suffered all this for the remission of our sins.

Wherefore we justly say with the apostle Paul that we know nothing *save Jesus Christ, and him crucified;* we *count all things but loss and refuse for the excellency of the knowledge of Christ Jesus our Lord,* in whose wounds we find all manner of consolation. Neither is it necessary to seek or invent any other means of being reconciled to God than this only sacrifice, once offered, by which *he hath perfected forever them that are sanctified.* This is also the reason why He was called by the angel of God, JESUS, that is to say, SAVIOR, because He would *save his people from their sins.*

ARTICLE XXII

OUR JUSTIFICATION THROUGH FAITH IN JESUS CHRIST

We believe that, to attain the true knowledge of this great mystery, the Holy Spirit kindles in our hearts an upright faith, which embraces Jesus Christ with all His merits, appropriates Him, and seeks nothing more besides Him. For it must needs follow, either that all things which are requisite to our salvation are not in Jesus Christ, or if all things are in Him, that then those who possess Jesus Christ through faith have complete salvation in Him. Therefore, for any to assert that Christ is not sufficient, but that something more is required besides Him, would be too gross a blasphemy; for hence it would follow that Christ was but half a Savior.

Therefore we justly say with Paul, that we *are justified by faith* alone, or *by faith apart from works.* However, to speak more clearly, we do not mean that faith itself justifies us, for it is only an instrument with which we embrace Christ our righteousness. But Jesus Christ, imputing to us all His merits, and so many holy works which He has done for us and in our stead, is our righteousness. And faith is an instrument that keeps us in communion with Him in all His benefits, which, when they become ours, are more than sufficient to acquit us of our sins.

ARTICLE XXIII

WHEREIN OUR JUSTIFICATION BEFORE GOD CONSISTS

We believe that our salvation consists in the remission of our sins for Jesus Christ's sake, and that therein our righteousness before God is implied; as David and Paul teach us, declaring this to be the blessedness of man that *God imputes righteousness to him apart from works.* And the same apostle says that we are *justified freely by his grace, through the redemption that is in Christ Jesus.*

And therefore we always hold fast this foundation, ascribing all the glory to God, humbling ourselves before Him, and acknowledging ourselves to be such as we really are, without presuming to trust in any thing in ourselves, or in any merit of ours, relying and resting upon the obedience of Christ crucified alone, which becomes ours when we believe in Him. This is sufficient to cover all our iniquities, and to give us confidence in approaching to God; freeing the conscience of fear, terror, and dread, without following the example of our first father, Adam, who, trembling, attempted to cover himself with fig-leaves. And, verily, if we should appear before God, relying on ourselves or on any other creature, though ever so little, we should, alas! be consumed. And therefore every one must pray with David: *O Jehovah, enter not into judgment with thy servant; for in thy sight no man living is righteous.*

ARTICLE XXIV

MAN'S SANCTIFICATION AND GOOD WORKS

We believe that this true faith, being wrought in man by the hearing of the Word of God and the operation of the Holy Spirit, regenerates him and makes him a new man, causing him to live a new life, and freeing him from the bondage of sin. Therefore it is so far from being true that this justifying faith makes men remiss in a pious and holy life, that on the contrary without it they would never do anything out of love to God, but only out of self-love or fear of damnation. Therefore it is impossible that this holy faith can be unfruitful in man; for we do not speak of a vain faith, but of such a faith which is called in Scripture a *faith working through love,* which excites man to the practice of those works which God has commanded in His Word.

These works, as they proceed from the good root of faith, are good and acceptable in the sight of God, forasmuch as they are all sanctified by His grace. Nevertheless they are of no account towards our justification, for it is by faith in Christ that we are justified, even before we do good works; otherwise they could not be good works, any more than the fruit of a tree can be good before the tree itself is good.

Therefore we do good works, but not to merit by them (for what can we merit?); nay, we are indebted to God for the good works we do, and not He to us, since it is He who *worketh in us both to will and to work, for his good pleasure.* Let us therefore attend to what is written: *When ye shall have done all the things that are commanded you, say, We are unprofitable servants; we have done that which it was our duty to do.* In the meantime we do not deny that God rewards good works, but it is through His grace that He crowns His gifts.

Moreover, though we do good works, we do not found our salvation upon them; for we can do no work but what is polluted by our flesh, and also punishable; and although we could perform such works, still the remembrance of one sin is sufficient to make God reject them. Thus, then, we would always be in doubt, tossed to and fro without any certainty, and our poor consciences would be continually vexed if they relied not on the merits of the suffering and death of our Savior.

ARTICLE XXV

THE ABOLISHING OF THE CEREMONIAL LAW

We believe that the ceremonies and symbols of the law ceased at the coming of Christ, and that all the shadows are accomplished; so that the use of them must be abolished among Christians; yet the truth and substance of them remain with us in Jesus Christ, in whom they have their completion. In the meantime we still use the testimonies taken out of the law and the prophets to confirm us in the doctrine of the gospel, and to regulate our life in all honorableness to the glory of God, according to His will.

ARTICLE XXVI

CHRIST'S INTERCESSION

We believe that we have no access unto God but alone through the only Mediator and Advocate, Jesus Christ the righteous; who therefore became man, having united in one person the divine and human natures, that we men might have access to the divine Majesty, which access would otherwise be barred against us. But this Mediator, whom the Father has appointed between Him and us, ought in no wise to affright us by His majesty, or cause us to seek another according to our fancy. For there is no creature, either in heaven or on earth, who loves us more than Jesus Christ; who, though *existing in the form of God,* yet *emptied himself, being made in the likeness of men and of a servant* for us, and *in all things was made like unto his brethren.* If, then, we should seek for another mediator who would be favorably inclined towards us, whom could we find who loved us more than He who laid down His life for us, even *while we were His enemies?* And if we seek for one who has power and majesty, who is there that has so much of both as He *who sits at the right hand of God* and *to whom hath been given all authority in heaven and on earth?* And who will sooner be heard than the own well beloved Son of God?

Therefore it was only through distrust that this practice of dishonoring, instead of honoring, the saints was introduced, doing that which they never have done nor required, but have on the contrary stedfastly rejected according to their bounden duty, as appears by their writings. Neither must we plead here our unworthiness; for the meaning is not that we should offer our prayers to God on the ground of our own worthiness, but only on the ground of the excellency and worthiness of the Lord Jesus Christ, whose righteousness is become ours by faith.

Therefore the apostle, to remove this foolish fear, or rather distrust, from us, rightly says that Jesus Christ *in all things was made like unto his brethren, that he might become a merciful and faithful high priest, to make propitiation for the sins of the people. For in that he himself hath suffered being tempted, he is able to succor them that are tempted.* And further to encourage us to go to Him, he says: *Having then a great high priest, who hath passed through the heavens, Jesus the Son of God, let us hold fast our confession. For we have not a high priest that cannot be touched with the feeling of our infirmities; but one that hath been in all points tempted like as* we are, yet *without sin. Let us therefore draw near with boldness unto the throne of grace, that we may receive mercy, and may find grace to help* us *in time of need.* The same apostle says: *Having boldness to enter into the holy place by the blood of Jesus, let us draw near with a true heart in fulness of faith,* etc. Likewise: Christ *hath his priesthood unchangeable; wherefore also he is able to save to the uttermost them that draw near unto God through him, seeing he ever liveth to make intercession for them.*

What more can be required? since Christ Himself says: *I am the way, and the truth, and the life: no one cometh unto the Father, but by me.* To what purpose should we, then, seek another advocate, since it has pleased God to give us His own Son as an Advocate? Let us not forsake Him to take another, or rather to seek after another, without ever being able to find him; for God well knew, when He gave Him to us, that we were sinners.

Therefore, according to the command of Christ, we call upon the heavenly Father through Jesus Christ our only Mediator, as we are taught in the Lord's Prayer; being assured that whatever we ask of the Father in His Name will be granted us.

ARTICLE XXVII

THE CATHOLIC CHRISTIAN CHURCH

We believe and profess one catholic or universal Church, which is a holy congregation of true Christian believers, all expecting their salvation in Jesus Christ, being washed by His blood, sanctified and sealed by the Holy Spirit.

This Church has been from the beginning of the world, and will be to the end thereof; which is evident from this that Christ is an eternal King, which without subjects He cannot be. And this holy Church is preserved or supported by God against the rage of the whole world; though it sometimes for a while appears very small, and in the eyes of men to be reduced to nothing; as during the perilous reign of Ahab the Lord reserved unto Him seven thousand men who had not bowed their knees to Baal.

Furthermore, this holy Church is not confined, bound, or limited to a certain place or to certain persons, but is spread and dispersed over the whole world; and yet is joined and united with heart and will, by the power of faith, in one and the same Spirit.

ARTICLE XXVIII

EVERY ONE IS BOUND TO JOIN HIMSELF TO THE TRUE CHURCH

We believe, since this holy congregation is an assembly of those who are saved, and outside of it there is no salvation, that no person of whatsoever state or condition he may be, ought to withdraw from it, content to be by himself; but that all men are in duty bound to join and unite themselves with it; maintaining the unity of the Church; submitting themselves to the doctrine and discipline thereof; bowing their necks under the yoke of Jesus Christ; and as mutual members of the same body, serving to the edification of the brethren, according to the talents God has given them.

And that this may be the more effectually observed, it is the duty of all believers, according to the Word of God, to separate themselves from all those who do not belong to the Church, and to join themselves to this congregation, wheresoever God has established it, even though the magistrates and edicts of princes were against it, yea, though they should suffer death or any other corporal punishment. Therefore all those who separate themselves from the same or do not join themselves to it act contrary to the ordinance of God.

ARTICLE XXIX

THE MARKS OF THE TRUE CHURCH, AND WHEREIN IT DIFFERS FROM THE FALSE CHURCH

We believe that we ought diligently and circumspectly to discern from the Word of God which is the true Church, since all sects which are in the world assume to themselves the name of the Church. But we speak not here of hypocrites, who are mixed in the Church with the good, yet are not of the Church, though externally in it; but we say that the body and communion of the true Church must be distinguished from all sects that call themselves the Church.

The marks by which the true Church is known are these: If the pure doctrine of the gospel is preached therein; if it maintains the pure administration of the sacraments as instituted by Christ; if church discipline is exercised in punishing of sin; in short, if all things are managed according to the pure Word of God, all things contrary thereto rejected, and Jesus Christ acknowledged as the only Head of the Church. Hereby the true Church may certainly be known, from which no man has a right to separate himself.

With respect to those who are members of the Church, they may be known by the marks of Christians; namely, by faith, and when, having received Jesus Christ the only Savior, they avoid sin, follow after righteousness, love the true God and their neighbor, neither turn aside to the right or left, and crucify the flesh with the works thereof. But this is not to be understood as if there did not remain in them great infirmities; but they fight against them through the Spirit all the days of their life, continually taking their refuge in the blood, death, passion, and obedience of our Lord Jesus Christ, in whom they have remission of sins, through faith in Him.

As for the false Church, it ascribes more power and authority to itself and its ordinances than to the Word of God, and will not submit itself to the yoke of Christ. Neither does it administer the sacraments as appointed by Christ in His Word, but adds to and takes from them, as it thinks proper; it relies more upon men than upon Christ; and persecutes those who live holily according to the Word of God and rebuke it for its errors, covetousness, and idolatry.

These two Churches are easily known and distinguished from each other.

ARTICLE XXX

THE GOVERNMENT OF THE CHURCH AND ITS OFFICES

We believe that this true Church must be governed by that spiritual polity which our Lord has taught us in His Word; namely, that there must be ministers or pastors to preach the Word of God and to administer the sacraments; also elders and deacons, who, together with the pastors, form the council of the Church; that by these means the true religion may be preserved, and the true doctrine everywhere propagated, likewise transgressors punished and restrained by spiritual means; also that the poor and distressed may be relieved and comforted, according to their necessities. By these means everything will be carried on in the Church with good order and decency, when faithful men are chosen, according to the rule prescribed by St. Paul in his Epistle to Timothy.

ARTICLE XXXI

THE MINISTERS, ELDERS, AND DEACONS

We believe that the ministers of God's Word, the elders, and the deacons ought to be chosen to their respective offices by a lawful election by the Church, with calling upon the name of the Lord, and in that order which the Word of God teaches. Therefore every one must take heed not to intrude himself by improper means, but is bound to wait till it shall please God to call him; that he may have testimony of his calling, and be certain and assured that it is of the Lord.

As for the ministers of God's Word, they have equally the same power and authority wheresoever they are, as they are all ministers of Christ, the only universal Bishop and the only Head of the Church.

Moreover, in order that this holy ordinance of God may not be violated or slighted, we say that every one ought to esteem the ministers of God's Word and the elders of the Church very highly for their work's sake, and be at peace with them without murmuring, strife, or contention, as much as possible.

ARTICLE XXXII

THE ORDER AND DISCIPLINE OF THE CHURCH

In the meantime we believe, though it is useful and beneficial that those who are rulers of the Church institute and establish certain ordinances among themselves for maintaining the body of the Church, yet that they ought studiously to take care that they do not depart from those things which Christ, our only Master, has instituted. And therefore we reject all human inventions, and all laws which man would introduce into the worship of God, thereby to bind and compel the conscience in any manner whatever. Therefore we admit only of that which tends to nourish and preserve concord and unity, and to keep all men in obedience to God. For this purpose, excommunication or church discipline is requisite, with all that pertains to it, according to the Word of God.

ARTICLE XXXIII

THE SACRAMENTS

We believe that our gracious God, taking account of our weakness and infirmities, has ordained the sacraments for us, thereby to seal unto us His promises, and to be pledges of the good will and grace of God towards us, and also to nourish and strengthen our faith; which He has joined to the Word of the gospel, the better to present to our senses both that which He declares to us by His Word and that which He works inwardly in our hearts, thereby confirming in us the salvation which He imparts to us. For they are visible signs and seals of an inward and invisible thing, by means whereof God works in us by the power of the Holy Spirit. Therefore the signs are not empty or meaningless, so as to deceive us. For Jesus Christ is the true object presented by them, without whom they would be of no moment.

Moreover, we are satisfied with the number of sacraments which Christ our Lord has instituted, which are two only, namely, the sacrament of baptism and the holy supper of our Lord Jesus Christ.

ARTICLE XXXIV

HOLY BAPTISM

We believe and confess that Jesus Christ, who is the end of the law, has made an end, by the shedding of His blood, of all other sheddings of blood which men could or would make as a propitiation or satisfaction for sin; and that He, having abolished circumcision, which was done with blood, has instituted the sacrament of baptism instead thereof; by which we are received into the Church of God, and separated from all other people and strange religions, that we may wholly belong to Him whose mark and ensign we bear; and which serves as a testimony to us that He will forever be our gracious God and Father.

Therefore He has commanded all those who are His to be baptized with pure water, *into the name of the Father and of the Son and of the Holy Spirit,* thereby signifying to us, that as water washes away the filth of the body when poured upon it, and is seen on the body of the baptized when sprinkled upon him, so does the blood of Christ by the power of the Holy Spirit internally sprinkle the soul, cleanse it from its sins, and regenerate us from children of wrath unto children of God. Not that this is effected by the external water, but by the sprinkling of the precious blood of the Son of God; who is our Red Sea, through which we must pass to escape the tyranny of Pharaoh, that is, the devil, and to enter into the spiritual land of Canaan.

The ministers, therefore, on their part administer the sacrament and that which is visible, but our Lord gives that which is signified by the sacrament, namely, the gifts and invisible grace; washing, cleansing, and purging our souls of all filth and unrighteousness; renewing our hearts and filling them with all comfort; giving unto us a true assurance of His fatherly goodness; putting on us the new man, and putting off the old man with all his deeds.

We believe, therefore, that every man who is earnestly studious of obtaining life eternal ought to be baptized but once with this only baptism, without ever repeating the same, since we cannot be born twice. Neither does this baptism avail us only at the time when the water is poured upon us and received by us, but also through the whole course of our life.

Therefore we detest the error of the Anabaptists, who are not content with the one only baptism they have once received, and moreover condemn the baptism of the infants of believers, who we believe ought to be baptized and sealed with the sign of the covenant, as the children in Israel formerly were circumcised upon the same promises which are made unto our children. And indeed Christ shed His blood no less for the washing of the children of believers than for adult persons; and therefore they ought to receive the sign and sacrament of that which Christ has done for them; as the Lord commanded in the law that they should be made partakers of the sacrament of Christ's suffering and death shortly after they were born, by offering for them a lamb, which was a sacrament of Jesus Christ. Moreover, what circumcision was to the Jews, baptism is to our children. And for this reason St. Paul calls baptism the *circumcision of Christ*.

ARTICLE XXXV

THE HOLY SUPPER OF OUR LORD JESUS CHRIST

We believe and confess that our Savior Jesus Christ did ordain and institute the sacrament of the holy supper to nourish and support those whom He has already regenerated and incorporated into His family, which is His Church.

Now those who are regenerated have in them a twofold life, the one corporal and temporal, which they have from the first birth and is common to all men; the other spiritual and heavenly, which is given them in their second birth, which is effected by the Word of the gospel, in the communion of the body of Christ; and this life is not common, but is peculiar to God's elect. In like manner God has given us, for the support of the bodily and earthly life, earthly and common bread, which is subservient thereto and is common to all men, even as life itself. But for the support of the spiritual and heavenly life which believers have He has sent a living bread, which descended from heaven, namely, Jesus Christ, who nourishes and strengthens the spiritual life of believers when they eat Him, that is to say, when they appropriate and receive Him by faith in the spirit.

In order that He might represent unto us this spiritual and heavenly bread, Christ has instituted an earthly and visible bread as a sacrament of His body, and wine as a sacrament of His blood, to testify by them unto us that, as certainly as we receive and hold this sacrament in our hands and eat and drink the same with our mouths, by which our life is afterwards nourished, we also do as certainly receive by faith (which is the hand and mouth of our soul) the true body and blood of Christ our only Savior in our souls, for the support of our spiritual life.

Now, as it is certain and beyond all doubt that Jesus Christ has not enjoined to us the use of His sacraments in vain, so He works in us all that He represents to us by these holy signs, though the manner surpasses our understanding and cannot be comprehended by us, as the operations of the Holy Spirit are hidden and incomprehensible. In the meantime we err not when we say that what is eaten and drunk by us is the proper and natural body and the proper blood of Christ. But the manner of our partaking of the same is not by the mouth, but by the spirit through faith. Thus, then, though Christ always sits at the right hand of His Father in the heavens, yet does He not therefore cease to make us partakers of Himself by faith. This feast is a spiritual table, at which Christ communicates Himself with all His benefits to us, and gives us there to enjoy both Himself and the merits of His sufferings and death: nourishing, strengthening, and comforting our poor comfortless souls by the eating of His flesh, quickening and refreshing them by the drinking of His blood.

Further, though the sacraments are connected with the thing signified nevertheless both are not received by all men. The ungodly indeed receives the sacrament to his condemnation, but he does not receive the truth of the sacrament, even as Judas and Simon the sorcerer both indeed received the sacrament but not Christ who was signified by it, of whom believers only are made partakers.

Lastly, we receive this holy sacrament in the assembly of the people of God, with humility and reverence, keeping up among us a holy remembrance of the death of Christ our Savior, with thanksgiving, making there confession of our faith and of the Christian religion. Therefore no one ought to come to this table without having previously rightly examined himself, lest by eating of this bread and drinking of this cup he eat and drink judgment to himself. In a word, we are moved by the use of this holy sacrament to a fervent love towards God and our neighbor.

Therefore we reject all mixtures and damnable inventions which men have added unto and blended with the sacraments, as profanations of them; and affirm that we ought to rest satisfied with the ordinance which Christ and His apostles have taught us, and that we must speak of them in the same manner as they have spoken.

ARTICLE XXXVI

THE MAGISTRACY (CIVIL GOVERNMENT)

We believe that our gracious God, because of the depravity of mankind, has appointed kings, princes, and magistrates; willing that the world should be governed by certain laws and policies; to the end that the dissoluteness of men might be restrained, and all things carried on among them with good order and decency. For this purpose He has invested the magistracy with *the sword for the punishment of evil-doers and for the protection of them that do well.*

Their office is not only to have regard unto and watch for the welfare of the civil state, but also to protect the sacred ministry,* that the kingdom of Christ may thus be promoted. They must therefore countenance the preaching of the Word of the gospel everywhere, that God may be honored and worshipped by every one, as He commands in His Word.

Moreover, it is the bounden duty of every one, of whatever state, quality,

---

* In the original text this sentence read as follows: "Their office is not only to have regard unto and watch for the welfare of the civil state, but also that they protect the sacred ministry, and thus may remove and prevent all idolatry and false worship, that the kingdom of antichrist may be thus destroyed and the kingdom of Christ promoted." The Synod of 1910, recognizing the unbiblical teaching, contained in this sentence, concerning freedom of religion and concerning the duty of the state to suppress false religion, saw fit to add an explanatory footnote. The synod of 1938, agreeing with the Synod of 1910 as to the unbiblical character of the teaching referred to, but recognizing a conflict between the objectionable clauses in the Article and its footnote, decided to eliminate the footnote and to make the change in the text of the Article which appears above, corresponding to the change adopted in 1905 by the General Synod of the "Gereformeerde Kerken in Nederland." (See *Acts of Synod, 1910,* pp. 9, 104-105; also *Acts of Synod, 1938,* p. 17.)

or condition he may be, to subject himself to the magistrates; to pay tribute, to show due honor and respect to them, and to obey them in all things which are not repugnant to the Word of God; to supplicate for them in their prayers that God may rule and guide them in all their ways, and *that we may lead a tranquil and quiet life in all godliness and gravity.*

Wherefore we detest the Anabaptists and other seditious people, and in general all those who reject the higher powers and magistrates and would subvert justice, introduce community of goods, and confound that decency and good order which God has established among men.

ARTICLE XXXVII

THE LAST JUDGMENT

Finally, we believe, according to the Word of God, when the time appointed by the Lord (which is unknown to all creatures) is come and the number of the elect complete, that our Lord Jesus Christ will come from heaven, corporally and visibly, as He ascended, with great glory and majesty to declare Himself Judge of the living and the dead, burning this old world with fire and flame to cleanse it.

Then all men will personally appear before this great Judge, both men and women and children, that have been from the beginning of the world to the end thereof, being summoned by *the voice of the archangel, and by the sound of the trump of God.* For all the dead shall be raised out of the earth, and their souls joined and united with their proper bodies in which they formerly lived. As for those who shall then be living, they shall not die as the others, but be changed in the twinkling of an eye, and from corruptible become incorruptible. Then *the books* (that is to say, the consciences) *shall be opened, and the dead judged* according to what they shall have done in this world, whether it be good or evil. Nay, all men *shall give account of every idle word they have spoken*, which the world only counts amusement and jest; and then the secrets and hypocrisy of men shall be disclosed and laid open before all.

And therefore the consideration of this judgment is justly terrible and dreadful to the wicked and ungodly, but most desirable and comfortable to the righteous and elect; because then their full deliverance shall be perfected, and there they shall receive the fruits of their labor and trouble which they have borne. Their innocence shall be known to all, and they shall see the terrible vengeance which God shall execute on the wicked, who most cruelly persecuted, oppressed, and tormented them in this world, and who shall be convicted by the testimony of their own consciences, and shall become immortal, but only to be tormented in *the eternal fire which is prepared for the devil and his angels.*

But on the contrary, the faithful and elect shall be crowned with glory and honor; and the Son of God will confess their names before God His Father and His elect angels; all tears shall be wiped from their eyes; and their cause which is now condemned by many judges and magistrates as heretical and impious will then be known to be the cause of the Son of God. And for a gracious reward, the Lord will cause them to possess such a glory as never entered into the heart of man to conceive.

Therefore we expect that great day with a most ardent desire, to the end that we may fully enjoy the promises of God in Christ Jesus our Lord. AMEN. *Amen, come, Lord Jesus.*—Rev. 22: 20.

HEIDELBERG CATECHISM

The second of our Doctrinal Standards is the Catechism. It is called the *Heidelberg Catechism* because it originated in Heidelberg, the capital of the German Electorate of the Palatinate, at the behest of the Elector, Frederick III. In order that the Calvinistic Reformation might gain the ascendancy in his domain, this pious ruler charged *Zacharias Ursinus*, professor at the Heidelberg University, and *Caspar Olevianus*, the court preacher, with the preparation of a manual for catechetical instruction. The result was a new Catechism, which, after having been approved by the Elector himself and by a gathering of prominent Calvinists, was published in the beginning of the year 1563. Its immediate popularity was indicated by the fact that the same year three more editions had to be printed. Moreover, the book was made to serve a new purpose, namely, to be used as a manual for doctrinal preaching on the Lord's Day. In the third edition the questions and answers were grouped into 52 sections, called *Lord's Days*, that the entire Catechism might be explained to the churches once a year.

In the Netherlands this Heidelberg Catechism became generally and favorably known almost as soon as it came from the press, mainly through the efforts of *Petrus Dathenus*, who translated it into the Dutch language and added this translation to his Dutch rendering of the Genevan Psalter, which was published in 1566. In the same year *Peter Gabriel* set the example of explaining this Catechism to his congregation at Amsterdam in his Sunday afternoon sermons. The National Synods of the 16th century adopted it as one of the Forms of Unity, the office-bearers being required to subscribe to it and the ministers to explain it to the churches. These requirements were strongly emphasized by the great Synod of Dort in 1618–19, and are still in force in the Christian Reformed Church and some other Reformed communions. At the present day the Heidelberg Catechism still has the distinction of being the most influential and the most generally accepted of the several Catechisms of Reformation times.

LORD'S DAY I

1. QUESTION. What is your only comfort in life and death?

ANSWER. That I, with body and soul, both in life and death[1], am not my own[2], but belong unto my faithful Savior Jesus Christ[3]; who with His precious blood has fully satisfied for all my sins[4], and delivered me from all the power of the devil[5]; and so preserves me[6] that without the will of my heavenly Father not a hair can fall from my head[7]; yea, that all things must be subservient to my salvation[8], wherefore by His Holy Spirit He also assures me of eternal life[9], and makes me heartily willing and ready, henceforth, to live unto Him[10].

[1] Rom. 14:8
[2] 1 Cor. 6:19
[3] 1 Cor. 3:23; Tit. 2:14
[4] 1 Pet. 1:18, 19; 1 John 1:7; 2:2, 12
[5] Heb. 2:14; 1 John 3:8; John 8:34–36

[6] John 6:39; 10:28, 29; 2 Thess. 3:3; 1 Pet. 1:5
[7] Matt. 10:30; Luke 21:18
[8] Rom. 8:28
[9] 2 Cor. 1:22; 5:5; Eph. 1:14; Rom. 8:16
[10] Rom. 8:14; 1 John 3:3

2. Q. How many things are necessary for you to know, that you in this comfort may live and die happily?

A. Three[1]; the first, how great my sins and misery are[2]; the second, how I am delivered from all my sins and misery[3]; the third, how I am to be thankful to God for such deliverance[4].

[1] Matt. 11:28–30; Eph. 5:8
[2] John 9:41; Matt. 9:12; Rom. 3:10; 1 John 1:9, 10
[3] John 17:3; Acts 4:12; 10:43
[4] Eph. 5:10; Ps. 50:14; Matt. 5:16; 1 Pet. 2:12; Rom. 6:13; 2 Tim. 2:15

THE FIRST PART

SIN AND MISERY

LORD'S DAY II

3. Q. Whence do you know your misery?

A. Out of the law of God[1].

[1] Rom. 3:20

4. Q. What does the law of God require of us?

A. Christ teaches that in a summary, Matt. 22:37–40, *Thou shalt love the Lord thy God with all thy heart, and with all thy soul, and with all thy mind. This is the great and first commandment. And a second like* unto it *is this, Thou shalt love thy neighbor as thyself. On these two commandments the whole law hangeth, and the prophets*[1].

[1] Deut. 6:5; Lev. 19:18; Mark 12:30; Luke 10:27

5. Q. Can you keep all this perfectly?

A. In no wise[1]; for I am prone by nature to hate God and my neighbor[2].

[1] Rom. 3:10, 20, 23; 1 John 1:8, 10
[2] Rom. 8:7; Eph. 2:3; Tit. 3:3; Gen. 6:5; 8:21; Jer. 17:9; Rom. 7:23

LORD'S DAY III

6. Q. Did God, then, create man so wicked and perverse?

A. By no means; but God created man good[1], and after His own image[2]; that is, in true righteousness and holiness, that he might rightly know God his Creator, heartily love Him, and live with Him in eternal blessedness to praise and glorify Him[3].

[1] Gen. 1:31   [2] Gen. 1:26, 27   [3] Eph. 4:24; Col. 3:10; 2 Cor. 3:18

7. Q. Whence, then, comes this depraved nature of man?

A. From the fall and disobedience of our first parents, Adam and Eve, in Paradise[1], whereby our nature became so corrupt that we all are conceived and born in sin[2].

[1] Gen. 3; Rom. 5:12, 18, 19   [2] Ps. 51:5; Gen. 5:3

8. Q. But are we so corrupt that we are wholly incapable of doing any good, and inclined to all evil?

A. Yes, indeed[1]; unless we are regenerated by the Spirit of God[2].

[1] Gen. 8:21; 6:5; Job 14:4; 15:14, 16, 35; John 3:6; Isa. 53:6
[2] John 3:3, 5; 1 Cor. 12:3; 2 Cor. 3:5

LORD'S DAY IV

9. Q. Does not God, then, wrong man by requiring of him in His law that which he cannot perform?

A. Not at all; for God made man capable of performing it[1]; but man, through the instigation of the devil[2], by his own wilful disobedience, deprived himself and all his posterity of these gifts[3].

[1] Eph. 4:24   [2] Gen. 3:13; 1 Tim. 2:13, 14   [3] Gen. 3:6; Rom. 5:12

10. Q. Will God suffer such disobedience and apostasy to go unpunished?

A. By no means; but He is terribly displeased[1] with our original as well as actual sins; and will punish them by a just judgment temporally and eternally[2], as He has declared, *Cursed is every one who continueth not in all things that are written in the book of the law, to do them*[3].

[1] Gen. 2:17; Rom. 5:12   [2] Ps. 50:21; 5:5; Nah. 1:2; Ex. 20:5; 34:7; Rom. 1:18; Eph. 5:6
[3] Deut. 27:26; Gal. 3:10

11. Q. Is, then, God not also merciful?

A. God is indeed merciful[1], but He is also just[2]; therefore His justice requires that sin which is committed against the most high majesty of God, be also punished with extreme, that is, with everlasting punishment of body and soul.

[1] Ex. 34:6, 7; 20:6   [2] Ps. 7:9; Ex. 20:5; 23:7; 34:7; Ps. 5:4, 5; Nah. 1:2, 3

The Second Part
DELIVERANCE
LORD'S DAY V

12. Q. Since, then, by the righteous judgment of God we deserve temporal and eternal punishment, is there no way by which we may escape that punishment and be again received into favor?

A. God will have His justice satisfied[1]; therefore we must make full satisfaction to the same, either by ourselves, or by another[2].

[1] Gen. 2:17; Ex. 23:7; Ezek. 18:4; Matt. 5:26; 2 Thess. 1:6; Luke 16:2
[2] Rom. 8:4

13. Q. But can we ourselves make this satisfaction?

A. By no means; on the contrary, we daily increase our debt[1].

[1] Job 9:2; 15:15, 16; 4:18, 19; Ps. 130:3; Matt. 6:12; 18:25; 16:26

14. Q. Can there be found anywhere a mere creature able to satisfy for us?

A. None; for, first, God will not punish any other creature for the sin which man has committed[1]; and, further, no mere creature can sustain the burden of God's eternal wrath against sin, and deliver others from it[2].

[1] Ezek. 18:4; Gen. 3:17   [2] Nah. 1:6; Ps. 130:3

15. Q. What manner of mediator and deliverer, then, must we seek?

A. One who is a true[1] and righteous[2] man, and yet more powerful than all creatures; that is, one who is withal true God[3].

[1] 1 Cor. 15:21   [2] Heb. 7:26   [3] Isa. 7:14; 9:6; Jer. 23:6; Luke 11:22

LORD'S DAY VI

16. Q. Why must He be a true and righteous man?

A. Because the justice of God requires that the same human nature which has sinned should make satisfaction for sin[1], and because one who himself is a sinner cannot satisfy for others[2].

[1] Ezek. 18:4, 20; Rom. 5:18; 1 Cor. 15:21; Heb. 2:14–16   [2] Heb. 7:26, 27; Ps. 49:8; 1 Pet. 3:18

17. Q. Why must He withal be true God?

A. That by the power of His Godhead[1] He might bear in His human nature[2] the burden of God's wrath[3]; and that He might obtain for us, and restore to us, righteousness and life[4].

[1] Isa. 9:6; 63:3
[2] Deut. 4:24; Nah. 1:6; Ps. 130:3
[3] Isa. 53:4, 11
[4] Isa. 53:5, 11

18. Q. But who is that Mediator who is at once true God[1] and a true[2], righteous man[3]?

A. Our Lord Jesus Christ[4], *who was made unto us wisdom from God, and righteousness and sanctification, and redemption[5].*

[1] 1 John 5:20; Rom. 9:5; 8:3; Gal. 4:4; Isa. 9:6; Jer. 23:6; Mal. 3:1
[2] Luke 1:42; 2:6, 7; Rom. 1:3; 9:5; Phil. 2:7; Heb. 2:14, 16, 17; 4:15
[3] Isa. 53:9, 11; Jer. 23:5; Luke 1:35; John 8:46; Heb. 4:15; 7:26; 1 Pet. 1:19; 2:22; 3:18
[4] 1 Tim. 2:5; Matt. 1:23; 1 Tim. 3:16; Luke 2:11; Heb. 2:9
[5] 1 Cor. 1:30

19. Q. Whence do you know this?

A. From the holy gospel, which God Himself first revealed in Paradise[1]; afterwards published by the holy patriarchs[2] and prophets[3], and foreshadowed by the sacrifices and other ceremonies of the law[4]; and lastly fulfilled by His only begotten Son[5].

[1] Gen. 3:15
[2] Gen. 22:18; 12:3; 49:10
[3] Isa. 53; 42:1–4; 43:25; 49:5, 6, 22, 23; Jer. 23:5, 6; 31:32, 33; 32:39–41; Mic. 7:18–20; Acts 10:43; 3:22–24; Rom. 1:2; Heb. 1:1
[4] Heb. 10:1, 7; Col. 2:7; John 5:46
[5] Rom. 10:4; Gal. 4:4; 3:24; Col. 2:17

LORD'S DAY VII

20. Q. Are all men, then, saved by Christ as they perished through Adam?

A. No[1]; but only those who by a true faith are ingrafted into Him and receive all His benefits[2].

[1] Matt. 7:14; 22:14
[2] Mark 16:16; John 1:12; 3:16, 18, 36; Isa. 53:11; Ps. 2:12; Rom. 11:20; 3:22; Heb. 4:3; 5:9; 10:39; 11:6

21. Q. What is true faith?

A. True faith is not only a sure knowledge, whereby I hold for truth all that God has revealed to us in His Word[1], but also a firm confidence[2] which the Holy Spirit[3] works in my heart by the gospel[4], that not only to others, but to me also, remission of sins, everlasting righteousness and salvation[5] are freely given by God, merely of grace, only for the sake of Christ's merits[6].

[1] Jas. 2:19
[2] Heb. 11:1, 7; Rom. 4:18–21; 10:10; Eph. 3:12; Heb. 4:16; Jas. 1:6
[3] Gal. 5:22; Matt. 16:17; 2 Cor. 4:13; John 6:29; Eph. 2:8; Phil. 1:19; Acts 16:14
[4] Rom. 1:16; 10:17; 1 Cor. 1:21; Acts 10:44; 16:14
[5] Rom. 1:17; Gal. 3:11; Heb. 10:10, 38; Gal. 2:16
[6] Eph. 2:8; Rom. 3:24; 5:19; Luke 1:77, 78

22. Q. What, then, is necessary for a Christian to believe?

A. All that is promised us in the gospel[1], which the articles of our catholic and undoubted Christian faith teach us in a summary.

[1] John 20:31; Matt. 28:19; Mark 1:15

23. Q. What are these articles?

A. I. *I believe in God the Father, Almighty, Maker of heaven and earth.*

II. *And in Jesus Christ, His only begotten Son, our Lord;*

III. *Who was conceived by the Holy Spirit, born of the virgin Mary;*

IV. *Suffered under Pontius Pilate; was crucified, dead, and buried;* **He** *descended into hell;*

V. *The third day He rose again from the dead;*

    VI.   *He ascended into heaven, and sitteth at the right hand of God the Father Almighty;*

   VII.   *From thence He shall come to judge the living and the dead.*

 VIII.   *I believe in the Holy Spirit.*

    IX.   *I believe a holy catholic Church, the communion of saints;*

     X.   *The forgiveness of sins;*

    XI.   *The resurrection of the body;*

   XII.   *And the life everlasting.*

LORD'S DAY VIII

24. Q.   How are these articles divided?

    A.   Into three parts: the first is of God the Father and our creation; the second of God the Son and our redemption; the third of God the Holy Spirit and our sanctification.

25. Q.   Since there is but one divine Being[1], why do you speak of three, Father, Son, and Holy Spirit?

    A.   Because God has so revealed Himself in His Word[2] that these three distinct persons are the one, true, and eternal God.

[1] Deut. 6:4; Eph. 4:6; Isa. 44:6; 45:5; 1 Cor. 8:4, 6
[2] Isa. 61:1; Luke 4:18; Gen. 1:2, 3; Ps. 33:6; Isa. 48:16; Matt. 3:16, 17; 28:19; 1 John 5:7 (A.V.); Isa. 6:1, 3; John 14:26; 15:26; 2 Cor. 13:14; Gal. 4:6; Eph. 2:18; Tit. 3:5, 6

LORD'S DAY IX

26. Q.   What do you believe when you say: *I believe in God the Father, Almighty, Maker of heaven and earth?*

    A.   That the eternal Father of our Lord Jesus Christ, who of nothing made heaven and earth with all that is in them[1], who likewise upholds and governs the same by His eternal counsel and providence[2], is for the sake of Christ His Son my God and my Father[3]; in whom I so trust as to have no doubt that He will provide me with all things necessary for body and soul[4]; and further, that whatever evil He sends upon me in this vale of tears, He will turn to my good[5]; for He is able to do it, being almighty God[6], and willing also, being a faithful Father[7].

[1] Gen. 1 and 2; Ex. 20:11; Job 33:4; Job 38 and 39; Acts 4:24; 14:15; Ps. 33:6; Isa. 45:7
[2] Heb. 1:3; Ps. 104:27–30; 115:3; Matt. 10:29; Eph. 1:11
[3] John 1:12; Rom. 8:15; Gal. 4:5–7; Eph. 1:5
[4] Ps. 55:22; Matt. 6:25, 26; Luke 12:22
[5] Rom. 8:28
[6] Isa. 46:4; Rom. 10:12
[7] Matt. 6:32, 33; 7:9, 10, 11

LORD'S DAY X

27. Q.   What do you mean by the providence of God?

    A.   The almighty and everywhere present power of God[1], whereby, as it were by His hand, He still upholds heaven, earth, and all creatures, and so governs them[2] that herbs and grass, rain and drought[3], fruitful and barren years, food and drink, health and sickness[4], riches and poverty[5], yea, all things, come not by chance but by His fatherly hand[6].

[1] Acts 17:25–28; Jer. 23:23, 24; Isa. 29:15, 16; Ezek. 8:12
[2] Heb. 1:3
[3] Jer. 5:24; Acts 14:17
[4] John 9:3
[5] Prov. 22:2
[6] Matt. 10:29; Prov. 16:33

28. Q.   What does it profit us to know that God has created, and by His providence still upholds, all things?

A. That we may be patient in adversity[1], thankful in prosperity[2], and with a view to the future may have good confidence in our faithful God and Father[3] that no creature shall separate us from His love[4], since all creatures are so in His hand that without His will they cannot so much as move[5].

[1] Rom. 5:3; Jas. 1:3; Ps. 39:9; Job 1:21, 22
[2] 1 Thess. 5:18; Deut. 8:10
[3] Ps. 55:22; Rom. 5:4
[4] Rom. 8:38, 39
[5] Job 1:12; 2:6; Prov. 21:1; Acts 17:25

LORD'S DAY XI

29. Q. Why is the Son of God called *Jesus*, that is, *Savior*?

A. Because He delivers us from all our sins and saves us[1]; and because no salvation is to be sought or found in any other[2].

[1] Matt. 1:21; Heb. 7:25   [2] Acts 4:12; John 15:4, 5; 1 Tim. 2:5; Isa. 43:11; 1 John 5:11

30. Q. Do such, then, believe in the only Savior Jesus who seek their salvation and welfare of saints, of themselves, or anywhere else?

A. They do not; for though they boast of Him in words, yet in deeds they deny the only Savior Jesus[1]; for one of two things must be true: either Jesus is not a complete Savior, or they who by a true faith receive this Savior must find in Him all things necessary to their salvation[2].

[1] 1 Cor. 1:13, 31; Gal. 5:4   [2] Heb. 12:2; Isa. 9:6; Col. 1:19, 20; 2:10; 1 John 1:7

LORD'S DAY XII

31. Q. Why is He called *Christ*, that is, *Anointed*?

A. Because He is ordained of God the Father, and anointed with the Holy Spirit[1], to be our chief Prophet and Teacher[2], who has fully revealed to us the secret counsel and will of God concerning our redemption[3]; and our only High Priest[4], who by the one sacrifice of His body has redeemed us[5], and makes continual intercession for us with the Father[6]; and our eternal King, who governs us by His Word and Spirit, and defends and preserves us in the salvation obtained for us[7].

[1] Ps. 45:7; Heb. 1:9; Isa. 61:1; Luke 4:18
[2] Deut. 18:15; Acts 3:22; 7:37; Isa. 55:4
[3] John 1:18; 15:15
[4] Ps. 110:4
[5] Heb. 10:12, 14; 9:12, 14, 28
[6] Rom. 8:34; Heb. 9:24; 1 John 2:1; Rom. 5:9, 10
[7] Ps. 2:6; Zech. 9:9; Matt. 21:5; Luke 1:33; Matt. 28:18; John 10:28; Rev. 12:10, 11

32. Q. But why are you called a Christian[1]?

A. Because I am a member of Christ by faith[2], and thus a partaker of His anointing[3], that I may confess His Name[4], present myself a living sacrifice of thankfulness to Him[5], and with a free and good conscience fight against sin and the devil in this life[6], and hereafter reign with Him eternally over all creatures[7].

[1] Acts 11:26
[2] 1 Cor. 6:15
[3] 1 John 2:27; Acts 2:17
[4] Matt. 10:32; Rom. 10:10
[5] Rom. 12:1; 1 Pet. 2:5, 9; Rev. 1:6; 5:8, 10
[6] 1 Pet. 2:11; Rom. 6:12, 13; Gal. 5:16, 17; Eph. 6:11; 1 Tim. 1:18, 10
[7] 2 Tim. 2:12; Matt. 25:34

LORD'S DAY XIII

33. Q. Why is He called God's *only begotten Son*, since we also are children of God?

A. Because Christ alone is the eternal, natural Son of God[1]; but we are children of God by adoption, through grace, for Christ's sake[2].

[1] John 1:14; Heb. 1:1, 2; John 3:16; 1 John 4:9; Rom. 8:32
[2] Rom. 8:16; John 1:12; Gal. 4:6; Eph. 1:5, 6

34. Q. Why do you call Him *our Lord*?

A. Because He has redeemed us, body and soul, from all our sins, not with gold or silver, but with His precious blood, and has delivered us from all the power of the devil, and has made us His own possession[1].

[1] 1 Pet. 1:18, 19; 2:9; 1 Cor. 6:20; 1 Tim. 2:6; John 20:28

LORD'S DAY XIV

35. Q. What does it mean that He was *conceived by the Holy Spirit, born of the virgin Mary?*

A. That God's eternal Son, who is[1] and continues[2] true and eternal God, took upon Himself the very nature of man of the flesh and blood of the virgin Mary[3], by the operation of the Holy Spirit[4], that He might also be the true seed of David[5], like unto His brethren in all things[6], sin excepted[7].

[1] 1 John 5:20; John 1:1; 17:3; Rom. 1:3; Col. 1:15
[2] Rom. 9:5
[3] Gal. 4:4; Luke 1:31, 42, 43
[4] Matt. 1:20; Luke 1:35
[5] Rom. 1:3; Ps. 132:11; 2 Sam. 7:12; Luke 1:32; Acts 2:30
[6] Phil. 2:7; Heb. 2:14, 17
[7] Heb. 4:15

36. Q. What benefit do you receive from the holy conception and birth of Christ?

A. That He is our Mediator[1], and with His innocence and perfect holiness covers, in the sight of God, my sin wherein I was conceived and brought forth[2].

[1] Heb. 7:26, 27　　[2] 1 Pet. 1:18, 19; 3:18; 1 Cor. 1:30, 31; Rom. 8:3, 4; Isa. 53:11; Ps. 32:1

LORD'S DAY XV

37. Q. What does it mean that He *suffered*?

A. That all the time He lived on earth, but especially at the end of His life, He bore, in body and soul, the wrath of God against the sin of the whole human race[1], in order that by His passion, as the only atoning sacrifice[2], He might redeem our body and soul from everlasting damnation[3] and obtain for us the grace of God, righteousness, and eternal life[4].

[1] Isa. 53:4; 1 Pet. 2:24; 3:18; 1 Tim. 2:6
[2] Isa. 53:10; Eph. 5:2; 1 Cor. 5:7; 1 John 2:2; Rom. 3:25; Heb. 9:28; 10:14
[3] Gal. 3:13; Col. 1:13; Heb. 9:12; 1 Pet. 1:18, 19
[4] Rom. 3:25; 2 Cor. 5:21; John 3:16; 6:51; Heb. 9:15; 10:19

38. Q. Why did He suffer *under Pontius Pilate* as judge?

A. That He, though innocent, might be condemned by a temporal judge[1], and thereby free us from the severe judgment of God to which we were subject[2].

[1] John 18:38; Matt. 27:24; Luke 23:14, 15; John 19:4
[2] Ps. 69:4; Isa. 53:4, 5; 2 Cor. 5:21; Gal. 3:13

39. Q. Is there anything more in His having been *crucified* than if He had died some other death?

A. Yes, since thereby I am assured that He took on Himself the curse which lay upon me[1]; for the death of the cross was accursed of God[2].

[1] Gal. 3:13　　[2] Deut. 21:23

LORD'S DAY XVI

40. Q. Why was it necessary for Christ to humble Himself even unto *death*?

A. Because, by reason of the justice and truth of God[1], satisfaction for our sins could be made no otherwise than by the death of the Son of God[2].

[1] Gen. 2:17　　[2] Rom. 8:3, 4; Heb. 2:14. 15

41. Q. Why was He *buried*?

A. To prove thereby that He was really dead[1].

[1] Acts 13:29; Matt. 27:59, 60; Luke 23:53; John 19:38

42. Q. Since, then, Christ died for us, why must we also die?

A. Our death is not a satisfaction for our sins[1], but only a dying to sins and entering into eternal life[2].

[1] Mark 8:37; Ps. 49:7   [2] Phil. 1:23; John 5:24; Rom. 7:24

43. Q. What further benefit do we receive from the sacrifice and death of Christ on the cross?

A. That by His power our old man is crucified, slain, and buried with Him[1], that so the evil lusts of the flesh may no more reign in us[2], but that we may offer ourselves unto Him a sacrifice of thanksgiving[3].

[1] Rom. 6:6   [2] Rom. 6:6, 12   [3] Rom. 12:1

44. Q. Why is there added, *He descended into hell*?

A. That in my greatest temptations I may be assured, and wholly comfort myself with this, that my Lord Jesus Christ, by His inexpressible anguish, pains, terrors, and hellish agony in which He was plunged during all His sufferings[1], but especially on the cross, has delivered me from the anguish and torment of hell[2].

[1] Ps. 18:4, 5; 116:3; Matt. 26:38; 27:46; Heb. 5:7   [2] Isa. 53:5

LORD'S DAY XVII

45. Q. What does the *resurrection* of Christ profit us?

A. First, by His resurrection He has overcome death, that He might make us partakers of the righteousness which He has obtained for us by His death[1]; second, we also are raised up by His power to a new life[2]; and third, the resurrection of Christ is to us a sure pledge of our blessed resurrection[3].

[1] Rom. 4:25; 1 Pet. 1:3; 1 Cor. 15:16   [3] 1 Cor. 15:20, 21
[2] Rom. 6:4; Col. 3:1, 3; Eph. 2:5, 6

LORD'S DAY XVIII

46. Q. How do you understand the words, *He ascended into heaven*?

A. That Christ, in the sight of His disciples, was taken up from earth into heaven[1], and there continues for our interest[2], until He comes again to judge the living and the dead[3].

[1] Acts 1:9; Mark 16:19; Luke 24:51   [3] Acts 1:11; Matt. 24:30
[2] Heb. 9:24; 4:14; Rom. 8:34; Col. 3:1

47. Q. Is Christ, then, not with us even to the end of the world, as He has promised[1]?

A. Christ is true man and true God: with respect to His human nature, He is no more on earth[2]; but with respect to His Godhead, majesty, grace, and Spirit, He is at no time absent from us[3].

[1] Matt. 28:20   [3] John 14:18; Matt. 28:20
[2] Heb. 8:4; Matt. 26:11; John 16:28; 17:11; Acts 3:21

48. Q. But if His human nature is not present wherever His Godhead is, are not then these two natures in Christ separated from one another?

A. Not at all; for since the Godhead is illimitable and omnipresent[1], it must follow that it is beyond the bounds of the human nature it has assumed[2], and yet none the less is in this human nature and remains personally united to it.

[1] Jer. 23:24; Acts 7:49   [2] Col. 2:9; John 3:13; 11:15; Matt. 28:6

49. Q. Of what advantage to us is Christ's ascension into heaven?

A. First, that He is our Advocate in the presence of His Father in heaven[1]; second, that we have our flesh in heaven as a sure pledge that He, as the Head, will also take us, His members, up to Himself[2]; third, that He sends us His Spirit as an earnest[3], by whose power we *seek the things that are above, where Christ is, seated on the right hand of God, and not the things that are upon the earth*[4].

[1] 1 John 2:1; Rom. 8:34
[2] John 14:2; 17:24; 20:17; Eph. 2:6
[3] John 14:16; 16:7; Acts 2:33; 2 Cor. 1:22; 5:5
[4] Col. 3:1

LORD'S DAY XIX

50. Q. Why is it added, *And sitteth at the right hand of God*?

A. Because Christ ascended into heaven for this end, that He might there appear as Head of His Church[1], by whom the Father governs all things[2].

[1] Eph. 1:20–23; Col. 1:18   [2] Matt. 28:18; John 5:22

51. Q. What profit unto us is this glory of Christ, our Head?

A. First, that by His Holy Spirit He sheds forth heavenly gifts in us, His members[1]; then, that by His power He defends and preserves us against all enemies[2].

[1] Acts 2:33; Eph. 4:8   [2] Ps. 2:9; 110:1, 2; John 10:28; Eph. 4:8

52. Q. What comfort is it to you that Christ *shall come to judge the living and the dead*?

A. That in all my sorrows and persecutions, with uplifted head I look for the very same Person who before has offered Himself for my sake to the tribunal of God, and has removed all curse from me, to come as Judge from heaven[1]; who shall cast all His and my enemies into everlasting condemnation[2], but shall take me with all His chosen ones to Himself into heavenly joy and glory[3].

[1] Phil. 3:20; Luke 21:28; Rom. 8:23; Tit. 2:13; 1 Thess. 4:16
[2] Matt. 25:41; 2 Thess. 1:6   [3] Matt. 25:34; 2 Thess. 1:7

LORD'S DAY XX

53. Q. What do you believe concerning *the Holy Spirit*?

A. First, that He is true and co-eternal God with the Father and the Son[1]; second, that He is also given me[2], to make me by a true faith partaker of Christ and all His benefits[3], to comfort me[4], and to abide with me forever[5].

[1] 1 John 5:7; Gen. 1:2; Isa. 48:16; 1 Cor. 3:16; 6:19; Acts 5:3, 4
[2] Gal. 4:6; Matt. 28:19, 20; 2 Cor. 1:22; Eph. 1:13   [4] John 15:26; Acts 9:31
[3] Gal. 3:14; 1 Pet. 1:2; 1 Cor. 6:17   [5] John 14:16; 1 Pet. 4:14

LORD'S DAY XXI

54. Q. What do you believe concerning the *holy catholic Church*?

A. That the Son of God[1], out of the whole human race[2], from the beginning to the end of the world[3], gathers, defends, and preserves for Himself[4], by His Spirit and Word[5], in the unity of the true faith[6], a Church chosen to everlasting life[7]; and that I am[8], and forever shall remain, a living member thereof[9].

[1] Eph. 5:26; John 10:11; Acts 20:28; Eph. 4:11–13
[2] Gen. 26:4; Rev. 5:9
[3] Ps. 71:17, 18; Isa. 59:21; 1 Cor. 11:26
[4] Matt. 16:18; John 10:28–30; Ps. 129:1–5
[5] Isa. 59:21; Rom. 1:16; 10:14–17; Eph. 5:26
[6] Acts 2:42; Eph. 4:3–5
[7] Rom. 8:29; Eph. 1:10–13
[8] 1 John 3:14, 19–21; 2 Cor. 13:5; Rom. 8:10
[9] Ps. 23:6; 1 Cor. 1:8, 9; John 10:28; 1 John 2:19; 1 Pet. 1:5

55. Q. What do you understand by *the communion of saints*?

A. First, that believers, all and every one, as members of Christ, are partakers of Him and of all His treasures and gifts[1]; second, that every one must know himself bound to employ his gifts readily and cheerfully for the advantage and salvation of other members[2].

[1] 1 John 1:3; Rom. 8:32; 1 Cor. 12:12, 13; 1 Cor. 6:17   [2] 1 Cor. 12:21; 13:1, 5; Phil. 2:4–8

56. Q. What do you believe concerning *the forgiveness of sins*?

A. That God, for the sake of Christ's satisfaction, will no more remember my sins, neither my sinful nature, against which I have to struggle all my life long[1]; but will graciously grant unto me the righteousness of Christ[2], that I may never come into condemnation[3].

[1] 1 John 2:2; 1:7; 2 Cor. 5:19   [3] John 3:18; 5:24
[2] Rom. 7:23–25; Jer. 31:34; Mic. 7:19; Ps. 103:3, 10, 12

LORD'S DAY XXII

57. Q. What comfort does *the resurrection of the body* afford you?

A. That not only my soul, after this life, shall immediately be taken up to Christ, its Head[1]; but also that this my body, raised by the power of Christ, shall again be united with my soul, and made like unto the glorious body of Christ[2].

[1] Luke 16:22; 23:43; Phil. 1:21, 23   [2] Job 19:25, 26; 1 John 3:2; Phil. 3:21

58. Q. What comfort do you derive from the article of *the life everlasting*?

A. That, since I now feel in my heart the beginning of eternal joy[1], after this life I shall possess perfect bliss, such as eye has not seen nor ear heard, neither has entered into the heart of man—therein to praise God forever[2].

[1] 2 Cor. 5:2, 3, 6   [2] 1 Cor. 2:9

LORD'S DAY XXIII

59. Q. But what does it profit you now that you believe all this?

A. That I am righteous in Christ before God, and an heir to eternal life[1].

[1] Hab. 2:4; Rom. 1:17; John 3:36

60. Q. How are you righteous before God?

A. Only by a true faith in Jesus Christ[1]; that is, though my conscience accuse me that I have grievously sinned against all the commandments of God and kept none of them[2], and am still inclined to all evil[3], yet God, without any merit of mine[4], of mere grace[5], grants and imputes to me[6] the perfect satisfaction[7], righteousness, and holiness of Christ[8], as if I had never had nor committed any sin, and myself had accomplished all the obedience which Christ has rendered for me[9]; if only I accept such benefit with a believing heart[10].

[1] Rom. 3:21–24; 5:1, 2; Gal. 2:16; Eph. 2:8, 9; Phil. 3:9   [6] Rom. 4:4; 2 Cor. 5:19
[2] Rom. 3:9   [7] 1 John 2:2
[3] Rom. 7:23   [8] 1 John 2:1
[4] Tit. 3:5; Deut. 9:6; Ezek. 36:22   [9] 2 Cor. 5:21
[5] Rom. 3:24; Eph. 2:8   [10] Rom. 3:22; John 3:18

61. Q. Why do you say that you are righteous only by faith?

A. Not that I am acceptable to God on account of the worthiness of my faith, but because only the satisfaction, righteousness, and holiness of Christ is my righteousness before God[1], and I can receive the same and make it my own in no other way than by faith only[2].

[1] 1 Cor. 1:30; 2:2   [2] 1 John 5:10

LORD'S DAY XXIV

62. Q.   But why cannot our good works be the whole or part of our righteousness before God?

A.   Because the righteousness which can stand before the tribunal of God must be absolutely perfect and wholly conformable to the divine law[1], while even our best works in this life are all imperfect and defiled with sin[2].

[1] Gal. 3:10; Deut. 27:26   [2] Isa. 64:6

63. Q.   What? do our good works then merit nothing, while God will yet reward them in this and in the future life?

A.   This reward is not of merit but of grace[1]..

Luke 17:10

64. Q.   But does not this doctrine make men careless and profane?

A.   By no means; for it is impossible that those who are implanted into Christ by a true faith should not bring forth fruits of thankfulness[1].

[1] Matt. 7:18; John 15:5

LORD'S DAY XXV

65. Q.   Since, then, we are made partakers of Christ and all His benefits by faith only, whence comes this faith?

A.   From the Holy Spirit[1], who works it in our hearts by the preaching of the holy gospel, and confirms it by the use of the holy sacraments[2].

[1] Eph. 2:8; 6:23; John 3:5; Phil. 1:29   [2] Matt. 28:19; 1 Pet. 1:22, 23

66. Q.   What are the sacraments?

A.   The sacraments are holy, visible signs and seals, appointed of God for this end, that by the use thereof He may the more fully declare and seal to us the promise of the gospel; namely, that He of grace grants us the remission of sins and life eternal, for the sake of the one sacrifice of Christ accomplished on the cross[1].

[1] Gen. 17:11; Rom. 4:11; Deut. 30:6; Lev. 6:25; Heb. 9:7, 8, 9, 24; Ezek. 20:12; Isa. 6:6, 7; 54:9

67. Q.   Are, then, both the Word and the sacraments designed to direct our faith to the sacrifice of Jesus Christ on the cross as the only ground of our salvation?

A.   Yes, indeed; for the Holy Spirit teaches us in the gospel and assures us by the sacraments that the whole of our salvation stands in the one sacrifice of Christ made for us on the cross[1].

[1] Rom. 6:3; Gal. 3:27

68. Q.   How many sacraments has Christ instituted in the new covenant or testament?

A.   Two: holy baptism and the holy supper.

LORD'S DAY XXVI

69. Q.   How is it signified and sealed unto you in holy baptism that you have part in the one sacrifice of Christ on the cross?

A.   Thus, that Christ has appointed this outward washing with water[1] and added the promise[2] that I am washed with His blood and Spirit from the pollution of my soul, that is, from all my sins[3], as certainly as I am washed outwardly with water, by which the filthiness of the body is commonly washed away.

[1] Matt. 28:19   [3] 1 Pet. 3:21; Mark 1:4; Luke 3:3

[2] Matt. 28:19; Mark 16:16; Acts 2:38; John 1:33; Matt. 3:11; Rom. 6:3, 4

70. Q.   What is it to be washed with the blood and Spirit of Christ?

A.   It is to have the forgiveness of sins from God, through grace, for the sake of Christ's blood, which He shed for us in His sacrifice on the cross[1]; and also to be renewed by the Holy Spirit, and sanctified to be members of Christ, that so we may more and more die unto sin and lead holy and unblamable lives[2].

[1] Heb. 12:24; 1 Pet. 1:2; Rev. 1:5; 7:14; Zech. 13:1; Ezek. 36:25
[2] John 1:33; 3:5; 1 Cor. 6:11; 12:13; Rom. 6:4; Col. 2:12

71. Q. Where has Christ assured us that we are washed with His blood and Spirit as certainly as we are washed with the water of baptism?

A. In the institution of baptism, which reads thus: *Go ye therefore, and make disciples of all the nations, baptizing them into the name of the Father and of the Son and of the Holy Spirit*, Matt. 28:19. And: *He that believeth and is baptized shall be saved; but he that disbelieveth shall be condemned*, Mark 16:16. This promise is also repeated where the Scripture calls baptism *the washing of regeneration* and *the washing away of sins*, Tit. 3:5; Acts 22:16.

LORD'S DAY XXVII

72. Q. Is, then, the outward washing with water itself the washing away of sin?

A. No[1], for only the blood of Jesus Christ and the Holy Spirit cleanse us from all sins[2].

[1] Matt. 3:11; 1 Pet. 3:21; Eph. 5:26   [2] 1 John 1:7; 1 Cor. 6:11

73. Q. Why, then, does the Holy Spirit call baptism *the washing of regeneration* and *the washing away of sins*?

A. God speaks thus not without great cause: to wit, not only to teach us thereby that as the filthiness of the body is taken away by water, so our sins are removed by the blood and Spirit of Jesus Christ[1]; but especially to assure us by this divine pledge and sign that we are spiritually cleansed from our sins as really as we are outwardly washed with water[2].

[1] Rev. 1:5; 7:14; 1 Cor. 6:11   [2] Mark 16:16; Gal. 3:27

74. Q. Are infants also to be baptized?

A. Yes; for since they, as well as adults, are included in the covenant and Church of God[1], and since both redemption from sin[2] and the Holy Spirit, the Author of faith, are through the blood of Christ promised to them no less than to adults[3], they must also by baptism, as a sign of the covenant, be ingrafted into the Christian Church, and distinguished from the children of unbelievers[4], as was done in the old covenant or testament by circumcision[5], instead of which baptism was instituted in the new covenant[6].

[1] Gen. 17:7   [3] Luke 1:15; Ps. 22:10; Isa. 44:1-3; Acts 2:39   [5] Gen. 17:14
[2] Matt. 19:14   [4] Acts 10:47   [6] Col. 2:11-13

LORD'S DAY XXVIII

75. Q. How is it signified and sealed unto you in the holy supper that you partake of the one sacrifice of Christ, accomplished on the cross, and of all His benefits?

A. Thus, that Christ has commanded me and all believers to eat of this broken bread and to drink of this cup in remembrance of Him, and has added these promises[1]: first, that His body was offered and broken on the cross for me, and His blood shed for me, as certainly as I see with my eyes the bread of the Lord broken for me, and the cup communicated to me; and further, that with His crucified body and shed blood He Himself feeds and nourishes my soul to everlasting life as assuredly as I receive from the hand of the minister, and taste with my mouth, the bread and cup of the Lord as sure signs of the body and blood of Christ.

[1] Matt. 26:26-28; Mark 14:22-24; Luke 22:19, 20: 1 Cor. 10:16, 17: 11:23-25: 12:13

76. Q. What is it to eat the crucified body and drink the shed blood of Christ?

A. It is not only to embrace with a believing heart all the sufferings and the death of Christ, and thereby to obtain the forgiveness of sins and life eternal[1], but, further, also to become more and more united to His sacred body, by the Holy Spirit, who dwells both in Christ and in us[2], so that, though Christ is in heaven[3] and we are on earth, we are nevertheless flesh of His flesh and bone of His bones[4], and live and are governed by one Spirit, as members of the same body are by one soul[5].

[1] John 6:35, 40, 47, 48, 50, 51, 53, 54
[2] John 6:55, 56
[3] Col. 3:1; Acts 3:21; 1 Cor. 11:26
[4] Eph. 5:29, 30; 3:16; 1 Cor. 6:15; 1 John 3:24; 4:13
[5] John 6:57; 15:1–6; Eph. 4:15, 16

77. Q. Where has Christ promised that He will as certainly feed and nourish believers with His body and blood as they eat of this broken bread and drink of this cup?

A. In the institution of the supper[1], which reads thus: *The Lord Jesus in the night in which he was betrayed took bread; and when he had given thanks, he brake it, and said, This is my body, which is for you; this do in remembrance of me. In like manner also the cup, after supper, saying, This cup is the new covenant in my blood; this do, as often as ye drink it, in remembrance of me. For as often as ye eat this bread, and drink the cup, ye proclaim the Lord's death till he come,* 1 Cor. 11:23–26. This promise is repeated by St. Paul, where he says: *The cup of blessing which we bless, is it not a communion of the blood of Christ? The bread which we break, is it not a communion of the body of Christ? seeing that we, who are many, are one bread, one body; for we all partake of the one bread,* 1 Cor. 10:16, 17.

[1] Matt. 26:26–28; Mark 14:22–24; Luke 22:19, 20

LORD'S DAY XXIX

78. Q. Do, then, the bread and wine become the real body and blood of Christ?

A. No[1]; but as the water in baptism neither is changed into the blood of Christ, nor is the washing away of sins itself, being only the divine token and confirmation thereof[2], so likewise the bread in the Lord's supper does not become the real body of Christ[3], though agreeably to the nature and property of sacraments[4] it is called the body of Christ Jesus.

[1] Matt. 26:29
[2] Eph. 5:26; Tit. 3:5
[3] 1 Cor. 10:16; 11:26
[4] Gen. 17:10, 11; Ex. 12:11, 13; 13:9; 1 Pet. 3:21; 1 Cor. 10:3, 4

79. Q. Why, then, does Christ call the bread *His body,* and the cup *His blood* or *the new covenant in His blood,* and Paul, *a communion of the body and blood of Christ?*

A. Christ speaks thus not without great cause; namely, not only to teach us thereby that, as bread and wine sustain this temporal life, so also His crucified body and shed blood are the true food and drink of our souls unto eternal life[1]; but much more, by these visible signs and pledges to assure us that we are as really partakers of His true body and blood, through the working of the Holy Spirit, as we receive by the mouth of the body these holy tokens in remembrance of Him[2]; and that all His sufferings and obedience are as certainly ours as if we ourselves had in our own persons suffered and made satisfaction to God for our sins.

[1] John 6:55
[2] 1 Cor. 10:16

LORD'S DAY XXX

80. Q. What difference is there between the Lord's supper and the popish mass?

A. The Lord's supper testifies to us that we have full pardon of all our sins by the only sacrifice of Jesus Christ, which He Himself has once accomplished on the cross[1]; and that by the Holy Spirit we are ingrafted into Christ[2], who according to His human nature is now not on earth but in heaven, at the right hand of God His Father[3], and wills there to be worshipped by us[4]; but the mass teaches that the living and the dead have not the forgiveness of sins through the sufferings of Christ unless Christ is still daily offered for them by the priests; and that Christ is bodily present under the form of bread and wine and is therefore to be worshipped in them. And thus the mass, at bottom, is nothing else than a denial of the one sacrifice and passion of Jesus Christ, and an accursed idolatry[5].

[1] Heb. 10:10, 12; 7:26, 27; 9:12, 25; John 19:30; Matt. 26:28; Luke 22:19
[2] 1 Cor. 10:16, 17; 6:17
[3] John 20:17; Col. 3:1; Heb. 1:3; 8:1
[4] Matt. 6:20, 21; John 4:21; Luke 24:52; Acts 7:55; Col. 3:1; Phil. 3:20; 1 Thess. 1:10
[5] Heb. 9:26; 10:12, 14

81. Q. For whom is the Lord's supper instituted?

A. For those who are truly displeased with themselves for their sins and yet trust that these are forgiven them for the sake of Christ, and that their remaining infirmity is covered by His passion and death; who also desire more and more to strengthen their faith and amend their life. But hypocrites and such as turn not to God with sincere hearts eat and drink judgment to themselves[1].

[1] 1 Cor. 11:28, 29; 10:19–22

82. Q. Are they also to be admitted to this supper who, by their confession and life, show themselves to be unbelieving and ungodly?

A. No; for in this way the covenant of God would be profaned and His wrath kindled against the whole congregation[1]; wherefore the Christian Church is in duty bound, according to the ordinance of Christ and His apostles, to exclude such persons by the keys of the kingdom of heaven, until they show amendment of life.

[1] 1 Cor. 11:20, 34; Isa. 1:11; 66:3; Jer. 7:21; Ps. 50:16

LORD'S DAY XXXI

83. Q. What are the keys of the kingdom of heaven?

A. The preaching of the holy gospel, and church discipline or excommunication out of the Christian Church. By these two the kingdom of heaven is opened to believers and shut against unbelievers.

84. Q. How is the kingdom of heaven opened and shut by the preaching of the holy gospel?

A. By proclaiming and openly witnessing, according to the command of Christ, to believers, one and all, that, whenever they receive the promise of the gospel by a true faith, all their sins are really forgiven them of God for the sake of Christ's merits; and on the contrary, by proclaiming and witnessing to all unbelievers and such as do not sincerely repent that the wrath of God and eternal condemnation abide on them so long as they are not converted[1]. According to this witness of the gospel God will judge, both in this life and in that which is to come.

[1] John 20:21–23; Matt. 16:19

85. Q. How is the kingdom of heaven shut and opened by church discipline?

A. By forbidding, according to the command of Christ, the use of the sacraments by those who under the Christian name maintain unchristian doctrines or practices; who will not, after repeated brotherly admonitions, renounce their errors and wicked course of life; and who, having been complained of to the church, or to those who are thereunto appointed by the church, despise their admonitions—by which censure they are excluded from the Christian Church, and by God himself from the kingdom of Christ; and by again receiving such as members of Christ and His Church when they promise and show real amendment[1].

[1] Matt. 18:15–17; 1 Cor. 5:4, 5, 11; 2 Cor. 2:6–8

THE THIRD PART
GRATITUDE

LORD'S DAY XXXII

86. Q. Since, then, we are delivered from our misery by grace alone, through Christ, without any merit of ours, why must we yet do good works?

A. Because Christ, having redeemed us by His blood, also renews us by His Holy Spirit after His own image, that with our whole life we may show ourselves thankful to God for His benefits[1], and that He may be praised by us[2]; then, also, that each of us may be assured in himself of his faith by the fruits thereof[3], and that by our godly walk our neighbors also may be won for Christ[4].

[1] Rom. 6:13; 12:1, 2; 1 Pet. 2:5, 9; 1 Cor. 6:20   [3] 2 Pet. 1:10; Matt. 7:17; Gal. 5:6, 22
[2] Matt. 5:16; 1 Pet. 2:12   [4] 1 Pet. 3:1, 2; Rom. 14:19

87. Q. Can they, then, not be saved who, continuing in their wicked and ungrateful lives, do not turn to God?

A. By no means; for the Scripture declares that no unchaste person, idolater, adulterer, thief, covetous man, drunkard, slanderer, robber, or any such like, shall inherit the kingdom of God[1].

[1] 1 Cor. 6:9, 10; Eph. 5:5, 6; 1 John 3:14

LORD'S DAY XXXIII

88. Q. Of how many parts does true conversion, or the turning of man to God, consist?

A. Two: the mortification of the old man, and the quickening of the new[1].

[1] Rom. 6:1, 4–6; Eph. 4:22–24; Col. 3:5, 6, 8–10; 1 Cor. 5:7; 2 Cor. 7:10

89. Q. What is the mortification of the old man?

A. It is heartfelt sorrow that we have provoked God by our sins, and more and more to hate them and flee from them[1].

[1] Rom. 8:13; Joel 2:13; Hos. 6:1

90. Q. What is the quickening of the new man?

A. It is heartfelt joy in God through Christ[1], and with love and delight to live according to the will of God in all good works[2].

[1] Rom. 5:1; 14:17; Isa. 57:15   [2] Rom. 6:10, 11; Gal. 2:20

91. Q. But what are good works?

A. Only those which are done from true faith[1], according to the law of God[2], and to His glory[3]; and not such as are based on our own opinions or the precepts of men[4].

[1] Rom. 14:23   [3] 1 Cor. 10:31
[2] Lev. 18:4; 1 Sam. 15:22; Eph. 2:10   [4] Ezek. 20:18, 19; Isa. 29:13; Matt. 15:7–9

LORD'S DAY XXXIV

92. Q. What is the law of God?

A. God spake all these words, saying[1]: *I am Jehovah thy God, who brought thee out of the land of Egypt, out of the house of bondage.*

I. *Thou shalt have no other gods before me.*

II. *Thou shalt not make unto thee a graven image, nor any likeness* of any thing *that is in heaven above, or that is in the earth beneath, or that is in the water under the earth; thou shalt not bow down thyself unto them, nor serve them; for I Jehovah thy God am a jealous God, visiting the iniquity of the fathers upon the children, upon the third and upon the fourth generation of them that hate me, and showing lovingkindness unto thousands of them that love me and keep my commandments.*

III. *Thou shalt not take the name of Jehovah thy God in vain: for Jehovah will not hold him guiltless that taketh his name in vain.*

IV. *Remember the sabbath day, to keep it holy. Six days shalt thou labor, and do all thy work; but the seventh day is a sabbath unto Jehovah thy God: in it thou shalt not do any work, thou, nor thy son, nor thy daughter, thy man-servant, nor thy maid-servant, nor thy cattle, nor thy stranger that is within thy gates: for in six days Jehovah made heaven and earth, the sea, and all that in them is, and rested the seventh day: wherefore Jehovah blessed the sabbath day, and hallowed it.*

V. *Honor thy father and thy mother, that thy days may be long in the land which Jehovah thy God giveth thee.*

VI. *Thou shalt not kill.*

VII. *Thou shalt not commit adultery.*

VIII. *Thou shalt not steal.*

IX. *Thou shalt not bear false witness against thy neighbor.*

X. *Thou shalt not covet thy neighbor's house, thou shalt not covet thy neighbor's wife, nor his man-servant, nor his maid-servant, nor his ox, nor his ass, nor anything that is thy neighbor's.*

[1] Ex. 20:1–17; cf. Deut. 5:6–21

93. Q. How are these commandments divided?

A. Into two tables[1]; the first of which teaches what must be our attitude toward God; the second, what duties we owe to our neighbor[2].

[1] Deut. 4:13; Ex. 34:28; Deut. 10:3, 4   [2] Matt. 22:37–40

94. Q. What does God require in the first commandment?

A. That, as much as I love my soul's salvation, I avoid and flee all idolatry[1], sorcery, soothsaying, superstition[2], invocation of saints or other creatures[3]; and that I rightly acknowledge the only true God[4], trust in Him alone[5], submit to Him[6] with all humility[7] and patience, expect all good[8] from Him only, and love[9], fear[10], and honor[11] Him with my whole heart; so that I leave and forsake all creatures rather than do even the least thing against His will[12].

[1] 1 John 5:21; 1 Cor. 6:10; 10:7, 14
[2] Lev. 19:31; Deut. 18:9, 10
[3] Matt. 4:10; Rev. 19:10; 22:8, 9
[4] John 17:3
[5] Jer. 17:5, 7
[6] Heb. 10:36; Col. 1:11; Rom. 5:3, 4; 1 Cor. 10:10; Phil. 2:14
[7] 1 Pet. 5:5
[8] Ps. 104:27; Isa. 45:7; Jas. 1:17
[9] Deut. 6:5; Matt. 22:37
[10] Deut. 6:2; Ps. 111:10; Prov. 1:7; 9:10; Matt. 10:28
[11] Matt. 4:10; Deut. 10:20
[12] Matt. 5:29; 10:37; Acts 5:29

95. Q. What is idolatry?

A. It is, instead of the one true God who has revealed Himself in His Word, or besides Him, to devise or have something else on which to place our trust[1].

[1] Eph. 5:5; 1 Chron. 16:26; Phil. 3:19; Gal. 4:8; Eph. 2:12; 1 John 2:23; 2 John 9; John 5:23.

LORD'S DAY XXXV

96. Q.   What does God require in the second commandment?

A.   That we in no wise make any image of God[1], nor worship Him in any other way than He has commanded in His Word[2].

[1] Isa. 40:18, 19, 25; Deut. 4:15, 16; Rom. 1:23; Acts 17:29
[2] 1 Sam. 15:23; Deut. 12:30; Matt. 15:9

97. Q.   May we, then, not make any image at all?

A.   God neither can nor may be visibly represented in any way[1]. As for creatures, though they may be visibly represented, yet God forbids us to make or have any likeness of them in order to worship them or serve God by them[2].

[1] Isa. 40:25   [2] Ex. 34:17; 23:24; 34:13; Num. 33:52

98. Q.   But may not images be tolerated in the churches as books for the laity?

A.   No; for we must not be wiser than God, who will not have His people taught by dumb images[1], but by the living preaching of His Word[2].

[1] Jer. 10:8; Hab. 2:18, 19   [2] Rom. 10:14, 15, 17; 2 Pet. 1:19; 2 Tim. 3:16, 17

LORD'S DAY XXXVI

99. Q.   What is required in the third commandment?

A.   That we must not by cursing[1] or perjury[2], nor by unnecessary swearing[3], profane or abuse the Name of God, nor by our silence or connivance become partakers of these horrible sins in others[4]; and briefly, that we use the holy Name of God no otherwise than with fear and reverence[5], to the end that He may be rightly confessed[6] and worshipped by us[7], and be glorified in all our words and works[8].

[1] Lev. 24:15, 16   [5] Jer. 4:2; Isa. 45:23
[2] Lev. 19:12   [6] Matt. 10:32; Rom. 10:9, 10
[3] Matt. 5:37; Jas. 5:12   [7] Ps. 50:14, 15; 1 Tim. 2:8
[4] Lev. 5:1; Prov. 29:24   [8] Col. 3:17; Rom. 2:24; 1 Tim. 6:1

100. Q.   Is, then, the profaning of God's Name by swearing and cursing so heinous a sin that His wrath is kindled even against those who do not, as much as in them lies, help to prevent and to forbid such cursing and swearing?

A.   Certainly[1]; for no sin is greater or more provoking to God than the profaning of His Name; wherefore, also, He has commanded this sin to be punished with death[2].

[1] Prov. 29:24; Lev. 5:1   [2] Lev. 24:16

LORD'S DAY XXXVII

101. Q.   But may we not swear by the Name of God in a godly manner?

A.   Yes; when the magistrate demands it of his subjects, or when otherwise necessity requires us thus to confirm fidelity and truth, for the glory of God and the welfare of our neighbor; for such swearing is grounded in God's Word[1], and therefore was rightly used by the saints in the Old and the New Testament[2].

[1] Deut. 6:13; 10:20; Isa. 48:1; Heb. 6:16
[2] Gen. 21:24; 31:53; Josh. 9:15; 1 Sam. 24:23; 2 Sam. 3:35; 1 Kings 1:29; Rom. 1:9; 9:1; 2 Cor. 1:23

102. Q.   May we also swear by saints or any other creatures?

A.   No; for a lawful oath is a calling upon God, as the only Searcher of hearts, to bear witness to the truth, and to punish me if I swear falsely[1]; which honor is due to no creature[2].

[1] 2 Cor. 1:23; Rom. 9:1   [2] Matt. 5:34–36; Jas. 5:12

LORD'S DAY XXXVIII

103. Q. What does God require in the fourth commandment?

A. First, that the ministry of the gospel and the schools be maintained[1]; and that I, especially on the Sabbath, that is, the day of rest, diligently attend the church of God[2], to learn God's Word[3], to use the sacraments[4], to call publicly upon the Lord[5], and to give Christian alms[6]. Second, that all the days of my life I rest from my evil works, let the Lord work in me by His Holy Spirit, and thus begin in this life the eternal Sabbath[7].

[1] Tit. 1:5; 2 Tim. 3:14; 1 Cor. 9:13, 14; 2 Tim. 2:2; 3:15
[2] Ps. 40:9, 10; 68:26; Acts 2:42
[3] 1 Tim. 4:13; 1 Cor. 14:29
[4] 1 Cor. 11:33
[5] 1 Tim. 2:1; 1 Cor. 14:16
[6] 1 Cor. 16:2
[7] Isa. 66:23

LORD'S DAY XXXIX

104. Q. What does God require in the fifth commandment?

A. That I show all honor, love, and fidelity to my father and mother, and to all in authority over me; submit myself with due obedience to their good instruction and correction[1]; and also bear patiently with their weaknesses and shortcomings[2], since it pleases God to govern us by their hand[3].

[1] Eph. 6:1, 2, 5; Col. 3:18, 20, 22; Eph. 5:22; Prov. 1:8; 4:1; 15:20; 20:20; Ex. 21:17; Rom. 13:1
[2] Prov. 23:22; Gen. 9:24; 1 Pet. 2:18
[3] Eph. 6:4, 9; Col. 3:20; Rom. 13:2, 3; Matt. 22:21

LORD'S DAY XL

105. Q. What does God require in the sixth commandment?

A. That I, neither in thought, nor in word or gesture, much less in deed, dishonor, hate, wound, or kill my neighbor, whether by myself or by another[1], but lay aside all desire of revenge[2]; moreover, that I harm not myself nor wilfully expose myself to any danger[3]. Therefore, also, the magistrate is armed with the sword to prevent murder[4].

[1] Matt. 5:21, 22; 26:52; Gen. 9:6
[2] Eph. 4:26; Rom. 12:19; Matt. 5:25; Matt. 18:35
[3] Rom. 13:14; Col. 2:23; Matt. 4:7
[4] Gen. 9:6; Ex. 21:14; Matt. 26:52; Rom. 13:4

106. Q. But this commandment seems to speak only of murder?

A. In forbidding murder, God teaches us that He abhors the root of murder, as envy[1], hatred[2], anger[3], and desire of revenge; and that He accounts all these as murder[4].

[1] Prov. 14:30; Rom. 1:29
[2] 1 John 2:11
[3] Jas. 1:20; Gal. 5:19–21
[4] 1 John 3:15

107. Q. But is it enough that we do not kill our neighbor in any such way?

A. No; for when God forbids envy, hatred, and anger, He commands us to love our neighbor as ourselves[1]: to show patience, peace, meekness, mercy, and all kindness towards him[2], prevent his hurt as much as in us lies[3], and do good even to our enemies[4].

[1] Matt. 22:39; 7:12; Rom. 12:10
[2] Eph. 4:2; Gal. 6:1, 2; Matt. 5:5; Rom. 12:18; Luke 6:36; Matt. 5:7; 1 Pet. 3:8; Col. 3:12
[3] Ex. 23:5
[4] Matt. 5:44, 45; Rom. 12:20

LORD'S DAY XLI

108. Q. What does the seventh commandment teach us?

A. That all unchastity is accursed of God[1]; and that we must, therefore, detest it from the heart[2], and live a chaste and continent life[3] both within and outside of holy wedlock[4].

[1] Lev. 18:28
[2] Jude:23
[3] 1 Thess. 4:3–5
[4] Heb. 13:4; 1 Cor. 7:7

109. Q. Does God in this commandment forbid nothing more than adultery and such like gross sins?

A. Since our body and soul are both temples of the Holy Spirit, it is His will that we keep both pure and holy; wherefore He forbids all unchaste actions, gestures, words[1], thoughts, desires[2], and whatever may entice one thereto[3].

[1] Eph. 5:3, 4; 1 Cor. 6:18, 19
[2] Matt. 5:27, 28
[3] Eph. 5:18; 1 Cor. 15:33

LORD'S DAY XLII

110. Q. What does God forbid in the eighth commandment?

A. God forbids not only such theft[1] and robbery[2] as are punished by the magistrate, but He also brands as theft all wicked tricks and devices whereby we aim to appropriate our neighbor's goods[3], whether by force or with show of right, as unjust weights, ells, measures, and wares[4], false coins, usury[5], or any other means forbidden by God; likewise all covetousness[6] and all abuse and waste of His gifts[7].

[1] 1 Cor. 6:10
[2] 1 Cor. 5:10; Isa. 33:1
[3] Luke 3:14; 1 Thess. 4:6
[4] Prov. 11:1; 16:11; Ezek. 45:9, 10; Deut. 25:13
[5] Ps. 15:5; Luke 6:35
[6] 1 Cor. 6:10
[7] Prov. 23:20, 21; 21:20

111. Q. But what does God require of you in this commandment?

A. That I further my neighbor's profit wherever I can or may, deal with him as I would have others deal with me[1], and labor faithfully that I may be able to relieve the needy[2].

[1] Matt. 7:12
[2] Eph. 4:28

LORD'S DAY XLIII

112. Q. What is required in the ninth commandment?

A. That I bear false witness against no man[1]; wrest no one's words[2]; be no backbiter or slanderer[3]; do not judge, or join in condemning, any man rashly or unheard[4]; but that I avoid all sorts of lies and deceit as the proper works of the devil[5], unless I would bring down upon myself the heavy wrath of God[6]; likewise, that in judicial and all other dealings I love the truth, speak it uprightly[7], and confess it; and that, as much as I am able, I defend and promote the honor and reputation of my neighbor[8].

[1] Prov. 19:5, 9; 21:28
[2] Ps. 15:3; 50:19, 20
[3] Rom. 1:30
[4] Matt. 7:1; Luke 6:37
[5] John 8:44
[6] Prov. 12:22; 13:5
[7] 1 Cor. 13:6; Eph. 4:25
[8] 1 Pet. 4:8

LORD'S DAY XLIV

113. Q. What does the tenth commandment require of us?

A. That not even the slightest inclination or thought contrary to any of God's commandments shall ever rise in our heart; but that at all times we shall hate all sin with our whole heart and delight in all righteousness[1].

[1] Rom. 7:7

114. Q. But can those who are converted to God keep these commandments perfectly?

A. No; but even the holiest men, while in this life, have only a small beginning of this obedience[1]; yet so that with earnest purpose they begin to live, not only according to some but according to all the commandments of God[2].

[1] 1 John 1:8; Rom. 7:14, 15; Eccl. 7:20; 1 Cor. 13:9   [2] Rom. 7:22; Ps. 1:2

115. Q. Why, then, will God have the ten commandments preached so strictly, since in this life no one can keep them?

A. First, that all our life long we may learn more and more to know our sinful nature[1], and so become the more earnest in seeking remission of sins and righteousness in Christ[2]; second, that we may constantly endeavor, and pray to God for the grace of the Holy Spirit, to be renewed more and more after the image of God, till after this life we arrive at the goal of perfection[3].

[1] Rom. 3:20; 1 John 1:9; Ps. 32:5   [3] 1 Cor. 9:24; Phil. 3:12–14
[2] Matt. 5:6; Rom. 7:24, 25

LORD'S DAY XLV

116. Q. Why is prayer necessary for Christians?

A. Because it is the chief part of the thankfulness which God requires of us[1], and because God will give His grace and Holy Spirit to those only who with hearty sighing unceasingly beg them of Him and thank Him for them[2].

[1] Ps. 50:14   [2] Matt. 7:7; Luke 11:9, 13; 1 Thess. 5:17

117. Q. What belongs to such prayer as God is pleased with and will hear?

A. First, that from the heart[1] we call upon the one true God only, who has revealed Himself in His Word[2], for all He has commanded us to ask of Him[3]; second, that we right thoroughly know our need and misery[4], in order to humble ourselves before the face of His majesty[5]; third, that we be firmly assured[6] that, notwithstanding we are unworthy of it, He will, for the sake of Christ our Lord, certainly hear our prayer[7], as He has promised us in His Word[8].

[1] John 4:24; Ps. 145:18   [5] Ps. 2:11; 34:18; Isa. 66:2
[2] Rev. 19:10; John 4:22–24   [6] Rom. 10:13; Jas. 1:6
[3] Rom. 8:26; 1 John 5:14; Jas. 1:5   [7] John 14:13; 16:23; Dan. 9:18
[4] 2 Chron. 20:12   [8] Matt. 7:8; Ps. 27:8

118. Q. What has God commanded us to ask of Him?

A. All things necessary for soul and body[1], which Christ our Lord has comprised in the prayer He Himself has taught us.

[1] Jas. 1:17; Matt. 6:33

119. Q. What is the Lord's Prayer?

A. *Our Father who art in heaven,*
Hallowed be thy name;
Thy kingdom come;
Thy will be done, as in heaven, so on earth.
Give us this day our daily bread;
And forgive us our debts, as we also have forgiven our debtors;

And bring us not into temptation, but deliver us from the evil one.
For thine is the kingdom, and the power, and the glory, for ever. Amen[1].
[1] Matt. 6:9–13; Luke 11:2–4

LORD'S DAY XLVI

120. Q. Why has Christ commanded us to address God thus, *Our Father*?

A. To awaken in us, at the very beginning of our prayer, that childlike reverence and trust toward God which should be the ground of our prayer; namely, that God has become our Father through Christ, and will much less deny us what we ask of Him in true faith than our parents will refuse us earthly things[1].

[1] Matt. 7:9–11; Luke 11:11–13

121. Q. Why is there added, *Who art in heaven*?

A. That we may have no earthly thought of the heavenly majesty of God[1], and may expect from His almighty power all things necessary for body and soul[2].

[1] Jer. 23:23, 24; Acts 17:24, 25, 27   [2] Rom. 10:12

LORD'S DAY XLVII

122. Q. What is the first petition?

A. *Hallowed by thy name.* That is: grant us, first, rightly to know Thee[1], and to sanctify, glorify, and praise Thee in all Thy works, in which Thy power, wisdom, goodness, justice, mercy, and truth shine forth[2]; further also, that we may so order and direct our whole life, thoughts, words, and actions, that Thy Name may not be blasphemed but honored and praised on our account[3].

[1] John 17:3; Jer. 9:24; 31:33, 34; Matt. 16:17; Jas. 1:5; Ps. 119:105
[2] Ps. 119:137; Luke 1:46, 47, 68, 69; Rom. 11:33   [3] Ps. 71:8; 115:1

LORD'S DAY XLVIII

123. Q. What is the second petition?

A. *Thy kingdom come.* That is: so rule us by Thy Word and Spirit that we may submit ourselves more and more to Thee[1]; preserve and increase Thy Church[2]; destroy the works of the devil, every power that exalts itself against Thee, and all wicked counsels conceived against Thy holy Word[3], until the perfection of Thy kingdom arrive[4] wherein Thou shalt be all in all[5].

[1] Ps. 143:10; 119:5; Matt. 6:33   [4] Rev. 22:20; Rom. 8:22, 23
[2] Ps. 51:18; 122:6   [5] 1 Cor. 15:28
[3] 1 John 3:8; Rom. 16:20

LORD'S DAY XLIX

124. Q. What is the third petition?

A. *Thy will be done, as in heaven, so on earth.* That is: grant that we and all men may renounce our own will[1], and without any gainsaying obey Thy will, which alone is good[2]; that so every one may discharge the duties of his office and calling[3] as willingly and faithfully as the angels in heaven[4].

[1] Matt. 16:24; Tit. 2:11, 12   [3] 1 Cor. 7:24
[2] Luke 22:42; Eph. 5:10; Rom. 12:2   [4] Ps. 103:20, 21

LORD'S DAY L

125. Q. What is the fourth petition?

A. *Give us this day our daily bread.* That is: be pleased to provide for all our bodily need[1], that we may thereby acknowledge Thee to be the only fountain of all good[2], and that without Thy blessing neither our care and labor nor Thy gifts can profit us[3]; and, therefore, that we may withdraw our trust from all creatures and place it alone in Thee[4].

[1] Ps. 145:15; 104:27; Matt. 6:26
[2] Jas. 1:17; Acts 14:17; 17:25
[3] 1 Cor. 15:58; Deut. 8:3; Ps. 37:16; 127:1, 2
[4] Ps. 55:22; 62:10; 146:3; Jer. 17:5, 7

LORD'S DAY LI

126. Q. What is the fifth petition?

A. *And forgive us our debts, as we also have forgiven our debtors.* That is: be pleased, for the sake of Christ's blood, not to impute to us, miserable sinners, any of our transgressions, nor the evil which always cleaves to us[1]; as also find this witness of Thy grace in us that it is our full purpose heartily to forgive our neighbor[2].

[1] Ps. 51:1; 143:2; 1 John 2:1; Rom. 8:1　　[2] Matt. 6:14

LORD'S DAY LII

127. Q. What is the sixth petition?

A. *And bring us not into temptation, but deliver us from the evil one.* That is: since we are so weak in ourselves that we cannot stand a moment[1], and besides, since our sworn enemies, the devil[2], the world[3], and our own flesh[4], cease not to assault us, be pleased to preserve and strengthen us by the power of Thy Holy Spirit, that we may not succumb in this spiritual warfare[5] but always offer strong resistance, till at last we obtain a complete victory[6].

[1] John 15:5; Ps. 103:14
[2] 1 Pet. 5:8; Eph. 6:12
[3] John 15:19
[4] Rom. 7:23; Gal. 5:17
[5] Matt. 26:41; Mark 13:33
[6] 1 Thess. 3:13; 5:23

128. Q. How do you conclude your prayer?

A. *For thine is the kingdom, and the power, and the glory for ever.* That is: all this we ask of Thee because Thou, as our King who hast power over all things, art both willing and able to give us all good[1], and that thereby not we but Thy holy Name may be glorified for ever[2].

[1] Rom. 10:12; 2 Pet. 2:9　　[2] John 14:13; Jer. 33:8, 9; Ps. 115:1

129. Q. What does the word *Amen* signify?

A. *Amen* signifies: it shall truly and surely be; for my prayer is more certainly heard of God than I feel in my heart that I desire these things of Him[1].

[1] 2 Cor. 1:20; 2 Tim. 2:13

CANONS OF DORT

The third of our Doctrinal Standards is the *Canons of Dort,* also called the *Five Articles Against the Remonstrants.* These are statements of doctrine adopted by the great Reformed Synod of Dordrecht in 1618–1619. This Synod had a truly international character, since it was composed not only of the delegates of the Reformed Church of the Netherlands but also of twenty seven delegates from foreign countries.

The Synod of Dordrecht was held in view of the serious disturbance in the Reformed Church by the rise and spread of Arminianism. Arminius, a theological professor at the University of Leyden, departed from the Reformed faith in his teaching concerning five important points. He taught conditional election on the ground of foreseen faith, universal atonement, partial depravity, resistible grace, and the possibility of a lapse from grace. These views were rejected by the Synod, and the opposite views were embodied in what is now called the Canons of Dort or the Five Articles Against the Remonstrants. In these Canons the Synod set forth the Reformed doctrine on these points, namely, unconditional election, limited atonement, total depravity, irresistible grace, and the perseverance of the saints.

Each of the Canons consists of a positive and a negative part, the former being an exposition of the Reformed doctrine on the subject, and the latter a repudiation of the corresponding Arminian error. Although in form there are only four chapters, occasioned by the combination of the third and fourth heads of doctrine into one, we speak properly of five Canons, and the third chapter is always designated as Chapter III–IV. All officebearers of our Church are required to subscribe to these Canons as well as to the Confession of Faith and the Heidelberg Catechism.

FIRST HEAD OF DOCTRINE

DIVINE ELECTION AND REPROBATION

ARTICLE 1

As all men have sinned in Adam, lie under the curse, and are deserving of eternal death, God would have done no injustice by leaving them all to perish and delivering them over to condemnation on account of sin, according to the words of the apostle: *That every mouth may be stopped, and all the world may be brought under the judgment of God* (Rom. 3:19). And: *For all have sinned, and fall short of the glory of God* (Rom. 3:23). And: *For the wages of sin is death* (Rom. 6:23).

ARTICLE 2

But in this the love of God was manifested, that He *sent his only begotten Son into the world, that whosoever believeth on him should not perish, but have eternal life* (1 John 4:9; John 3:16).

ARTICLE 3

And that men may be brought to believe, God mercifully sends the messengers of these most joyful tidings to whom He will and at what time He pleases; by whose ministry men are called to repentance and faith in Christ crucified. *How then shall they call on him in whom they have not believed? And how shall they believe in him whom they have not heard? And how shall they hear without a preacher? And how shall they preach except they be sent?* (Rom. 10:14, 15).

ARTICLE 4

The wrath of God abides upon those who believe not this gospel. But such as receive it and embrace Jesus the Savior by a true and living faith are by Him delivered from the wrath of God and from destruction, and have the gift of eternal life conferred upon them.

ARTICLE 5

The cause or guilt of this unbelief as well as of all other sins is no wise in God, but in man himself; whereas faith in Jesus Christ and salvation through Him is the free gift of God, as it is written: *By grace have ye been saved through faith; and that not of yourselves,* it is *the gift of God* (Eph. 2:8). Likewise: *To you it hath been granted in the behalf of Christ, not only to believe on him,* etc. (Phil. 1:29).

ARTICLE 6

That some receive the gift of faith from God, and others do not receive it, proceeds from God's eternal decree. *For known unto God are all his works from the beginning of the world* (Acts 15:18, A.V.). *Who worketh all things after the counsel of his will* (Eph. 1:11). According to which decree He graciously softens the hearts of the elect, however obstinate, and inclines them to believe; while He leaves the non-elect in His just judgment to their own wickedness and obduracy. And herein is especially displayed the profound, the merciful, and at the same time the righteous discrimination between men equally involved in ruin; or that decree of election and reprobation, revealed in the Word of God, which, though men of perverse, impure, and unstable minds wrest it to their own destruction, yet to holy and pious souls affords unspeakable consolation.

ARTICLE 7

Election is the unchangeable purpose of God, whereby, before the foundation of the world, He has out of mere grace, according to the sovereign good pleasure of His own will, chosen from the whole human race, which had fallen through their own fault from their primitive state of rectitude into sin and destruction, a certain number of persons to redemption in Christ, whom He from eternity appointed the Mediator and Head of the elect and the foundation of salvation. This elect number, though by nature neither better nor more deserving than others, but with them involved in one common misery, God has decreed to give to Christ to be saved by Him, and effectually to call and draw them to His communion by His Word and Spirit; to bestow upon them true faith, justification, and sanctification; and having powerfully preserved them in the fellowship of His Son, finally to glorify them for the demonstration of His mercy, and for the praise of the riches of His glorious grace: as it is written: *Even as he chose us in him before the foundation of the world, that we should be holy and without blemish before him in love: having foreordained us unto adoption as sons through Jesus Christ unto himself, according to the good pleasure of his will, to the praise of the glory of his grace, which he freely bestowed on us in the Beloved* (Eph. 1:4, 5, 6). And elsewhere: *Whom he foreordained, them he also called: and whom he called, them he also justified: and whom he justified, them he also glorified* (Rom. 8:30).

ARTICLE 8

There are not various decrees of election, but one and the same decree respecting all those who shall be saved, both under the Old and the New Testament; since the Scripture declares the good pleasure, purpose, and counsel of the divine will to be one, according to which He has chosen us from eternity, both to grace and to glory, to salvation and to the way of salvation, which He has ordained that we should walk therein (Eph. 1:4, 5; 2:10).

ARTICLE 9

This election was not founded upon foreseen faith and the obedience of faith, holiness, or any other good quality or disposition in man, as the prerequisite, cause, or condition on which it depended; but men are chosen to faith and to the obedience of faith, holiness, etc. Therefore election is the fountain of every saving good, from which proceed faith, holiness, and the other gifts of salvation, and finally eternal life itself, as its fruits and effects, according to the testimony of the apostle: *He hath chosen us* (not because we were, but) *that we should be holy, and without blemish before him in love* (Eph. 1:4).

ARTICLE 10

The good pleasure of God is the sole cause of this gracious election; which does not consist herein that out of all possible qualities and actions of men God has chosen some as a condition of salvation, but that He was pleased out of the common mass of sinners to adopt some certain persons as a peculiar people to Himself, as it is written: *For* the children *being not yet born, neither having done anything good or bad,* etc., *it was said unto her* (namely, to Rebekah), *The elder shall serve the younger. Even as it is written, Jacob I loved, but Esau I hated* (Rom. 9:11, 12, 13). *And as many as were ordained to eternal life believed* (Acts 13:48).

ARTICLE 11

And as God Himself is most wise, unchangeable, omniscient, and omnipotent, so the election made by Him can neither be interrupted nor changed, recalled, or annulled; neither can the elect be cast away, nor their number diminished.

ARTICLE 12

The elect in due time, though in various degrees and in different measures, attain the assurance of this their eternal and unchangeable election, not by inquisitively prying into the secret and deep things of God, but by observing in themselves with a spiritual joy and holy pleasure the infallible fruits of election pointed out in the Word of God—such as, a true faith in Christ, filial fear, a godly sorrow for sin, a hungering and thirsting after righteousness, etc.

ARTICLE 13

The sense and certainty of this election afford to the children of God additional matter for daily humiliation before Him, for adoring the depth of His mercies, for cleansing themselves, and rendering grateful returns of ardent love to Him who first manifested so great love towards them. The consideration of this doctrine of election is so far from encouraging remissness in the observance of the divine commands or from sinking men in carnal security, that these, in the just judgment of God, are the usual effects of rash presumption or of idle and wanton trifling with the grace of election, in those who refuse to walk in the ways of the elect.

ARTICLE 14

As the doctrine of divine election by the most wise counsel of God was declared by the prophets, by Christ Himself, and by the apostles, and is clearly revealed in the Scriptures both of the Old and the New Testament, so it is still to be published in due time and place in the Church of God, for which it was peculiarly designed, provided it be done with reverence, in the spirit of discretion and piety, for the glory of God's most holy Name, and for enlivening and comforting His people, without vainly attempting to investigate the secret ways of the Most High (Acts 20:27; Rom. 11:33, 34; 12:3; Heb. 6:17, 18).

ARTICLE 15

What peculiarly tends to illustrate and recommend to us the eternal and unmerited grace of election is the express testimony of sacred Scripture that not all, but some only, are elected, while others are passed by in the eternal decree; whom God, out of His sovereign, most just, irreprehensible, and unchangeable good pleasure, has decreed to leave in the common misery into which they have wilfully plunged themselves, and not to bestow upon them saving faith and the grace of conversion; but, permitting them in His just judgment to follow their own ways, at last, for the declaration of His justice, to condemn and punish them forever, not only on account of their unbelief, but also for all their other sins. And this is the decree of reprobation, which by no means makes God the Author of sin (the very thought of which is blasphemy), but declares Him to be an awful, irreprehensible, and righteous Judge and Avenger thereof.

ARTICLE 16

Those in whom a living faith in Christ, an assured confidence of soul, peace of conscience, an earnest endeavor after filial obedience, a glorying in God through Christ, is not as yet strongly felt, and who nevertheless make use of the means which God has appointed for working these graces in us, ought not to be alarmed at the mention of reprobation, nor to rank themselves among the reprobate, but diligently to persevere in the use of means, and with ardent desires devoutly and humbly to wait for a season of richer grace. Much less cause to be terrified by the doctrine of reprobation have they who, though they seriously desire to be turned to God, to please Him only, and to be delivered from the body of death, cannot yet reach that measure of holiness and faith to which they aspire; since a merciful God has promised that He will not quench the smoking flax, nor break the bruised reed. But this doctrine is justly terrible to those who, regardless of God and of the Savior Jesus Christ, have wholly given themselves up to the cares of the world and the pleasures of the flesh, so long as they are not seriously converted to God.

ARTICLE 17

Since we are to judge of the will of God from His Word, which testifies that the children of believers are holy, not by nature, but in virtue of the covenant of grace, in which they together with the parents are comprehended, godly parents ought not to doubt the election and salvation of their children whom it pleases God to call out of this life in their infancy (Gen. 17:7; Acts 2:39; 1 Cor. 7:14).

ARTICLE 18

To those who murmur at the free grace of election and the just severity of reprobation we answer with the apostle: *Nay but, O man, who art thou that repliest against God?* (Rom. 9:20), and quote the language of our Savior: *Is it not lawful for me to do what I will with mine own?* (Matt. 20:15). And therefore, with holy adoration of these mysteries, we exclaim in the words of the apostle: *O the depth of the riches both of the wisdom and the knowledge of God! how unsearchable are his judgments, and his ways past tracing out! For who hath known the mind of the Lord, or who hath been his counsellor? or who hath first given to him, and it shall be recompensed unto him again? For of him, and through him, and unto him are all things. To him* be *the glory for ever. Amen.* (Rom. 11:33–36).

REJECTION OF ERRORS

The true doctrine concerning election and reprobation having been explained, the Synod rejects the errors of those:

PARAGRAPH 1

Who teach: That the will of God to save those who would believe and would persevere in faith and in the obedience of faith is the whole and entire decree of election unto salvation, and that nothing else concerning this decree has been revealed in God's Word.

For these deceive the simple and plainly contradict the Scriptures, which declare that God will not only save those who will believe, but that He has also from eternity chosen certain particular persons to whom, above others, He will grant, in time, both faith in Christ and perseverance; as it is written: *I manifested thy name unto the men whom thou gavest me out of the world* (John 17:6). *And as many as were ordained to eternal life believed* (Acts 13:48). And: *Even as he chose us in him before the foundation of the world, that we should be holy and without blemish before him in love* (Eph. 1:4).

PARAGRAPH 2

Who teach: That there are various kinds of election of God unto eternal life: the one general and indefinite, the other particular and definite; and that the latter in turn is either incomplete, revocable, non-decisive, and conditional, or complete, irrevocable, decisive, and absolute. Likewise: That there is one election unto faith and another unto salvation, so that election can be unto justifying faith, without being a decisive election unto salvation.

For this is a fancy of men's minds, invented regardless of the Scriptures, whereby the doctrine of election is corrupted, and this golden chain of our salvation is broken: *And whom he foreordained, them he also called: and whom he called, them he also justified: and whom he justified, them he also glorified* (Rom. 8:30).

PARAGRAPH 3

Who teach: That the good pleasure and purpose of God, of which Scripture makes mention in the doctrine of election, does not consist in this, that God chose certain persons rather than others, but in this, that He chose out of all possible conditions (among which are also the works of the law), or out of the whole order of things, the act of faith which from its very nature is undeserving, as well as its incomplete obedience, as a condition of salvation, and that He would graciously consider this in itself as a complete obedience and count it worthy of the reward of eternal life.

For by this injurious error the pleasure of God and the merits of Christ are made of none effect, and men are drawn away by useless questions from the truth of gracious justification and from the simplicity of Scripture, and this declaration of the apostle is charged as untrue: *Who saved us, and called us with a holy calling, not according to our works, but according to his own purpose and grace, which was given us in Christ Jesus before times eternal* (2 Tim. 1:9).

PARAGRAPH 4

Who teach: That in the election unto faith this condition is beforehand demanded that man should use the light of nature aright, be pious, humble, meek, and fit for eternal life, as if on these things election were in any way dependent.

For this savors of the teaching of Pelagius, and is opposed to the doctrine of the apostle when he writes: *Among whom we also all once lived in the lusts of our flesh, doing the desires of the flesh and of the mind, and were by nature children of wrath, even as the rest; but God, being rich in mercy, for his great love wherewith he loved us, even when we were dead through our trespasses, made us alive together with Christ (by grace have ye been saved), and raised us up with him, and made us to sit with him in the heavenly places, in Christ Jesus; that in the ages to come he might show the exceeding riches of his grace in kindness towards us in Christ Jesus; for by grace have ye been saved through faith; and that not of yourselves, it is the gift of God; not of works, that no man should glory* (Eph. 2:3–9).

PARAGRAPH 5

Who teach: That the incomplete and non-decisive election of particular persons to salvation occurred because of a foreseen faith, conversion, holiness, godliness, which either began or continued for some time; but that the complete and decisive election occurred because of foreseen perseverance unto the end in faith, conversion, holiness, and godliness; and that this is the gracious and evangelical worthiness, for the sake of which he who is chosen is more worthy than he who is not chosen; and that therefore faith, the obedience of faith, holiness, godliness, and perseverance are not fruits of the unchangeable election unto glory, but are conditions which, being required beforehand, were foreseen as being met by those who will be fully elected, and are causes without which the unchangeable election to glory does not occur.

This is repugnant to the entire Scripture, which constantly inculcates this and similar declarations: Election is *not of works, but of him that calleth* (Rom. 9:11). *And as many as were ordained to eternal life believed* (Acts 13:48). *He chose us in him before the foundation of the world, that we should be holy* (Eph. 1:4). *Ye did not choose me, but I chose you* (John 15:16). *But if it is by grace, it is no more of works* (Rom. 11:6). *Herein is love, not that we loved God, but that he loved us, and sent his Son* (1 John 4:10).

PARAGRAPH 6

Who teach: That not every election unto salvation is unchangeable, but that some of the elect, any decree of God notwithstanding, can yet perish and do indeed perish.

By this gross error they make God to be changeable, and destroy the comfort which the godly obtain out of the firmness of their election, and contradict the Holy Scripture, which teaches that *the elect can not be led astray* (Matt. 24:24), that Christ *does not lose those whom the Father gave him* (John 6:39), and that *God also glorified those whom he foreordained, called, and justified* (Rom. 8:30).

PARAGRAPH 7

Who teach: That there is in this life no fruit and no consciousness of the unchangeable election to glory, nor any certainty, except that which depends on a changeable and uncertain condition.

For not only is it absurd to speak of an uncertain certainty, but also contrary to the experience of the saints, who by virtue of the consciousness of their election rejoice with the apostle and praise this favor of God (Eph. 1); who according to Christ's admonition rejoice with his disciples that *their names are written in heaven* (Luke 10:20); who also place the consciousness of their election over against the fiery darts of the devil, asking: *Who shall lay anything to the charge of God's elect?* (Rom. 8:33).

PARAGRAPH 8

Who teach: That God, simply by virtue of His righteous will, did not decide either to leave anyone in the fall of Adam and in the common state of sin and condemnation, or to pass anyone by in the communication of grace which is necessary for faith and conversion.

For this is firmly decreed: *He hath mercy on whom he will, and whom he will he hardeneth* (Rom. 9:18). And also this: *Unto you it is given to know the mysteries of the kingdom of heaven, but to them it is not given* (Matt. 13:11). Likewise: *I thank thee, O Father, Lord of heaven and earth, that thou didst hide these things from the wise and understanding, and didst reveal them unto babes; yea, Father, for so it was well-pleasing in thy sight* (Matt. 11:25, 26).

PARAGRAPH 9

Who teach: That the reason why God sends the gospel to one people rather than to another is not merely and solely the good pleasure of God, but rather the fact that one people is better and worthier than another to which the gospel is not communicated.

For this Moses denies, addressing the people of Israel as follows: *Behold, unto Jehovah thy God belongeth heaven and the heaven of heavens, the earth, with all that is therein. Only Jehovah had a delight in thy fathers to love them, and he chose their seed after them, even you above all peoples, as at this day* (Deut. 10:14, 15). And Christ said: *Woe unto thee, Chorazin! woe unto thee, Bethsaida! for if the mighty works had been done in Tyre and Sidon which were done in you, they would have repented long ago in sackcloth and ashes* (Matt. 11:21).

SECOND HEAD OF DOCTRINE

THE DEATH OF CHRIST, AND THE REDEMPTION OF MEN THEREBY

ARTICLE 1

God is not only supremely merciful, but also supremely just. And His justice requires (as He has revealed Himself in His Word) that our sins committed against His infinite majesty should be punished, not only with temporal but with eternal punishments, both in body and soul; which we cannot escape, unless satisfaction be made to the justice of God.

ARTICLE 2

Since, therefore, we are unable to make that satisfaction in our own persons, or to deliver ourselves from the wrath of God, He has been pleased of His infinite mercy to give His only begotten Son for our Surety, who was made sin, and became a curse for us and in our stead, that He might make satisfaction to divine justice on our behalf.

ARTICLE 3

The death of the Son of God is the only and most perfect sacrifice and satisfaction for sin, and is of infinite worth and value, abundantly sufficient to expiate the sins of the whole world.

ARTICLE 4

This death is of such infinite value and dignity because the person who submitted to it was not only really man and perfectly holy, but also the only begotten Son of God, of the same eternal and infinite essence with the Father and the Holy Spirit, which qualifications were necessary to constitute Him a Savior for us; and, moreover, because it was attended with a sense of the wrath and curse of God due to us for sin.

ARTICLE 5

Moreover, the promise of the gospel is that whosoever believes in Christ crucified shall not perish, but have eternal life. This promise, together with the command to repent and believe, ought to be declared and published to all nations, and to all persons promiscuously and without distinction, to whom God out of His good pleasure sends the gospel.

ARTICLE 6

And, whereas many who are called by the gospel do not repent nor believe in Christ, but perish in unbelief, this is not owing to any defect or insufficiency in the sacrifice offered by Christ upon the cross. but is wholly to be imputed to themselves.

ARTICLE 7

But as many as truly believe, and are delivered and saved from sin and destruction through the death of Christ, are indebted for this benefit solely to the grace of God given them in Christ from everlasting, and not to any merit of their own.

ARTICLE 8

For this was the sovereign counsel and most gracious will and purpose of God the Father that the quickening and saving efficacy of the most precious death of His Son should extend to all the elect, for bestowing upon them alone the gift of justifying faith, thereby to bring them infallibly to salvation; that is, it was the will of God that Christ by the blood of the cross, whereby He confirmed the new covenant, should effectually redeem out of every people, tribe, nation, and language, all those, and those only, who were from eternity chosen to salvation and given to Him by the Father; that He should confer upon them faith, which, together with all the other saving gifts of the Holy Spirit, He purchased for them by His death; should purge them from all sin, both original and actual, whether committed before or after believing; and having faithfully preserved them even to the end, should at last bring them, free from every spot and blemish, to the enjoyment of glory in His own presence forever.

ARTICLE 9

This purpose, proceeding from everlasting love towards the elect, has from the beginning of the world to this day been powerfully accomplished, and will henceforward still continue to be accomplished, notwithstanding all the ineffectual opposition of the gates of hell; so that the elect in due time may be gathered together into one, and that there never may be wanting a Church composed of believers, the foundation of which is laid in the blood of Christ; which may stedfastly love and faithfully serve Him as its Savior (who, as a bridegroom for his bride, laid down His life for them upon the cross); and which may celebrate His praises here and through all eternity.

REJECTION OF ERRORS

The true doctrine having been explained, the Synod rejects the errors of those:

PARAGRAPH 1

Who teach: That God the Father has ordained His Son to the death of the cross without a certain and definite decree to save any, so that the necessity, profitableness, and worth of what Christ merited by His death might have existed, and might remain in all its parts complete, perfect, and intact, even if the merited redemption had never in fact been applied to any person.

For this doctrine tends to the despising of the wisdom of the Father and of the merits of Jesus Christ, and is contrary to Scripture. For thus says our Savior: *I lay down my life for the sheep, and I know them* (John 10:15, 27). And the prophet Isaiah says concerning the Savior: *When thou shalt make his soul an offering for sin, he shall see his seed, he shall prolong his days, and the pleasure of Jehovah shall prosper in his hand* (Is. 53:10). Finally, this contradicts the article of faith according to which we believe the catholic Christian Church.

Paragraph 2

Who teach: That it was not the purpose of the death of Christ that He should confirm the new covenant of grace through His blood, but only that He should acquire for the Father the mere right to establish with man such a covenant as He might please, whether of grace or of works.

For this is repugnant to Scripture which teaches that *Christ hath become the surety and mediator of a better, that is, the new covenant,* and that *a testament is of force where there hath been death* (Heb. 7:22; 9:15, 17).

Paragraph 3

Who teach: That Christ by His satisfaction merited neither salvation itself for anyone, nor faith, whereby this satisfaction of Christ unto salvation is effectually appropriated; but that He merited for the Father only the authority or the perfect will to deal again with man, and to prescribe new conditions as He might desire, obedience to which, however, depended on the free will of man, so that it therefore might have come to pass that either none or all should fulfil these conditions.

For these adjudge too contemptuously of the death of Christ, in no wise acknowledge the most important fruit or benefit thereby gained, and bring again out of hell the Pelagian error.

Paragraph 4

Who teach: That the new covenant of grace, which God the Father, through the mediation of the death of Christ, made with man, does not herein consist that we by faith, in as much as it accepts the merits of Christ, are justified before God and saved, but in the fact that God, having revoked the demand of perfect obedience of faith, regards faith itself and the obedience of faith, although imperfect, as the perfect obedience of the law, and does esteem it worthy of the reward of eternal life through grace.

For these contradict the Scriptures: *Being justified freely by his grace through the redemption that is in Christ Jesus; whom God set forth* to be *a propitiation, through faith, in his blood* (Rom. 3:24, 25). And these proclaim, as did the wicked Socinus, a new and strange justification of man before God, against the consensus of the whole Church

Paragraph 5

Who teach: That all men have been accepted unto the state of reconciliation and unto the grace of the covenant, so that no one is worthy of condemnation on account of original sin, and that no one shall be condemned because of it, but that all are free from the guilt of original sin.

For this opinion is repugnant to Scripture which teaches that we are *by nature children of wrath* (Eph. 2:3).

Paragraph 6

Who use the difference between meriting and appropriating, to the end that they may instil into the minds of the imprudent and inexperienced this teaching that God, as far as He is concerned, has been minded to apply to all equally the benefits gained by the death of Christ; but that, while some obtain the pardon of sin and eternal life, and others do not, this difference depends on their own free will, which joins itself to the grace that is offered without exception, and that it is not dependent on the special gift of mercy, which powerfully works in them, that they rather than others should appropriate unto themselves this grace.

For these, while they feign that they present this distinction in a sound sense, seek to instil into the people the destructive poison of the Pelagian errors.

PARAGRAPH 7

Who teach: That Christ neither could die, nor needed to die, and also did not die, for those whom God loved in the highest degree and elected to eternal life, since these do not need the death of Christ.

For they contradict the apostle, who declares: *Christ loved me, and gave himself up for me* (Gal. 2:20). Likewise: *Who shall lay anything to the charge of God's elect? It is God that justifieth; who is he that condemneth? It is Christ Jesus that died* (Rom. 8:33, 34), namely, for them; and the Savior who says: *I lay down my life for the sheep* (John 10:15). And: *This is my commandment, that ye love one another, even as I have loved you. Greater love hath no man than this, that a man lay down his life for his friends* (John 15:12, 13).

THIRD AND FOURTH HEADS OF DOCTRINE

THE CORRUPTION OF MAN, HIS CONVERSION TO GOD, AND THE MANNER THEREOF

ARTICLE 1

Man was originally formed after the image of God. His understanding was adorned with a true and saving knowledge of his Creator, and of spiritual things; his heart and will were upright, all his affections pure, and the whole man was holy. But, revolting from God by the instigation of the devil and by his own free will, he forfeited these excellent gifts; and in the place thereof became involved in blindness of mind, horrible darkness, vanity, and perverseness of judgment; became wicked, rebellious, and obdurate in heart and will, and impure in his affections.

ARTICLE 2

Man after the fall begat children in his own likeness. A corrupt stock produced a corrupt offspring. Hence all the posterity of Adam, Christ only excepted, have derived corruption from their original parent, not by imitation, as the Pelagians of old asserted, but by the propagation of a vicious nature, in consequence of the just judgment of God.

ARTICLE 3

Therefore all men are conceived in sin, and are by nature children of wrath, incapable of saving good, prone to evil, dead in sin, and in bondage thereto; and without the regenerating grace of the Holy Spirit, they are neither able nor willing to return to God, to reform the depravity of their nature, or to dispose themselves to reformation.

ARTICLE 4

There remain, however, in man since the fall, the glimmerings of natural light, whereby he retains some knowledge of God, of natural things, and of the difference between good and evil, and shows some regard for virtue and for good outward behavior. But so far is this light of nature from being sufficient to bring him to a saving knowledge of God and to true conversion that he is incapable of using it aright even in things natural and civil. Nay further, this light, such as it is, man in various ways renders wholly polluted, and hinders in unrighteousness, by doing which he becomes inexcusable before God.

ARTICLE 5

In the same light are we to consider the law of the decalogue, delivered by God to His peculiar people, the Jews, by the hands of Moses. For though it reveals the greatness of sin, and more and more convinces man thereof, yet, as it neither points out a remedy nor imparts strength to extricate him from this misery, but, being weak through the flesh, leaves the transgressor under the curse, man cannot by this law obtain saving grace.

ARTICLE 6

What, therefore, neither the light of nature nor the law could do, that God performs by the operation of the Holy Spirit through the word or ministry of reconciliation; which is the glad tidings concerning the Messiah, by means whereof it has pleased God to save such as believe, as well under the Old as under the New Testament.

ARTICLE 7

This mystery of His will God revealed to but a small number under the Old Testament; under the New Testament (the distinction between various peoples having been removed) He reveals it to many. The cause of this dispensation is not to be ascribed to the superior worth of one nation above another, nor to their better use of the light of nature, but results wholly from the sovereign good pleasure and unmerited love of God. Hence they to whom so great and so gracious a blessing is communicated, above their desert, or rather notwithstanding their demerits, are bound to acknowledge it with humble and grateful hearts, and with the apostle to adore, but in no wise curiously to pry into, the severity and justice of God's judgments displayed in others to whom this grace is not given.

ARTICLE 8

As many as are called by the gospel are unfeignedly called. For God has most earnestly and truly declared in His Word what is acceptable to Him, namely, that those who are called should come unto Him. He also seriously promises rest of soul and eternal life to all who come to Him and believe.

ARTICLE 9

It is not the fault of the gospel, nor of Christ offered therein, nor of God, who calls men by the gospel and confers upon them various gifts, that those who are called by the ministry of the Word refuse to come and be converted. The fault lies in themselves; some of whom when called, regardless of their danger, reject the Word of life; others, though they receive it, suffer it not to make a lasting impression on their heart; therefore, their joy, arising only from a temporary faith, soon vanishes, and they fall away; while others choke the seed of the Word by perplexing cares and the pleasures of this world, and produce no fruit. This our Savior teaches in the parable of the sower (Matt. 13).

ARTICLE 10

But that others who are called by the gospel obey the call and are converted is not to be ascribed to the proper exercise of free will, whereby one distinguishes himself above others equally furnished with grace sufficient for faith and conversion (as the proud heresy of Pelagius maintains); but it must be wholly ascribed to God, who, as He has chosen His own from eternity in Christ, so He calls them effectually in time, confers upon them faith and repentance, rescues them from the power of darkness, and translates them into the kingdom of His own Son; that they may show forth the praises of Him who has called them out of darkness into His marvelous light, and may glory not in themselves but in the Lord, according to the testimony of the apostles in various places.

ARTICLE 11

But when God accomplishes His good pleasure in the elect, or works in them true conversion, He not only causes the gospel to be externally preached to them, and powerfully illuminates their minds by His Holy Spirit, that they may rightly understand and discern the things of the Spirit of God; but by the efficacy of the same regenerating Spirit He pervades the inmost recesses of man; He opens the closed and softens the hardened heart, and circumcises that which was uncircumcised; infuses new qualities into the will, which, though heretofore dead, He quickens; from being evil, disobedient, and refractory, He renders it good, obedient, and pliable; actuates and strengthens it, that like a good tree, it may bring forth the fruits of good actions.

ARTICLE 12

And this is that regeneration so highly extolled in Scripture, that renewal, new creation, resurrection from the dead, making alive, which God works in us without our aid. But this is in no wise effected merely by the external preaching of the gospel, by moral suasion, or such a mode of operation that, after God has performed His part, it still remains in the power of man to be regenerated or not, to be converted or to continue unconverted; but it is evidently a supernatural work, most powerful, and at the same time most delightful, astonishing, mysterious, and ineffable; not inferior in efficacy to creation or the resurrection from the dead, as the Scripture inspired by the Author of this work declares; so that all in whose heart God works in this marvelous manner are certainly, infallibly, and effectually regenerated, and do actually believe. Whereupon the will thus renewed is not only actuated and influenced by God, but in consequence of this influence becomes itself active. Wherefore also man himself is rightly said to believe and repent by virtue of that grace received.

ARTICLE 13

The manner of this operation cannot be fully comprehended by believers in this life. Nevertheless, they are satisfied to know and experience that by this grace of God they are enabled to believe with the heart and to love their Savior.

Article 14

Faith is therefore to be considered as the gift of God, not on account of its being offered by God to man, to be accepted or rejected at his pleasure, but because it is in reality conferred upon him, breathed and infused into him; nor even because God bestows the power or ability to believe, and then expects that man should by the exercise of his own free will consent to the terms of salvation and actually believe in Christ, but because He who works in man both to will and to work, and indeed all things in all, produces both the will to believe and the act of believing also.

Article 15

God is under no obligation to confer this grace upon any; for how can He be indebted to one who had no previous gifts to bestow as a foundation for such recompense? Nay, how can He be indebted to one who has nothing of his own but sin and falsehood? He, therefore, who becomes the subject of this grace owes eternal gratitude to God, and gives Him thanks forever. Whoever is not made partaker thereof is either altogether regardless of these spiritual gifts and satisfied with his own condition, or is in no apprehension of danger, and vainly boasts the possession of that which he has not. Further, with respect to those who outwardly profess their faith and amend their lives, we are bound, after the example of the apostle, to judge and speak of them in the most favorable manner; for the secret recesses of the heart are unknown to us. And as to others who have not yet been called, it is our duty to pray for them to God, who calls the things that are not as if they were. But we are in no wise to conduct ourselves towards them with haughtiness, as if we had made ourselves to differ.

Article 16

But as man by the fall did not cease to be a creature endowed with understanding and will, nor did sin which pervaded the whole race of mankind deprive him of the human nature, but brought upon him depravity and spiritual death; so also this grace of regeneration does not treat men as senseless stocks and blocks, nor take away their will and its properties, or do violence thereto; but it spiritually quickens, heals, corrects, and at the same time sweetly and powerfully bends it, that where carnal rebellion and resistance formerly prevailed, a ready and sincere spiritual obedience begins to reign; in which the true and spiritual restoration and freedom of our will consist. Wherefore, unless the admirable Author of every good work so deal with us, man can have no hope of being able to rise from his fall by his own free will, by which, in a state of innocence, he plunged himself into ruin.

Article 17

As the almighty operation of God whereby He brings forth and supports this our natural life does not exclude but require the use of means by which God, of His infinite mercy and goodness, has chosen to exert His influence, so also the aforementioned supernatural operation of God by which we are regenerated in no wise excludes or subverts the use of the gospel, which the most wise God has ordained to be the seed of regeneration and food of the soul. Wherefore, as the apostles and the teachers who succeeded them piously instructed the people concerning this grace of God, to His glory and to the abasement of all pride, and in the meantime, however, neglected not to keep them, by the holy admonitions of the gospel, under the influence of the Word, the sacraments, and ecclesiastical discipline; so even now it should be far from those who give or receive instruction in the Church to presume to tempt God by separating what He of His good pleasure has most intimately joined together. For grace is conferred by means of admonitions; and the more readily we perform our duty, the more clearly this favor of God, working in us, usually manifests itself, and the more directly His work is advanced; to whom alone all the glory, both for the means and for their saving fruit and efficacy, is forever due. Amen.

REJECTION OF ERRORS

The true doctrine having been explained, the Synod rejects the errors of those:

PARAGRAPH 1

Who teach: That it cannot properly be said that original sin in itself suffices to condemn the whole human race or to deserve temporal and eternal punishment.

For these contradict the apostle, who declares: *Therefore, as through one man sin entered into the world, and death through sin; and so death passed unto all men, for that all sinned* (Rom. 5:12). And: *The judgment came of one unto condemnation* (Rom. 5:16). And: *The wages of sin is death* (Rom. 6:23).

PARAGRAPH 2

Who teach: That the spiritual gifts or the good qualities and virtues, such as goodness, holiness, righteousness, could not belong to the will of man when he was first created, and that these, therefore, cannot have been separated therefrom in the fall.

For such is contrary to the description of the image of God which the apostle gives in Eph. 4:24, where he declares that it consists in righteousness and holiness, which undoubtedly belong to the will.

PARAGRAPH 3

Who teach: That in spiritual death the spiritual gifts are not separate from the will of man, since the will in itself has never been corrupted, but only hindered through the darkness of the understanding and the irregularity of the affections; and that, these hindrances having been removed, the will can then bring into operation its native powers, that is, that the will of itself is able to will and to choose, or not to will and not to choose, all manner of good which may be presented to it.

This is an innovation and an error, and tends to elevate the powers of the free will, contrary to the declaration of the prophet: *The heart is deceitful above all things, and it is exceedingly corrupt* (Jer. 17:9); and of the apostle: *Among whom* (sons of disobedience) *we also all once lived in the lusts of our flesh, doing the desires of the flesh and of the mind* (Eph. 2:3).

PARAGRAPH 4

Who teach: That the unregenerate man is not really nor utterly dead in sin, nor destitute of all powers unto spiritual good, but that he can yet hunger and thirst after righteousness and life, and offer the sacrifice of a contrite and broken spirit, which is pleasing to God.

For these things are contrary to the express testimony of Scripture: *Ye were dead through your trespasses and sins* (Eph. 2:1, 5). And: *Every imagination of the thoughts of his heart was only evil continually* (Gen. 6:5; 8:21). Moreover, to hunger and thirst after deliverance from misery and after life, and to offer unto God the sacrifice of a broken spirit, is peculiar to the regenerate and those that are called blessed (Ps. 51:17; Matt. 5:6).

PARAGRAPH 5

Who teach: That the corrupt and natural man can so well use the common grace (by which they understand the light of nature), or the gifts still left him after the fall, that he can gradually gain by their good use a greater, that is, the evangelical or saving grace, and salvation itself; and that in this way God on His part shows Himself ready to reveal Christ unto all men, since He applies to all sufficiently and efficiently the means necessary to conversion.

For both the experience of all ages and the Scriptures testify that this is untrue. *He showeth his word unto Jacob, his statutes and his ordinances unto Israel. He hath not dealt so with any nation; and as for his ordinances, they have not known them* (Ps. 147:19, 20). *Who in the generations gone by suffered all the nations to walk in their own way* (Acts 14:16). And: *And they* (Paul and his companions) *having been forbidden of the Holy Spirit to speak the word in Asia, when they were come over against Mysia, they assayed to go into Bithynia, and the Spirit of Jesus suffered them not* (Acts 16: 6, 7).

PARAGRAPH 6

Who teach: That in the true conversion of man no new qualities, powers, or gifts can be infused by God into the will, and that therefore faith, through which we are first converted and because of which we are called believers, is not a quality or gift infused by God but only an act of man, and that it cannot be said to be a gift, except in respect of the power to attain to this faith.

For thereby they contradict the Holy Scriptures, which declare that God infuses new qualities of faith, of obedience, and of the consciousness of His love into our hearts: *I will put my law in their inward parts, and in their heart will I write it* (Jer. 31:33). And: *I will pour water upon him that is thirsty, and streams upon the dry ground; I will pour my Spirit upon thy seed* (Is. 44:3). And: *The love of God hath been shed abroad in our hearts through the Holy Spirit which was given unto us* (Rom. 5:5). This is also repugnant to the constant practice of the Church, which prays by the mouth of the prophet thus: *Turn thou me, and I shall be turned* (Jer. 31:18).

PARAGRAPH 7

Who teach: That the grace whereby we are converted to God is only a gentle advising, or (as others explain it) that this is the noblest manner of working in the conversion of man, and that this manner of working, which consists in advising, is most in harmony with man's nature; and that there is no reason why this advising grace alone should not be sufficient to make the natural man spiritual; indeed, that God does not produce the consent of the will except through this manner of advising; and that the power of the divine working, whereby it surpasses the working of Satan, consists in this that God promises eternal, while Satan promises only temporal goods.

But this is altogether Pelagian and contrary to the whole Scripture, which, besides this, teaches yet another and far more powerful and divine manner of the Holy Spirit's working in the conversion of man, as in Ezekiel: *A new heart also will I give you, and a new spirit will I put within you; and I will take away the stony heart out of your flesh, and I will give you a heart of flesh* (Ezek. 36:26).

PARAGRAPH 8

Who teach: That God in the regeneration of man does not use such powers of His omnipotence as potently and infallibly bend man's will to faith and conversion; but that all the works of grace having been accomplished, which God employs to convert man, man may yet so resist God and the Holy Spirit, when God intends man's regeneration and wills to regenerate him, and indeed that man often does so resist that he prevents entirely his regeneration, and that it therefore remains in man's power to be regenerated or not.

For this is nothing less than the denial of all the efficiency of God's grace in our conversion, and the subjecting of the working of Almighty God to the will of man, which is contrary to the apostles, who teach that *we believe according to the working of the strength of his might* (Eph. 1:19); and that *God fulfils every desire of goodness and every work of faith with power* (2 Thess. 1:11); and that *his divine power hath granted unto us all things that pertain unto life and godliness* **(2 Peter 1:3).**

PARAGRAPH 9

Who teach: That grace and free will are partial causes which together work the beginning of conversion, and that grace, in order of working, does not precede the working of the will; that is, that God does not efficiently help the will of man unto conversion until the will of man moves and determines to do this.

For the ancient Church has long ago condemned this doctrine of the Pelagians according to the words of the apostle: *So then it is not of him that willeth, nor of him that runneth, but of God that hath mercy* (Rom. 9:16). Likewise: *For who maketh thee to differ? and what hast thou that thou didst not receive?* (1 Cor. 4:7). And: *For it is God who worketh in you both to will and to work, for his good pleasure* (Phil. 2:13).

FIFTH HEAD OF DOCTRINE

THE PERSEVERANCE OF THE SAINTS

ARTICLE 1

Those whom God, according to His purpose, calls to the communion of His Son, our Lord Jesus Christ, and regenerates by the Holy Spirit, He also delivers from the dominion and slavery of sin, though in this life He does not deliver them altogether from the body of sin and from the infirmities of the flesh.

ARTICLE 2

Hence spring forth the daily sins of infirmity, and blemishes cleave even to the best works of the saints. These are to them a perpetual reason to humiliate themselves before God and to flee for refuge to Christ crucified; to mortify the flesh more and more by the spirit of prayer and by holy exercises of piety; and to press forward to the goal of perfection, until at length, delivered from this body of death, they shall reign with the Lamb of God in heaven.

ARTICLE 3

By reason of these remains of indwelling sin, and also because of the temptations of the world and of Satan, those who are converted could not persevere in that grace if left to their own strength. But God is faithful, who, having conferred grace, mercifully confirms and powerfully preserves them therein, even to the end.

ARTICLE 4

Although the weakness of the flesh cannot prevail against the power of God, who confirms and preserves true believers in a state of grace, yet converts are not always so influenced and actuated by the Spirit of God as not in some particular instances sinfully to deviate from the guidance of divine grace, so as to be seduced by and to comply with the lusts of the flesh; they must, therefore, be constant in watching and prayer, that they may not be led into temptation. When these are neglected, they are not only liable to be drawn into great and heinous sins by the flesh, the world, and Satan, but sometimes by the righteous permission of God actually are drawn into these evils. This, the lamentable fall of David, Peter, and other saints described in Holy Scripture, demonstrates.

ARTICLE 5

By such enormous sins, however, they very highly offend God, incur a deadly guilt, grieve the Holy Spirit, interrupt the exercise of faith, very grievously wound their consciences, and sometimes for a while lose the sense of God's favor, until, when they change their course by serious repentance, the light of God's fatherly countenance again shines upon them.

ARTICLE 6

But God, who is rich in mercy, according to His unchangeable purpose of election, does not wholly withdraw the Holy Spirit from His own people even in their grievous falls; nor suffers them to proceed so far as to lose the grace of adoption and forfeit the state of justification, or to commit the sin unto death or against the Holy Spirit; nor does He permit them to be totally deserted, and to plunge themselves into everlasting destruction.

ARTICLE 7

For in the first place, in these falls He preserves in them the incorruptible seed of regeneration from perishing or being totally lost; and again, by His Word and Spirit He certainly and effectually renews them to repentance, to a sincere and godly sorrow for their sins, that they may seek and obtain remission in the blood of the Mediator, may again experience the favor of a reconciled God, through faith adore His mercies, and henceforward more diligently work out their own salvation with fear and trembling.

ARTICLE 8

Thus it is not in consequence of their own merits or strength, but of God's free mercy, that they neither totally fall from faith and grace nor continue and perish finally in their backslidings; which, with respect to themselves is not only possible, but would undoubtedly happen; but with respect to God, it is utterly impossible, since His counsel cannot be changed nor His promise fail; neither can the call according to His purpose be revoked, nor the merit, intercession, and preservation of Christ be rendered ineffectual, nor the sealing of the Holy Spirit be frustrated or obliterated.

ARTICLE 9

Of this preservation of the elect to salvation and of their perseverance in the faith, true believers themselves may and do obtain assurance according to the measure of their faith, whereby they surely believe that they are and ever will continue true and living members of the Church, and that they have the forgiveness of sins and life eternal.

ARTICLE 10

This assurance, however, is not produced by any peculiar revelation contrary to or independent of the Word of God, but springs from faith in God's promises, which He has most abundantly revealed in His Word for our comfort; from the testimony of the Holy Spirit, witnessing with our spirit that we are children and heirs of God (Rom. 8:16); and lastly, from a serious and holy desire to preserve a good conscience and to perform good works. And if the elect of God were deprived of this solid comfort that they shall finally obtain the victory, and of this infallible pledge of eternal glory, they would be of all men the most miserable.

ARTICLE 11

The Scripture moreover testifies that believers in this life have to struggle with various carnal doubts, and that under grievous temptations they do not always feel this full assurance of faith and certainty of persevering. But God, who is the Father of all consolation, does not suffer them to be tempted above that they are able, but will with the temptation make also the way of escape, that they may be able to endure it (1 Cor. 10:13), and by the Holy Spirit again inspires them with the comfortable assurance of persevering.

ARTICLE 12

This certainty of perseverance, however, is so far from exciting in believers a spirit of pride, or of rendering them carnally secure, that on the contrary it is the real source of humility, filial reverence, true piety, patience in every tribulation, fervent prayers, constancy in suffering and in confessing the truth, and of solid rejoicing in God; so that the consideration of this benefit should serve as an incentive to the serious and constant practice of gratitude and good works, as appears from the testimonies of Scripture and the examples of the saints.

ARTICLE 13

Neither does renewed confidence of persevering produce licentiousness or a disregard of piety in those who are recovered from backsliding; but it renders them much more careful and solicitous to continue in the ways of the Lord, which He has ordained, that they who walk therein may keep the assurance of persevering; lest, on account of their abuse of His fatherly kindness, God should turn away His gracious countenance from them (to behold which is to the godly dearer than life, and the withdrawal of which is more bitter than death) and they in consequence thereof should fall into more grievous torments of conscience.

ARTICLE 14

And as it has pleased God, by the preaching of the gospel, to begin this work of grace in us, so He preserves, continues, and perfects it by the hearing and reading of His Word, by meditation thereon, and by the exhortations, threatenings, and promises thereof, and by the use of the sacraments.

ARTICLE 15

The carnal mind is unable to comprehend this doctrine of the perseverance of the saints and the certainty thereof, which God has most abundantly revealed in His Word, for the glory of His Name and the consolation of pious souls, and which He impresses upon the hearts of the believers. Satan abhors it, the world ridicules it, the ignorant and hypocritical abuse it, and the heretics oppose it. But the bride of Christ has always most tenderly loved and constantly defended it as an inestimable treasure; and God, against whom neither counsel nor strength can prevail, will dispose her so to continue to the end. Now to this one God, Father, Son, and Holy Spirit, be honor and glory forever. Amen.

REJECTION OF ERRORS

The true doctrine having been explained, the Synod rejects the errors of those:

PARAGRAPH 1

Who teach: That the perseverance of the true believers is not a fruit of election, or a gift of God gained by the death of Christ, but a condition of the new covenant, which (as they declare) man before his decisive election and justification must fulfil through his free will.

For the Holy Scripture testifies that this follows out of election, and is given the elect in virtue of the death, the resurrection, and intercession of Christ: *But the election obtained it, and the rest were hardened* (Rom. 11:7). Likewise: *He that spared not his own Son, but delivered him up for us all, how shall he not also with him freely give us all things? Who shall lay anything to the charge of God's elect? It is God that justifieth; who is he that condemneth? It is Christ Jesus that died, yea rather, that was raised from the dead, who is at the right hand of God, who also maketh intercession for us. Who shall separate us from the love of Christ?* (Rom. 8:32–35).

PARAGRAPH 2

Who teach: That God does indeed provide the believer with sufficient powers to persevere, and is ever ready to preserve these in him if he will do his duty; but that, though all things which are necessary to persevere in faith and which God will use to preserve faith are made use of, even then it ever depends on the pleasure of the will whether it will persevere or not.

For this idea contains an outspoken Pelagianism, and while it would make men free, it makes them robbers of God's honor, contrary to the prevailing agreement of the evangelical doctrine, which takes from man all cause of boasting, and ascribes all the praise for this favor to the grace of God alone; and contrary to the apostle, who declares that it is God, *who shall also confirm you unto the end,* that ye be *unreprovable in the day of our Lord Jesus Christ* (1 Cor. 1:8).

Who teach: That the true believers and regenerate not only can fall from justifying faith and likewise from grace and salvation wholly and to the end, but indeed often do fall from this and are lost forever.

For this conception makes powerless the grace, justification, regeneration, and continued preservation by Christ, contrary to the expressed words of the apostle Paul: *That, while we were yet sinners, Christ died for us. Much more then, being now justified by his blood, shall we be saved from the wrath* of God *through him* (Rom. 5:8, 9). And contrary to the apostle John: *Whosoever is begotten of God doeth no sin, because his seed abideth in him; and he can not sin, because he is begotten of God* (1 John 3:9). And also contrary to the words of Jesus Christ: *I give unto them eternal life; and they shall never perish, and no one shall snatch them out of my hand. My Father, who hath given* them *to me, is greater than all; and no one is able to snatch* them *out of the Father's hand* (John 10:28, 29).

Who teach: That true believers and regenerate can sin the sin unto death or against the Holy Spirit.

Since the same apostle John, after having spoken in the fifth chapter of his first epistle, vs. 16 and 17, of those who sin unto death and having forbidden to pray for them, immediately adds to this in vs. 18: *We know that whosoever is begotten of God sinneth not* (meaning a sin of that character), *but he that was begotten of God keepeth himself, and the evil one toucheth him not* (1 John 5:18).

Who teach: That without a special revelation we can have no certainty of future perseverance in this life.

For by this doctrine the sure comfort of the true believers is taken away in this life, and the doubts of the papist are again introduced into the Church, while the Holy Scriptures constantly deduce this assurance, not from a special and extraordinary revelation, but from the marks proper to the children of God and from the very constant promises of God. So especially the apostle Paul: *No creature shall be able to separate us from the love of God, which is in Christ Jesus our Lord* (Rom. 8:39). And John declares: *And he that keepeth his commandments abideth in him, and he in him. And hereby we know that he abideth in us, by the Spirit which he gave us* (1 John 3:24).

Who teach: That the doctrine of the certainty of perseverance and of salvation from its own character and nature is a cause of indolence and is injurious to godliness, good morals, prayers, and other holy exercises, but that on the contrary it is praiseworthy to doubt.

For these show that they do not know the power of divine grace and the working of the indwelling Holy Spirit. And they contradict the apostle John, who teaches the opposite with express words in his first epistle: *Beloved, now are we children of God, and it is not yet made manifest what we shall be. We know that, if he shall be manifested, we shall be like him; for we shall see him even as he is. And every one that hath this hope set on him purifieth himself, even as he is pure* (1 John 3:2, 3). Furthermore, these are contradicted by the example of the saints, both of the Old and the New Testament, who though they were assured of their perseverance and salvation, were nevertheless constant in prayers and other exercises of godliness.

Paragraph 7

Who teach: That the faith of those who believe for a time does not differ from justifying and saving faith except only in duration.

For Christ Himself, in Matt. 13:20, Luke 8:13, and in other places, evidently notes, besides this duration, a threefold difference between those who believe only for a time and true believers, when He declares that the former receive the seed in stony ground, but the latter in the good ground or heart; that the former are without root, but the latter have a firm root; that the former are without fruit, but that the latter bring forth their fruit in various measure, with constancy and stedfastness.

Paragraph 8

Who teach: That it is not absurd that one having lost his first regeneration is again and even often born anew.

For these deny by this doctrine the incorruptibleness of the seed of God, whereby we are born again; contrary to the testimony of the apostle Peter: *Having been begotten again, not of corruptible seed, but of incorruptible* (Peter 1-23).

Paragraph 9

Who teach: That Christ has in no place prayed that believers should infallibly continue in faith.

For they contradict Christ Himself, who says: *I made supplication for thee* (Simon), *that thy faith fail not* (Luke 22:32), and the evangelist John, who declares that Christ has not prayed for the apostles only, but also for those who through their word would believe: *Holy Father, keep them in thy name*, and: *I pray not that thou shouldest take them from the world, but that thou shouldest keep them from the evil one* (John 17:11, 15, 20).

Conclusion

And this is the perspicuous, simple, and ingenuous declaration of the orthodox doctrine respecting the five articles which have been controverted in the Belgic Churches; and the rejection of the errors, with which they have for some time been troubled. This doctrine the Synod judges to be drawn from the Word of God, and to be agreeable to the confession of the Reformed Churches. Whence it clearly appears that some, whom such conduct by no means became, have violated all truth, equity, and charity, in wishing to persuade the public:

'That the doctrine of the Reformed Churches concerning predestination, and the points annexed to it, by its own genius and necessary tendency, leads off the minds of men from all piety and religion; that it is an opiate administered by the flesh and the devil; and the stronghold of Satan, where he lies in wait for all, and from which he wounds multitudes, and mortally strikes through many with the darts both of despair and security; that it makes God the author of sin, unjust, tyrannical, hypocritical; that it is nothing more than an interpolated Stoicism, Manicheism, Libertinism, Turcism; that it renders men carnally secure, since they are persuaded by it that nothing can hinder the salvation of the elect, let them live as they please; and, therefore, that they may safely perpetrate every species of the most atrocious crimes; and that, if the reprobate should even perform truly all the works of the saints, their obedience would not in the least contribute to their salvation; that the same doctrine teaches that God, by a mere arbitrary act of his will, without the least respect or view to any sin, has predestinated the greatest part of the world to eternal damnation, and has created them for this very purpose; that in the same manner in which the election is the fountain and cause of faith and good works, reprobation is the cause of unbelief and impiety; that many children of the faithful are torn, guiltless, from their mothers' breasts, and tyrannically plunged into hell: so that neither baptism nor the prayers of the Church at their baptism can at all profit them;' and many other things of the same kind which the Reformed Churches not only do not acknowledge, but even detest with their whole soul.

Wherefore, this Synod of Dort, in the name of the Lord, conjures as many as piously call upon the name of our Saviour Jesus Christ to judge of the faith of the Reformed Churches, not from the calumnies which on every side are heaped upon it, nor from the private expressions of a few among ancient and modern teachers, often dishonestly quoted, or corrupted and wrested to a meaning quite foreign to their intention; but from the public confessions of the Churches themselves, and from this declaration of the orthodox doctrine, confirmed by the unanimous consent of all and each of the members of the whole Synod. Moreover, the Synod warns calumniators themselves to consider the terrible judgment of God which awaits them, for bearing false witness against the confessions of so many Churches; for distressing the consciences of the weak; and for laboring to render suspected the society of the truly faithful.

Finally, this Synod exhorts all their brethren in the gospel of Christ to conduct themselves piously and religiously in handling this doctrine, both in the universities and churches; to direct it, as well in discourse as in writing, to the glory of the Divine name, to holiness of life, and to the consolation of afflicted souls; to regulate, by the Scripture, according to the analogy of faith, not only their sentiments, but also their language, and to abstain from all those phrases which exceed the limits necessary to be observed in ascertaining the genuine sense of the Holy Scriptures, and may furnish insolent sophists with a just pretext for violently assailing, or even vilifying, the doctrine of the Reformed Churches.

May Jesus Christ, the Son of God, who, seated at the Father's right hand, gives gifts to men, sanctify us in the truth; bring to the truth those who err; shut the mouths of the calumniators of sound doctrine, and endue the faithful ministers of his Word with the spirit of wisdom and discretion, that all their discourses may tend to the glory of God, and the edification of those who hear them. Amen.

ECUMENICAL CREEDS

In Article IX of our Confession of Faith three writings, dating from the first centuries of the Christian Church, are named as creeds which "we do willingly receive." They are: the Apostles' Creed, the Nicene Creed, and the Athanasian Creed. The adoption of this Confession of Faith by the Synods of the Reformed Churches in the Netherlands, held in the last part of the sixteenth century and the beginning of the seventeenth, constituted therefore at the same time an implicit approval of the three Creeds mentioned above. They are called *Ecumenical* (general, universal) because they have been approved and accepted by nearly all the churches of Christendom.

APOSTLES' CREED

This Creed is called the *Apostles' Creed*, not because it is a production of the apostles themselves, but because it contains a brief summary of their teachings. It sets forth their doctrine, as has been well said, "in sublime simplicity, in unsurpassable brevity, in beautiful order, and with liturgical solemnity." In its present form it is of no later date than the fourth century. More than any other creed of Christendom, it may justly be called an ecumenical symbol of faith.

    I. I believe in God the Father, Almighty, Maker of heaven and earth.

    II. And in Jesus Christ, His only begotten Son, our Lord;

    III. Who was conceived by the Holy Spirit, born of the virgin Mary;

    IV. Suffered under Pontius Pilate; was crucified, dead, and buried; He descended into hell;

    V. The third day He rose again from the dead;

    VI. He ascended into heaven, and sitteth at the right hand of God the Father Almighty;

    VII. From thence He shall come to judge the living and the dead.

    VIII. I believe in the Holy Spirit.

    IX. I believe a holy catholic Church, the communion of saints;

    X. The forgiveness of sins;

    XI. The resurrection of the body;

    XII. And the life everlasting. AMEN.

NICENE CREED

The Nicene Creed, also called the *Nicaeno-Constantinopolitan Creed*, is a statement of the orthodox faith of the early Christian Church, in opposition to certain heresies, especially Arianism. These heresies disturbed the Church during the fourth century, and concerned the doctrine of the Trinity and of the person of Christ. Both the Greek, or Eastern, and the Latin, or Western, Church held this Creed in honor, though with one important difference. The Western Church insisted on the inclusion of the phrase *and the Son* (known as the *Filioque*) in the article on the procession of the Holy Spirit, which phrase to this day is repudiated by the Eastern Church. Though in its present form this Creed does not go back to the Council of Nicea (325 A.D.), nor to the Council of Constantinople (381 A.D.), as was erroneously held until recent times, it is in substance an accurate and majestic formulation of the Nicene faith.

I believe in one God, the Father Almighty, Maker of heaven and earth, and of all things visible and invisible.

And in one Lord Jesus Christ, the only-begotten Son of God, begotten of the Father before all worlds; God of God, Light of Light, very God of very God; begotten, not made, being of one substance with the Father, by whom all things were made.

Who, for us men and for our salvation, came down from heaven, and was incarnate by the Holy Spirit of the virgin Mary, and was made man; and was crucified also for us under Pontius Pilate; He suffered and was buried; and the third day He rose again, according to the Scriptures; and ascended into heaven, and sitteth on the right hand of the Father; and He shall come again, with glory, to judge the living and the dead; whose kingdom shall have no end.

And I believe in the Holy Spirit, the Lord and Giver of life; who proceedeth from the Father and the Son; who with the Father and the Son together is worshipped and glorified; who spake by the prophets.

And I believe one holy catholic and apostolic Church. I acknowledge one baptism for the remission of sins; and I look for the resurrection of the dead, and the life of the world to come. AMEN.

ATHANASIAN CREED

This Creed is named after Athanasius (293–373 A.D.), the champion of orthodoxy over against Arian attacks upon the doctrine of the Trinity. Although Athanasius did not write this Creed and it is improperly named after him, the name persists because until the seventeenth century it was commonly ascribed to him. Another name for it is the *Symbol Quicunque*, this being its opening word in the Latin original. Its author is unknown, but in its present form it probably does not date back farther than the sixth century. It is not from Greek Eastern, but from Latin Western origin, and is not recognized by the Greek Church today. Apart from the opening and closing sentences, this symbol consists of two parts, the first setting forth the orthodox doctrine of the Trinity (3–28), and the second dealing chiefly with the incarnation and the two natures doctrine (29–43). This Creed, though more explicit and advanced theologically than the Apostles' and the Nicene Creeds, cannot be said to possess the simplicity, spontaneity, and majesty of these. For centuries it has been the custom of the Roman and Anglican Churches to chant this Creed in public worship on certain solemn occasions.

---

(1) Whosoever will be saved, before all things it is necessary that he hold the catholic faith; (2) Which faith except every one do keep whole and undefiled, without doubt he shall perish everlastingly.

(3) And the catholic faith is this: That we worship one God in Trinity, and Trinity in Unity; (4) Neither confounding the persons, nor dividing the substance. (5) For there is one person of the Father, another of the Son, and another of the Holy Spirit. (6) But the Godhead of the Father, of the Son, and of the Holy Spirit is all one, the glory equal, the majesty co-eternal. (7) Such as the Father is, such is the Son, and such is the Holy Spirit. (8) The Father uncreate, the Son uncreate, and the Holy Spirit uncreate. (9) The Father incomprehensible, the Son incomprehensible, and the Holy Spirit incomprehensible. (10) The Father eternal, the Son eternal, and the Holy Spirit eternal. (11) And yet they are not three eternals, but one eternal. (12) As also there are not three uncreated nor three incomprehensibles, but one uncreated and one incomprehensible. (13) So likewise the Father is almighty, the Son almighty, and the Holy Spirit almighty; (14) And yet they are not three almighties, but one almighty. (15) So the Father is God, the Son is God, and the Holy Spirit is God; (16) And yet they are not three Gods, but one God. (17) So likewise the Father is Lord, the Son Lord, and the Holy Spirit Lord; (18) And yet they are not three Lords, but one Lord. (19) For like as we are compelled by the Christian verity to acknowledge every person by himself to be God and Lord; (20) So are we forbidden by the catholic religion to say: There are three Gods or three Lords. (21) The Father is made of none, neither created nor begotten. (22) The Son is of the Father alone; not made nor created, but begotten. (23) The Holy Spirit is of the Father and of the Son; neither made, nor created, nor begotten, but proceeding. (24) So there is one Father, not three Fathers; one Son, not three Sons; one Holy Spirit, not three Holy Spirits. (25) And in this Trinity none is afore, or after another; none

is greater, or less than another.   (26) But the whole three persons are co-eternal, and co-equal.   (27) So that in all things, as aforesaid, the Unity in Trinity and the Trinity in Unity is to be worshipped.   (28) He therefore that will be saved must thus think of the Trinity.

(29) Furthermore it is necessary to everlasting salvation that he also believe rightly the incarnation of our Lord Jesus Christ.   (30) For the right faith is that we believe and confess that our Lord Jesus Christ, the Son of God, is God and man. (31) God of the substance of the Father, begotten before the worlds; and man of the substance of His mother, born in the world.   (32) Perfect God and perfect man, of a reasonable soul and human flesh subsisting.   (33) Equal to the Father as touching His Godhead, and inferior to the Father as touching His manhood.   (34) Who, although He is God and man, yet He is not two, but one Christ.   (35) One, not by conversion of the Godhead into flesh, but by taking of the manhood into God. (36) One altogether, not by confusion of substance, but by unity of person.   (37) For as the reasonable soul and flesh is one man, so God and man is one Christ; (38) Who suffered for our salvation, descended into hell, rose again the third day from the dead; (39) He ascended into heaven, He sitteth on the right hand of the Father, God Almighty; (40) From thence He shall come to judge the living and the dead.   (41) At whose coming all men shall rise again with their bodies; (42) And shall give account of their own works.   (43) And they that have done good shall go into life everlasting, and they that have done evil into everlasting fire.

(44) This is the catholic faith, which except a man believe faithfully, he cannot be saved.

FORM OF SUBSCRIPTION

We, the undersigned, Professors of the Christian Reformed Church, Ministers of the Gospel, Elders and Deacons of the Christian Reformed congregation of ...., of the Classis of...................., do hereby, sincerely and in good conscience before the Lord, declare by this our subscription that we heartily believe and are persuaded that all the articles and points of doctrine contained in the Confession and Catechism of the Reformed Churches, together with the explanation of some points of the aforesaid doctrine made by the National Synod of Dordrecht, 1618–'19, do fully agree with the Word of God.

We promise therefore diligently to teach and faithfully to defend the aforesaid doctrine, without either directly or indirectly contradicting the same by our public preaching or writing.

We declare, moreover, that we not only reject all errors that militate against this doctrine and particularly those which were condemned by the above mentioned Synod, but that we are disposed to refute and contradict these and to exert ourselves in keeping the Church free from such errors. And if hereafter any difficulties or different sentiments respecting the aforesaid doctrines should arise in our minds, we promise that we will neither publicly nor privately propose, teach, or defend the same, either by preaching or writing, until we have first revealed such sentiments to the Consistory, Classis, or Synod, that the same may there be examined, being ready always cheerfully to submit to the judgment of the Consistory, Classis, or Synod, under the penalty, in case of refusal, of being by that very fact suspended from our office.

And further, if at any time the Consistory, Classis, or Synod, upon sufficient grounds of suspicion and to preserve the uniformity and purity of doctrine, may deem it proper to require of us a further explanation of our sentiments respecting any particular article of the Confession of Faith, the Catechism, or the explanation of the National Synod, we do hereby promise to be always willing and ready to comply with such requisition, under the penalty above mentioned, reserving for ourselves, however, the right of appeal in case we should believe ourselves aggrieved by the sentence of the Consistory or the Classis; and until a decision is made upon such an appeal, we will acquiesce in the determination and judgment already passed.

LITURGY

OF THE

CHRISTIAN REFORMED CHURCH

CONSISTING OF

A COLLECTION OF CHRISTIAN PRAYERS

FOR

Church and Family and Individual Use

AND

THE LITURGICAL FORMS

FOR

THE ADMINISTRATION OF THE SACRAMENTS AND CHURCH DISCIPLINE

THE ORDINATION OF CHURCH OFFICERS

AND

THE SOLEMNIZATION OF MARRIAGE

PUBLICATION COMMITTEE OF THE CHRISTIAN REFORMED CHURCH
PUBLISHERS
GRAND RAPIDS, MICHIGAN

INTRODUCTORY

The Liturgy of the Christian Reformed Church consists of two parts:

I. *A Collection of Christian Prayers for Church and Family and Individual Use.*

These prayers all date from the time of the Reformation. With exception of the last, which was added in the beginning of the seventeenth century, they were first published in the Netherlands in an edition of the Dutch Psalter by *Petrus Dathenus* in the year 1566. Some of these prayers seem to have been composed by him, while others were taken in whole or in part from Calvin's liturgy or other liturgies based upon that of Calvin. Although they gradually fell into disuse, they have to the present time always been printed in every edition of the Liturgy of the Reformed Churches in the Netherlands.

The collection now appears for the first time in our praise book. A committee was appointed by the synod of 1930 to translate these prayers into the English language. Their work was submitted to the synod of 1932, and with a few slight revisions adopted by the synod of 1934. One of the prayers, namely, the Prayer for all the Needs of Christendom, was considerably abridged, but all the others are faithful renderings of the original.

These prayers are for voluntary use. Neither the Reformed Churches in the Netherlands nor the Christian Reformed Church in our country imposes the use of prescribed forms of public prayer in worship. They are offered here, partly because of their historical interest, and partly because of the profitable aid they can render to those who are called to lead in public prayer.

II. *The Liturgical Forms for the Administration of the Sacraments and Church Discipline, the Ordination of Church Officers, and the Solemnization of Marriage.*

All these forms, with a few exceptions noted below, date from Reformation times. The forms for the administration of infant baptism, the Lord's supper, and the solemnization of marriage first appeared in the above-mentioned edition of the Dutch Psalter by *Petrus Dathenus.* In their composition he availed himself to a very large extent of existing liturgies based upon the liturgy of Calvin. The forms for the administration of church discipline, the ordination of ministers, and the ordination of elders and deacons were added by the synod of The Hague in 1586, and the form for the administration of adult baptism by the great synod of Dordrecht in 1618–19.

These forms have been in constant use in the Reformed Churches in the Netherlands to the present time. Only recently a few changes were made in some of the forms which were very much in need of revision.

Until now our Church has availed itself of a translation of these forms which was originally prepared in the Netherlands for the use of churches composed of English and Scottish refugees, and later revised and adopted by the Reformed Church in America. This translation, slightly revised and corrected, was adopted by our synod of 1912 for the use of our English speaking churches.

A more thorough revision of these forms is now published for the first time in this volume. The forms for the ordination of elders and deacons and for the solemnization of marriage, although in general of the same content as the existing forms, were entirely re-written by a committee, whose work was adopted by the synod of 1934. The committee for the preparation of this Psalter Hymnal took upon itself the revision of the translation of the other forms mentioned above, and the synod of 1934 adopted this revision, which offers a more faithful translation of the original in more idiomatic English.

The forms for the public profession of faith, the installation of professors of theology, and the ordination of missionaries are of recent date. These were not inherited by us from the Churches in the Netherlands, but are original compositions, which were adopted by our Church during the present century.

The use of these liturgical forms is obligatory. Article 58 of our Church Order reads: "In the ceremony of baptism, both of children and of adults, the minister shall use the respective forms drawn up for the administration of this sacrament." Similar requirements with respect to the other forms are found in Articles 4, 5, 62, 70, 76, and 78 of the Church Order.

74

CHRISTIAN PRAYERS

PRAYER AT THE BEGINNING OF PUBLIC WORSHIP

Our help is in the name of Jehovah, who made heaven and earth. AMEN

A GENERAL CONFESSION OF SINS, AND PRAYER BEFORE THE SERMON AND ON DAYS OF
FASTING AND PRAYER

O eternal God and merciful Father, we humble ourselves before Thy great majesty, against which we have frequently and grievously sinned. We acknowledge that if Thou shouldst enter into judgment with us, we would deserve nothing less than eternal death. We are deeply conscious of the fact that, on account of our original sin, we are unclean before Thee and children of wrath. Since we are conceived and born in sin, all manner of evil desires against Thee and our neighbor fill our soul. We continually transgress Thy commandments, failing to do what Thou hast commanded us, and doing that which Thou hast expressly forbidden. We all like sheep have gone astray; we have turned everyone to his own way. We acknowledge our waywardness, and are heartily sorry for all our sins. We confess to our humiliation and to the praise of Thy mercy that our transgressions are innumerable, and that our debt is so great that we cannot even begin to repay. We are not worthy to be called Thy children, nor to lift up our eyes heavenward to Thee in prayer.

Nevertheless, O Lord God and gracious Father, we know that Thou dost not desire the death of the sinner, but rather that he should turn to Thee and live; we know that Thy mercy toward those who turn to Thee is infinite; and so we take courage to call upon Thee from the depths of our hearts, trusting in our Mediator Jesus Christ, the Lamb of God that takes away the sin of the world. We pray that Thou, forgiving all our sins for Christ's sake, wilt have compassion upon us in our infirmities. Wash us in the pure fountain of His blood, so that we may become clean and white as snow. Cover our nakedness with His innocence and righteousness, for the glory of Thy Name. Deliver our understanding from all blindness, and our hearts from all wilfulness and rebellion.

Open now the mouth of Thy servant, and fill it with Thy wisdom and knowledge, that he may boldly proclaim Thy Word in all its purity. Prepare our hearts to receive it, to understand it, and to preserve it. Inscribe Thy law, as Thou hast promised, upon the tablet of our heart, and give us the desire and the strength to walk in the ways of Thy precepts, to the praise and glory of Thy Name, and to the edification of the Church.

All this, gracious Father, we implore in the Name of Jesus Christ, who taught us to pray, saying:

Our Father who art in heaven, etc. AMEN.

A PRAYER FOR ALL THE NEEDS OF CHRISTENDOM, TO BE USED ON THE SABBATH AFTER THE FIRST SERMON

Almighty and merciful God, we realize and confess before Thee that if Thou shouldst regard our merits, we would indeed be unworthy to lift up our eyes towards heaven and present our prayers before Thee. Our consciences accuse us, and our sins testify against us. We also know that Thou art a righteous Judge, punishing the sins of those who transgress Thy commandments. But Thou, O Lord, hast commanded us to call upon Thee in all our needs, and hast in mercy promised to hearken to our petitions. This is not because of our merits, for we have none, but because of the merits of our Lord Jesus Christ, whom Thou hast appointed as our Mediator and Advocate. Therefore we spurn all other help and take our refuge in Thy mercy alone.

We acknowledge that Thou hast showered upon us so many blessings that we are not able to comprehend them, much less to enumerate them. It behooves us especially to acknowledge that Thou hast led us to the light of Thy truth and to the knowledge of Thy holy gospel. Yet we, being ungrateful, have forgotten Thy benefits. We have departed from Thee and have followed the desires of our own heart. We have not honored Thee as we ought. We have grievously sinned against Thee. If Thou shouldst bring us into judgment, we could expect nothing but eternal death and condemnation. But, O Lord, behold the face of Thy Anointed and hide Thine eyes from our sins, that Thy wrath through His intercession may be removed. Work mightily within us by Thy Spirit, in order that we may daily mortify our sinful flesh more and more. And do Thou renew us to a better life.

And since it pleases Thee that we should pray for all mankind, we beseech Thee that Thou wilt cause Thy benediction to rest upon Thy holy gospel, that it may be proclaimed everywhere and universally received. May the world be filled with Thy knowledge, may the ignorant be converted, and the weak strengthened; may every one by word and deed magnify Thy holy Name. To this end send forth faithful servants into Thy harvest, and qualify them in such a manner that they may faithfully perform their duties. But destroy, we pray Thee, all false teachers, ravenous wolves, and hirelings, who seek their own honor and profit rather than the honor of Thy holy Name or the salvation and welfare of souls.

Wilt Thou also graciously govern Thy Church, and preserve it in the unity of true faith and in godliness of life. May Thy kingdom increase day by day; may the kingdom of Satan be destroyed, until the kingdom of God be perfected, and Thou shalt be all in all.

We also pray for all civil magistrates. Particularly would we remember those whom Thou hast set in authority over us. Grant that they may fulfil their task in such a manner that the King of kings may reign over them and us, and that the kingdom of Satan, which is a kingdom of shame and iniquity, may through them as Thy servants be more and more opposed and destroyed, and that we may live a peaceful life in all godliness and honor.

Furthermore we pray for all our brethren who are suffering affliction because of civil or ecclesiastical persecution. Comfort them with Thy Holy Spirit, and grant them deliverance. Permit not the memory of Thy Name to be removed from the earth, and give the enemies no occasion to dishonor or blaspheme Thy Name. But should it be Thy will that persecuted Christians must by their death witness to Thy truth, grant them comfort in their sufferings; may they accept their trial as from Thy hand, and, doing Thy will, may they remain firm in life and death to Thy honor, to the edification of the Church, and to their salvation.

We remember before Thee also all those whom Thou art chastening with poverty, imprisonment, physical illness, or spiritual distress. Comfort them all, O Lord, according to their several needs. Grant that their chastening may lead them to acknowledge their sins and to amend their lives. Give them unwavering patience, alleviate their sufferings, and deliver them, that they may rejoice because of Thy goodness, and may eternally praise Thy Name. Comfort all widows and orphans, and be to them a Father. Strengthen those who are weak, and heal those who are ill in body. Remember also those who are mentally ill, and strengthen within them the gift of understanding, that they may use it to the magnifying of Thy Name and the edifying of their neighbors.

Finally, O Lord, wilt Thou take us and our dear ones and all that concern us into Thy care and keeping. Remember particularly those who are journeying afar over land and sea, along dangerous trails for the promotion of Thy kingdom, for the benefit of our country, or for the promotion of honorable personal interests. Bless also the products of the soil. Grant favorable weather and fruitful increase. Grant that in our several callings we may live according to Thy will. May we so use the talents which we have received from Thy hand that they may not hinder but rather promote the interests of our spiritual life. In all temptations strengthen us, so that we may be victorious in the battle, and thereafter may with Christ possess eternal life.

We pray Thee for all these things, even as our faithful Lord and Savior, Jesus Christ, Himself has taught us, saying:

Our Father who art in heaven, etc. AMEN.

Strengthen us in the true Christian faith that we may increase daily therein. Of this faith we make confession with mouth and heart, saying:

I believe in God the Father, Almighty, etc. AMEN.

¶*Afterward the congregation is dismissed with the usual blessing:*

Lift up your hearts unto God and receive the blessing of the Lord:
Jehovah bless thee, and keep thee;
Jehovah make his face to shine upon thee, and be gracious unto thee;
Jehovah lift up his countenance upon thee, and give thee peace. AMEN.

A PUBLIC CONFESSION OF SINS, AND PRAYER BEFORE THE SERMON

Heavenly Father, eternal and merciful God, we acknowledge and confess before Thy divine majesty that we are poor miserable sinners. We were conceived and born in utter wickedness and corruption and are prone to all manner of evil and incapable by nature of doing any good. By our sinful life we transgress Thy holy commandments without ceasing, and thereby incur Thy wrath and bring down upon ourselves eternal damnation according to Thy righteous judgment.

But we are penitent, Lord, and we grieve because of our sins whereby we provoked Thy wrath. We bring accusation against ourselves and lay transgression to our own charge. Yet we make bold to desire that Thou mayest in mercy regard our miseries. Have compassion on us, most merciful God and Father, and be pleased to forgive all our sins for the sake of the passion of Thy dear Son, Jesus Christ.

Grant us also the grace of Thy Holy Spirit, in order that He may teach us to confess our sins in sincerity of heart, to abhor ourselves indeed, and may lead us to the mortification of sin in our lives. For we earnestly desire to return to a life that is truly holy and righteous and that is acceptable to Thee through Jesus Christ.

May it also please Thee to lead us into the comprehension of Thy holy Word according to Thy divine will, in order that we may be taught to put our trust wholly in Thee and not to repose confidence in any creature. May our old nature with all its lusts be increasingly mortified day by day, and may we offer ourselves as a living sacrifice to Thee, to the honor of Thy Name and the edification of our neighbor.

We also beseech Thee, gracious God, to turn unto Thyself in true penitence all that depart from Thy truth, for we eagerly desire that we all of one accord may serve Thee in holiness and righteousness all the days of our life.

This we ask of Thee through Jesus Christ our Lord, who taught and commanded us to pray, saying:

Our Father who art in heaven, etc. AMEN.

A BRIEF FORM OF PRAYER AFTER THE SERMON

O Lord, Almighty God, we pray that Thy holy Name may not be blasphemed on account of our sins. For we have sinned against Thee in many ways. We do not obey Thy holy Word as it behooves us. Through ignorance, unthankfulness, and discontent, we daily provoke Thee to wrath. We confess, Lord, that Thou art just in inflicting punishment upon us.

But we beseech Thee, O Lord, remember Thy great mercy and have compassion upon us. Teach us truly to know our sins and sincerely to mourn for them and to amend our life. Strengthen the ministers of Thy Church in order that they may faithfully and stedfastly preach Thy holy Word. Likewise, Lord, give strength to our rulers that they may wield the sword of civil authority in justice and equity.

We pray thee particularly for N— . . .

Keep us, we beseech Thee, from all hypocrisy and unfaithfulness, and frustrate all evil and subtle designs against Thy Word and Thy Church. O Lord, do not withhold from us Thy Word and Thy Spirit, but grant us increase in faith, and patience and stedfastness in all suffering and adversity. Succor Thy Church, and deliver Thy people from opposition, ridicule, and tyranny, which it suffers at the hands of wicked men. Impart from on high strength to those that are sorely burdened with sorrow. And visit upon us Thy peace through Jesus Christ, our Lord, who gave us this sure promise: *Verily, verily, I say unto you, If ye shall ask anything of the Father, he will give it you in my name,* and would have us pray, saying:

Our Father who art in heaven, etc. AMEN.

PRAYER BEFORE THE EXPLANATION OF THE CATECHISM

O heavenly Father, Thy Word is perfect, restoring the soul, making wise the simple, and enlightening the eyes of the blind, and a power of God unto salvation for every one that believes. We, however, are by nature blind and incapable of doing anything good, and Thou wilt succor only those who have a broken and contrite heart and who revere Thy Word. We beseech Thee, therefore, that Thou wilt illumine our darkened minds with Thy Holy Spirit and give us a humble heart, free from all haughtiness and carnal wisdom, in order that we, hearing Thy Word, may rightly understand it and may regulate our lives accordingly. Wilt Thou also graciously convert those who are straying from the truth, that we all in unity may serve Thee in true holiness and righteousness all the days of our life. These things we crave of Thee only for the sake of Christ, who promised to hear us and also taught us to pray in His Name, saying:

Our Father who art in heaven, etc. AMEN.

PRAYER AFTER THE EXPLANATION OF THE CATECHISM

O gracious and merciful God and Father, we thank Thee that Thou hast established Thy covenant with believers and their seed. This Thou hast not only sealed by holy baptism, but Thou daily showest it by perfecting Thy praise out of the mouths of babes and sucklings, thus putting to shame the wise and prudent of this world. We beseech Thee that Thou wilt increase Thy grace in them, in order that they may unceasingly grow in Christ, Thy Son, until they have reached complete maturity in all wisdom and righteousness. Give us grace to instruct them in Thy knowledge and fear, according to Thy commandment. May by their godliness the kingdom of Satan be destroyed and the kingdom of Jesus Christ in this and other congregations strengthened, unto the glory of Thy holy Name and unto their eternal salvation, through Jesus Christ, Thy Son and our Lord, who taught us to pray, saying:

Our Father who art in heaven, etc. AMEN.

PRAYER BEFORE MEALS

Ps. 145:15, 16—*The eyes of all wait for thee; and thou givest them their food in due season. Thou openest thy hand, and satisfiest the desire of every living thing.*

Lord God Almighty, Thou hast made the worlds; Thou dost uphold all things by the word of Thy power. Thou didst sustain the children of Israel in the wilderness with food from on high. Wilt Thou also bless us, Thy humble servants, and sanctify to us these gifts which we have received from Thy generous hand. May we use them temperately; help us to devote them to their proper purpose. May we thus acknowledge that Thou art our Father and the source of all good things. Grant also that we may at all times and above all things yearn for the spiritual bread of Thy Word. May our souls thus be nourished unto eternal life, which Thou hast prepared for us through the precious blood of Thy beloved Son, our Lord Jesus Christ. AMEN.

Our Father who art in heaven, etc. AMEN.

Even so we are admonished by our Lord Jesus Christ, according to Luke 21:34, 35—

But take heed to yourselves, lest haply your hearts be overcharged with surfeiting, and drunkenness, and cares of this life, and that day come on you suddenly as a snare: for so shall it come upon all them that dwell on the face of the earth.

THANKSGIVING AFTER MEALS

Thus speaks the Lord in the fifth book of Moses, Deut. 8:10, 11—*And thou shalt eat and be full, and thou shalt bless Jehovah thy God for the good land which he hath given thee. Beware lest thou forget Jehovah thy God, in not keeping his commandments, and his ordinances, and his statutes, which I command thee this day.*

Lord God, our heavenly Father, we thank Thee for all Thy benefits, which we so unceasingly receive from Thy bountiful hand. We thank Thee that it pleases Thee to sustain us in this temporal life and to supply all our needs. We are especially grateful that Thou hast regenerated us unto the hope of a better life, which Thou hast revealed unto us in Thy holy gospel. We pray Thee, merciful God and Father, that our hearts may not become too deeply attached to these earthly and perishable things, but that we may always look heavenward, expecting our Savior Jesus Christ, until He shall appear upon the clouds unto our deliverance. AMEN.

Our Father who art in heaven, etc. AMEN.

Psalm 106:1—*Praise ye Jehovah. Oh give thanks unto Jehovah, for he is good; for his lovingkindness* endureth *forever.* AMEN.

PRAYER FOR THE SICK AND THE SPIRITUALLY DISTRESSED

Eternal and merciful God and Father, the eternal salvation of the living and the eternal life of the dying, Thou alone hast life and death in Thy hands. Thou dost continually care for us in such a way that neither health nor sickness, neither good nor evil can befall us, yea, not even a hair can fall from our heads without Thy will. Thou dost order all things for the good of believers.

We beseech Thee that Thou wilt grant us the grace of the Holy Spirit, that He may teach us to know truly our miseries, and to bear patiently Thy chastisements, which as far as our merits are concerned might have been ten thousand times more severe. We know that they are not tokens of Thy wrath but of Thy fatherly love towards us, that we might not be condemned with the world.

Increase, O Lord, our faith, by Thy Holy Spirit, that we may become more and more united with Christ, our spiritual Head, to whom Thou dost desire to conform us both in suffering and glory. Lighten our cross so that we in our weakness may be able to bear it. We submit ourselves without reserve to Thy holy will, regardless whether Thou wouldst leave our souls here in these earthly tabernacles or whether Thou wouldst take them home unto Thyself. We have no fear because we belong to Christ, and therefore shall not perish. We even desire to depart from this weak body in the hope of a blessed resurrection, knowing that then it will be restored to us in a much more glorious form.

Grant that we may experience the blessed comfort of the remission of sins and justification in Christ. May we with that defense overcome all the assaults of Satan. May Jesus' innocent blood wash away our stain and may His righteousness cover our unrighteousness in Thy judgment at last. Arm us with faith and hope, that we may not be put to shame by any fear of death. May the eyes of our soul be fastened upon Thee when the eyes of our body become dim. When Thou shalt have taken from us the power of speech, may our hearts never cease to call upon Thee. O Lord, we commit our souls into Thy hands; do not forsake us in the hour of death. This we pray only for the sake of Christ, who taught us to say:

Our Father who art in heaven, etc. AMEN.

Or as follows:

O Almighty, eternal, and righteous God, our merciful Father: Thou art the Lord of life and death; without Thy will nothing occurs in heaven or upon earth. We are not worthy to call upon Thy Name, nor to hope that Thou wilt hearken unto us, when we consider how we have hitherto spent our time. Yet we pray Thee that Thou wilt, according to Thy mercy, look upon us in Him who has taken upon Himself all our infirmities. We acknowledge that we have within ourselves nothing but evil inclinations and inability to do any good. On this account also we have merited this affliction, yea, have deserved far more.

But Lord, Thou knowest that we are Thy people and that Thou art our God. Thy mercy, which Thou hast never withheld from those who turn to Thee, is our only refuge. Therefore we pray, count not our sins against us, but impute to us the wisdom, righteousness, and holiness of our Savior. For His sake deliver us from this suffering in order that the evil one may not regard us as forsaken of God. And if it please Thee to prolong our trial, give us patience and strength to bear it all according to Thy will; and may it thus in Thy wisdom redound to our edification.

Rather chastise us here, Lord, than that we should have to perish with the world hereafter. Grant that we may die to this world and to all earthly things, that we may be renewed daily after the image of Jesus Christ. Suffer us never to be separated from Thy love, but draw us daily closer and closer to Thee, that at last we may enter with joy upon the end of our divine calling, which is to die with Christ, rise with Him triumphantly, and live with Him eternally. We also believe that Thou wilt hear us through Jesus Christ, who has taught us to pray, saying:

Our Father who art in heaven, etc. AMEN.

Strengthen us also in the true faith which we confess with heart and mouth, saying:

I believe in God the Father, Almighty, etc. AMEN.

MORNING PRAYER

O merciful Father, we thank Thee that Thou didst keep watch over us this past night, in Thy great faithfulness. We pray that Thou mayest strengthen and guide us henceforth by Thy Holy Spirit, that we may put this day as well as all the days of our life to the service of holiness and righteousness. Grant, we pray Thee, that in all our undertakings we may always have an eye single to Thy glory. May we ever labor in the consciousness of our dependence upon Thy beneficence for the success of our work.

We beseech Thee to forgive all our sins according to Thy promise, for the sake of the passion and blood of our Lord Jesus Christ, for we are truly sorry for all our transgressions. Illumine our hearts, we pray Thee, that we may lay aside all works of darkness and as children of light may lead new lives in all godliness.

May it please Thee to bless us also as we engage in the proclamation of the divine

Word. Frustrate all the works of the devil. Endue all the ministers of the Church who are faithful to Thee with strength, and make the magistrates of Thy people strong. Instil comfort in the hearts of all that are distressed, through Jesus Christ, Thy beloved Son. For He has assured us that Thou wilt surely grant us all that we ask of Thee in His Name, and has enjoined us to pray after this fashion, saying:

Our Father who art in heaven, etc. AMEN.

May grace also be given us, we pray Thee, to order our lives according to Thy will which thou didst reveal in Thy law as contained in the Ten Commandments:

I am Jehovah thy God, who brought thee out of the land of Egypt, out of the house of bondage.
Thou shalt have no other gods before me, etc. AMEN.

EVENING PRAYER

O merciful God, light eternal shining in the darkness, Thou dispellest the night of our sins and the blindness of our hearts. Since Thou didst ordain that man should rest in the night and labor during the day, we pray Thee that our bodies may rest in peace and quiet, in order that they may be enabled to sustain the labors to which we shall again be called. Control our sleep and rule our hearts while we slumber, in order that we may not be defiled in either body or soul, but may glorify Thee even in our nightly rest. Enlighten once more, we beseech Thee, the eyes of our mind, lest we enter upon the sleep of death. Grant that we may ever cherish the expectation of our redemption from the misery of the life that now is. Defend us against all assaults of the devil and take us in Thy holy protection.

We confess that we have not spent this day without grievously sinning against Thee. We pray Thee to cover our sins in Thy mercy, even as Thou dost shroud all the things of earth in the darkness of the night, lest we be cast away from Thy face. Be pleased to bestow comfort and rest upon all that are sick, bowed down with grief, or afflicted with distress of soul, through our Lord Jesus Christ, who would have us pray, saying:

Our Father who art in heaven, etc. AMEN.

OPENING PRAYER FOR ECCLESIASTICAL ASSEMBLIES

Heavenly Father, eternal and merciful God: It has pleased Thee according to Thy infinite wisdom and lovingkindness to gather a Church unto Thyself out of the peoples of all the earth, and to govern Thy Church through the service of men. Thou hast graciously called us to this office of government, and hast enjoined us to watch over ourselves and to bestow due care upon the flock which Christ purchased with His precious blood.

We are now assembled in this place in Thy holy Name, in order to deal, after the fashion of the apostolic churches, with such matters as shall come before us and concern the edification and· welfare of Thy churches, agreeably to our office. We confess that we are unworthy and unable of ourselves to accomplish any good thing. We beseech Thee, therefore, faithful God and Father, that, in accordance with Thy promise, Thou wilt abide in the midst of the present assembly through Thy Holy Spirit. and that He may lead us into all the truth.

Remove all misunderstandings and guard us against the influence of our sinful hearts. Grant that Thy Word may be our only rule and standard, in order that our deliberations may redound to the glory of Thy Name, the edification of Thy churches, and the peace of our own consciences.

This we ask in the Name of Christ Jesus, Thy Son, who with Thee and the Holy Spirit, the only and true God, is deserving of eternal praise and glory. AMEN.

CLOSING PRAYER FOR ECCLESIASTICAL ASSEMBLIES

Lord God, heavenly Father, we thank Thee from our hearts that it pleases Thee to gather a Church in our land and to employ our services to that end. Thou dost graciously so order all things that we can preach the gospel without any hindrance and may engage in public worship. Thou hast also been present with Thy Holy Spirit in our assembly, guiding our deliberations according to Thy will, and binding our hearts together in mutual peace and unity.

Wilt Thou, O faithful God and Father, graciously bless the efforts that we purpose to put forth, and wilt Thou finish in power the work which Thou hast begun. Continue to gather unto Thyself a true Church, and cause it to preserve the purity of doctrine; guide it in the proper use of the holy sacraments; and inspire it with zeal for the maintenance of church purity.

Bring to nought all wicked and subtle counsels that are devised against Thy Word and Church. Give strength to all whom Thou hast placed in authority over Thy Church, to the end that they may preach Thy Word in faithfulness and stedfastness.

Strengthen the civil magistrates of Thy people, in order that they may wield the sword of worldly power in justice and with wise restraint. In particular do we pray for the civil rulers, both higher and lower officers of government, whom Thou hast been pleased to appoint over us. We commend unto Thee especially the esteemed council of this city. Grant that their rule may be entirely directed toward the supremacy of the King of kings over rulers and ruled alike. May through their labors the shameful and wicked dominion of Satan be increasingly disturbed and broken down. May it be given unto us to lead a quiet and peaceable life in all godliness and gravity.

Hear us, O God and Father, through Thy dear Son, Jesus Christ, who with Thee and the Holy Spirit, the only and true God, is worthy of eternal praise and glory. AMEN.

OPENING PRAYER FOR THE MEETINGS OF THE DEACONS

Merciful God and Father, Thou hast not only declared that we shall always have the poor with us, but hast also commanded us to succor them in their need. Thou hast ordained the service of the deacons for Thy Church, in order that its needy members may receive the aid they require. Since we whom Thou hast called to the deaconal office in this church are now met in Thy Name to discuss matters pertaining to our office, we humbly beseech Thee that Thou mayest, for the sake of Jesus Christ, dwell among us with the spirit of discrimination. May Thy Spirit help us to distinguish between those really poor and those who feign destitution, and to distribute the alms that have been collected as each one's need may render necessary, in the spirit of joy and fidelity. May we neither fail to comfort the needy members of Thy dear Son, nor dispense gifts to those who are not in want.

Kindle fervent love to the poor in men's hearts, in order that they may contribute generously of their temporal possessions over which Thou didst appoint them stewards, and we may have command of sufficient means to bring relief to those that are indigent, and may faithfully perform our task with true liberality of heart and without difficulty.

Bestow upon us also the grace we need, not only to relieve want by means of external gifts, but also to instil the comfort of Thy holy Word in hearts afflicted with misery. Truly, man lives not by bread alone, but by every word that proceeds out of Thy mouth. We pray, therefore, that Thou wilt bless our ministrations and wilt multiply the bread of the poor, to the end that both they and we may have reasons to praise and thank Thee; meanwhile awaiting the blessed appearance of Thy dear Son, Jesus Christ, who for our sakes became poor that He might enrich us with eternal treasures. AMEN.

LITURGICAL FORMS

FORM FOR THE BAPTISM OF INFANTS

Beloved congregation in the Lord Jesus Christ:

The principal parts of the doctrine of holy baptism are these three:

First: That we with our children are conceived and born in sin, and therefore are children of wrath, so that we cannot enter into the kingdom of God, except we are born again. This, the dipping in or sprinkling with water teaches us, whereby the impurity of our souls is signified, that we may be admonished to loathe ourselves, humble ourselves before God, and seek for our purification and salvation apart from ourselves.

Second: Holy baptism witnesses and seals unto us the washing away of our sins through Jesus Christ. Therefore we are baptized into the Name of God, the Father and the Son and the Holy Spirit. For when we are baptized into the Name of the Father, God the Father witnesses and seals unto us that He makes an eternal covenant of grace with us and adopts us for His children and heirs, and therefore will provide us with every good thing and avert all evil or turn it to our profit. And when we are baptized into the Name of the Son, the Son seals unto us that He washes us in His blood from all our sins, incorporating us into the fellowship of His death and resurrection, so that we are freed from our sins and accounted righteous before God. Likewise, when we are baptized into the Name of the Holy Spirit, the Holy Spirit assures us by this holy sacrament that He will dwell in us, and sanctify us to be members of Christ, imparting to us that which we have in Christ, namely, the washing away of our sins and the daily renewing of our lives, till we shall finally be presented without spot among the assembly of the elect in life eternal.

Third: Whereas in all covenants there are contained two parts, therefore are we by God, through baptism, admonished of and obliged unto new obedience, namely, that we cleave to this one God, Father, Son, and Holy Spirit; that we trust in Him, and love Him with all our heart, with all our soul, with all our mind, and with all our strength; that we forsake the world, crucify our old nature, and walk in a godly life. And if we sometimes through weakness fall into sins, we must not therefore despair of God's mercy, nor continue in sin, since baptism is a seal and indubitable testimony that we have an eternal covenant with God.

And although our children do not understand these things, we may not therefore exclude them from baptism, since they are without their knowledge partakers of the condemnation in Adam, and so again are received unto grace in Christ; as God speaks unto Abraham, the father of all believers, and therefore also to us and our children, saying: *I will establish my covenant between me and thee and thy seed after thee throughout their generations for an everlasting covenant, to be a God unto thee and to thy seed after thee* (Gen. 17:7). This also Peter testifies with these words: *For to you is*

85

the promise, and to your children, and to all that are afar off, even *as many as the Lord our God shall call unto him* (Acts 2:39). Therefore God formerly commanded to circumcise them, which was a seal of the covenant and of the righteousness of faith; as also Christ embraced them, laid His hands upon them, and blessed them (Mark 10:16). Since, then, baptism has come in the place of circumcision (Col. 2:11-13), the children should be baptized as heirs of the kingdom of God and of His covenant; and as they grow up, the parents shall be bound to give them further instruction in these things.

That we, therefore, may administer this holy ordinance of God to His glory, to our comfort, and to the edification of the church, let us call upon His holy Name:

O almighty, eternal God, Thou who hast according to Thy severe judgment punished the unbelieving and unrepentant world with the flood, and hast according to Thy great mercy saved and protected believing Noah and his family; Thou who hast drowned the obstinate Pharaoh and all his host in the Red Sea and led Thy people Israel through the midst of the sea upon dry ground—by which baptism was signified—we beseech Thee that Thou wilt be pleased of Thine infinite mercy, graciously to look upon these Thy children and incorporate them by Thy Holy Spirit into Thy Son Jesus Christ, that they may be buried with Him through baptism into death and be raised with Him in newness of life; that they, daily following Him, may joyfully bear their cross, cleaving unto Him in true faith, firm hope, and ardent love; that they, being comforted in Thee, may leave this life, which is nothing but a constant death, and at the last day may appear without terror before the judgment seat of Christ Thy Son, through Him, our Lord Jesus Christ, who with Thee and the Holy Spirit, one only God, lives and reigns forever. AMEN.

ADDRESS TO THE PARENTS

Beloved in Christ the Lord, you have heard that baptism is an ordinance of God to seal unto us and our seed His covenant; therefore it must be used for that end, and not out of custom or superstition. That it may, then, be manifest that you are thus minded, you are to answer sincerely to these questions:

First: Do you acknowledge that our children, though conceived and born in sin and therefore subject to all manner of misery, yea, to condemnation itself, are sanctified in Christ, and therefore as members of His Church ought to be baptized?

Second: Do you acknowledge the doctrine which is contained in the Old and the New Testament, and in the articles of the Christian faith, and which is taught here in this Christian church, to be the true and complete doctrine of salvation?

Third: Do you promise and intend to instruct these children, as soon as they are able to understand, in the aforesaid doctrine, and cause them to be instructed therein, to the utmost of your power?

Answer: We do (*or in case only one of the parents is a confessing member:* I do)

¶ *Then the minister of God's Word, in baptizing, shall say:*

N——, I baptize you into the Name of the Father and of the Son and of the Holy Spirit.

THANKSGIVING

Almighty God and merciful Father, we thank and praise Thee that Thou hast forgiven us and our children all our sins, through the blood of Thy beloved Son Jesus Christ, and received us through Thy Holy Spirit as members of Thine only begotten Son, and so adopted us to be Thy children, and sealed and confirmed the same unto us by holy baptism. We beseech Thee also, through Him, Thy beloved Son, that Thou wilt always govern these children by Thy Holy Spirit, that they may be nurtured in the Christian faith and in godliness, and grow and increase in the Lord Jesus Christ, in order that they may acknowledge Thy fatherly goodness and mercy, which Thou hast shown to them and to us all, and live in all righteousness under our only Teacher, King, and High Priest, Jesus Christ; and manfully fight against and overcome sin, the devil, and his whole dominion, to the end that they may eternally praise and magnify Thee, and Thy Son Jesus Christ, together with the Holy Spirit, the one only true God. AMEN.

FORM FOR THE PUBLIC PROFESSION OF FAITH

Beloved in the Lord Jesus Christ:

We thank our God concerning you for the grace of God which was given you in Christ Jesus, that you were made desirous of professing your faith publicly, here in the presence of God and His holy church, and of obtaining the privileges of full communion with the people of God.

You are now requested to answer sincerely the following questions:

First: Do you heartily believe the doctrine contained in the Old and the New Testament, and in the articles of the Christian faith, and taught in this Christian church, to be the true and complete doctrine of salvation, and do you promise by the grace of God stedfastly to continue in this profession?

Second: Do you openly accept God's covenant promise, which has been signified and sealed unto you in your baptism, and do you confess that you abhor and humble yourselves before God because of your sins, and that you seek your life not in yourselves, but only in Jesus Christ your Savior?

Third: Do you declare that you love the Lord, and that it is your heartfelt desire to serve Him according to His Word, to forsake the world, to mortify your old nature, and to lead a godly life?

Fourth: Do you promise to submit to the government of the church and also, if you should become delinquent either in doctrine or in life, to submit to its admonition and discipline?

N——, what is your answer?

Answer: I do (*to be given by each individually*).

I charge you, then, beloved, that you, by the diligent use of the means of grace and with the assistance of your God, continue in the profession which you have just made. In the Name of Christ Jesus our Lord, I now welcome you to full communion with the people of God. Rest assured that all the privileges of such communion are now yours. *And the God of all grace, who called you unto his eternal glory in Christ, after that ye have suffered a little while, shall himself perfect, establish, strengthen you. To him be the dominion for ever and ever.* AMEN.

PRAYER (*optional*)

Heavenly Father, we thank Thee that Thou hast from the beginning embraced in Thy covenant the children together with their parents. We thank Thee that Thou from the first didst cast the lot of these Thy servants in the Christian Church, and didst grant them all the manifold blessings of Christian culture. We bless Thee that in their case Thou didst add the special grace of Thy Holy Spirit, so that of their own will they come here today to profess Thy truth and to consecrate their lives to Thy service. We earnestly beseech Thee that Thou wilt continue to carry on the good work Thou hast begun in them unto the day of complete redemption. Increase in them daily the manifold gifts of Thy grace, the spirit of wisdom and understanding, the spirit of counsel and might, the spirit of knowledge and of the fear of the Lord. Grant them the happiness of promoting the glory of their Lord and the edification of His people. Deliver them in the temptations of this life and in the final trial of death. And in that day when Thou makest up Thy jewels, set also these Thy servants in Thy crown, that they may shine as stars, to Thy praise, for ever and ever. AMEN.

FORM FOR THE BAPTISM OF ADULTS

¶ *When those who were not baptized in their youth, upon coming to the years of discretion, desire to receive Christian baptism, they shall first be thoroughly instructed in the fundamentals of the Christian religion. And when they have made a good profession thereof before the consistory, they shall be permitted to make public profession and receive holy baptism; in the administration of which the following form shall be used.*

Beloved congregation in the Lord Jesus Christ:

The principal parts of the doctrine of holy baptism are these three:

First: That we with our children are conceived and born in sin, and therefore are children of wrath, so that we cannot enter into the kingdom of God, except we are born again. This, the dipping in or sprinkling with water teaches us, whereby the impurity of our souls is signified, that we may be admonished to loathe ourselves, humble ourselves before God, and seek for our purification and salvation apart from ourselves.

Second: Holy baptism witnesses and seals unto us the washing away of our sins through Jesus Christ. Therefore we are baptized into the Name of God, the Father and the Son and the Holy Spirit. For when we are baptized into the Name of the Father, God the Father witnesses and seals unto us that He makes an eternal covenant of grace with us and adopts us for His children and heirs, and therefore will provide us with every good thing and avert all evil or turn it to our profit. And when we are baptized into the Name of the Son, the Son seals unto us that He washes us in His blood from all our sins, incorporating us into the fellowship of His death and resurrection, so that we are freed from our sins and accounted righteous before God. Likewise, when we are baptized into the Name of the Holy Spirit, the Holy Spirit assures us by this holy sacrament that He will dwell in us, and sanctify us to be members of Christ, imparting to us that which we have in Christ, namely, the washing away of our sins and the daily renewing of our lives, till we shall finally be presented without spot among the assembly of the elect in life eternal.

Third: Whereas in all covenants there are contained two parts, therefore are we by God, through baptism, admonished of and obliged unto new obedience, namely, that we cleave to this one God, Father, Son, and Holy Spirit; that we trust in Him, and love Him with all our heart, with all our soul, with all our mind, and with all our strength; that we forsake the world, crucify our old nature, and walk in a godly life. And if we sometimes through weakness fall into sins, we must not therefore despair of God's mercy, nor continue in sin, since baptism is a seal and indubitable testimony that we have an eternal covenant with God.

And although the children of Christians, notwithstanding their inability to understand these things, must be baptized by virtue of the covenant, yet it is not lawful to baptize adults, unless they first feel their sins and make confession of their repentance and of their faith in Christ. For this cause did not only John the Baptist,

89

according to the command of God, preach *the baptism of repentance unto the remission of sins*, and baptize those who confessed their sins (Mark 1:4, 5 and Luke 3:3), but also our Lord Jesus Christ commanded His apostles *to make disciples of all the nations*, and *to baptize them into the Name of the Father and of the Son and of the Holy Spirit* (Matt. 28:19), adding thereunto this promise: *He that believeth and is baptized shall be saved* (Mark 16:16). According to this rule the apostles, as appears from the book of Acts, baptized no other adults but such as made confession of their repentance and faith. Therefore it is not lawful now to baptize any other adults than those who have learned and understand, from the preaching of the holy gospel, the mysteries of holy baptism, and are able to give an account thereof and of their faith by the profession of their mouths.

That we therefore may administer this holy ordinance of God to His glory, to our comfort, and to the edification of the church, let us call upon His holy Name:

O almighty, eternal God, Thou who hast according to Thy severe judgment punished the unbelieving and unrepentant world with the flood, and hast according to Thy great mercy saved and protected believing Noah and his family; Thou who hast drowned the obstinate Pharaoh and all his host in the Red Sea and led Thy people Israel through the midst of the sea upon dry ground—by which baptism was signified—we beseech Thee that Thou wilt be pleased of Thine infinite mercy, graciously to look upon this brother (*sister*) and incorporate him (*her*) by Thy Holy Spirit into Thy Son Jesus Christ, that he (*she*) may be buried with Him through baptism into death and be raised with Him in newness of life; that he (*she*), daily following Him, may joyfully bear his (*her*) cross, cleaving unto Him in true faith, firm hope, and ardent love; that he (*she*), being comforted in Thee, may leave this life, which is nothing but a constant death, and at the last day may appear without terror before the judgment seat of Christ Thy Son, through Him, our Lord Jesus Christ, who with Thee and the Holy Spirit, one only God, lives and reigns forever. AMEN.

ADDRESS TO THE PERSON TO BE BAPTIZED

N——, since, then, you desire to receive holy baptism, that it may be to you a seal of your incorporation in the Church of God—that it may now appear that you not only accept the Christian religion, in which you have been instructed by us, and of which you have made profession before us, but also that you intend to direct your life in accordance therewith, you are to answer these questions sincerely before God and His church:

First: Do you believe in the only true God, distinct in three Persons, Father, Son, and Holy Spirit, who of nothing has made heaven and earth and all that is in them, and still upholds and governs them, so that nothing comes to pass, either in heaven or on earth, without His divine will?

Answer: I do.

Second: Do you believe that you are conceived and born in sin and therefore a child of wrath, by nature wholly incapable of doing any good and prone to all evil; and that you, in thought, word, and deed, have frequently transgressed the commandments of the Lord; and do you sincerely repent of these your sins?

Answer: I do.

Third: Do you believe that Jesus Christ, who is both true and eternal God and very man, who assumed His human nature from the flesh and blood of the virgin Mary, is given you of God as a Savior; and that you by this faith receive remission of sins in His blood, and that you by the power of the Holy Spirit became a member of Jesus Christ and of His Church?

Answer: I do.

Fourth: Do you assent to all the articles of the Christian religion, as they are taught here in this Christian church from the Word of God, and do you purpose to continue stedfastly in the same doctrine to the end of your life; and do you also reject all heresies and errors conflicting with this doctrine, and promise that you will persevere in the fellowship of this Christian church, not only in the hearing of the divine Word, but also in the use of the holy supper?

Answer: I do.

Fifth: Do you firmly resolve always to lead a Christian life, to forsake the world and its evil lusts, as is becoming to the members of Christ and of His Church, and to submit cheerfully to all Christian admonitions?

Answer: I do.

The good and great God mercifully grant you His grace and blessing in this your holy purpose, through our Lord Jesus Christ. AMEN.

¶ *Then the minister of God's Word, in baptizing, shall say:*

N——, I baptize you into the Name of the Father and of the Son and of the Holy Spirit.

THANKSGIVING

Almighty God and merciful Father, we thank and praise Thee, that Thou hast forgiven us and our children all our sins, through the blood of Thy beloved Son Jesus Christ, and received us through Thy Holy Spirit as members of Thine only begotten Son, and so adopted us to be Thy children, and sealed and confirmed the same unto us by holy baptism. We beseech Thee also, through Him, Thy beloved Son, that Thou wilt always govern this brother (*sister*) by Thy Holy Spirit, that he (*she*) may lead a Christian and godly life, and grow and increase in the Lord Jesus Christ, in order that he (*she*) may acknowledge Thy fatherly goodness and mercy, which Thou hast shown to him (*her*) and to us all, and live in all righteousness under our only Teacher, King, and High Priest, Jesus Christ; and manfully fight against and overcome sin, the devil, and his whole dominion, to the end that he (*she*) may eternally praise and magnify Thee, and Thy Son Jesus Christ, together with the Holy Spirit, the one only true God. AMEN.

FORM FOR THE LORD'S SUPPER

Beloved in the Lord Jesus Christ, attend to the words of the institution of the holy supper of our Lord Jesus Christ, as they are delivered by the holy apostle Paul (1 Cor. 11:23–29):

For I received of the Lord that which also I delivered unto you, that the Lord Jesus in the night in which he was betrayed took bread; and when he had given thanks, he brake it, and said, This is my body, which is for you: this do in remembrance of me. In like manner also the cup, after supper, saying, This cup is the new covenant in my blood: this do, as often as ye drink it, in remembrance of me. For as often as ye eat this bread, and drink the cup, ye proclaim the Lord's death till he come. Wherefore whosoever shall eat the bread or drink the cup of the Lord in an unworthy manner, shall be guilty of the body and blood of the Lord. But let a man prove himself, and so let him eat of the bread, and drink of the cup. For he that eateth and drinketh, eateth and drinketh judgment unto himself, if he discern not the body.

That we may now celebrate the supper of the Lord to our comfort, it is necessary, before all things, rightly to examine ourselves; and further, to direct it to that end for which Christ has ordained and instituted the same—namely, to His remembrance.

The true examination of ourselves consists of these three parts:

First: Let every one consider by himself his sins and accursedness, that he may abhor himself and humble himself before God, considering that the wrath of God against sin is so great that He, rather than to leave it unpunished, has punished it in His beloved Son, Jesus Christ, with the bitter and shameful death of the cross.

Second: Let every one examine his heart whether he also believes this sure promise of God that all his sins are forgiven him only for the sake of the passion and death of Jesus Christ, and that the complete righteousness of Christ is imputed and freely given him as his own—yea, so completely as if he himself, in his own person, had satisfied for all his sins and fulfilled all righteousness.

Third: Let every one examine his conscience whether he is minded henceforth to show true thankfulness to God in his whole life, and to walk sincerely before His face; likewise, whether he, without any hypocrisy, heartily laying aside all enmity, hatred, and envy, earnestly resolves henceforward to live in true love and unity with his neighbor.

All those, then, who are thus minded, God will certainly receive in grace and count them worthy partakers of the table of His Son Jesus Christ. On the contrary, those who do not feel this testimony in their hearts eat and drink judgment to themselves. Wherefore we also, according to the command of Christ and of the apostle Paul, admonish all who know themselves to be defiled with the following gross sins to abstain from the table of the Lord, and declare to them that they have no part in the kingdom of Christ: such as, all idolaters; all who invoke deceased saints, angels, or other creatures; all who show honor to images; all who resort to or confide in sorcery, fortune-telling, charms, or other forms of superstition; all despisers of God, of His Word, and of the holy sacraments; all blasphemers; all who seek to raise discord, sects, and mutiny in Church or State; all perjurers; all who are disobedient to their parents and superiors; all murderers, quarrelsome persons, and those who live in hatred and envy against their neighbors; all adulterers, fornicators, drunkards, thieves, usurers, robbers, gamblers, covetous persons, and all who lead offensive lives. All these, while they continue in such sins, shall abstain from this food, which Christ has appointed only for His believers, lest their judgment and condemnation be made the heavier.

But this is not designed, dearly beloved brethren and sisters, to discourage the contrite hearts of the believers, as if none might come to the supper of the Lord but he that is without sin. For we do not come to this supper to testify thereby that we are perfect and righteous in ourselves, but on the contrary, considering that we seek our life apart from ourselves in Jesus Christ, we acknowledge thereby that we lie in the midst of death. Therefore, although we find many shortcomings and miseries in ourselves, as namely, that we have not perfect faith, and that we do not give ourselves to serve God with that zeal as we are bound, but have to strive daily with the weakness of our faith and the evil lusts of our flesh, yet, since we are, by the grace of the Holy Spirit, heartily sorry for these shortcomings and desirous to fight against our unbelief and to live according to all the commandments of God, therefore we rest assured that no sin or infirmity which still remains in us against our will can hinder us from being received of God in grace and from being made worthy partakers of this heavenly food and drink.

Let us now also consider to what end the Lord has instituted His supper; namely, that we should do it in remembrance of Him. Now after this manner are we to remember Him by it:

First of all, let us be fully persuaded in our hearts that our Lord Jesus Christ, according to the promises made to the forefathers in the Old Testament, was sent of the Father into this world; that He assumed our flesh and blood; that He has borne for us the wrath of God, under which we should have perished everlastingly, from the beginning of His incarnation to the end of His life upon earth, and has fulfilled for us all obedience and righteousness of the divine law, especially when the weight of our sins and of the wrath of God pressed out of Him the bloody sweat in the garden, where He was bound that we might be loosed from our sins; that afterwards He suffered innumerable reproaches that we might never be confounded; that He was innocently condemned to death that we might be acquitted at the judgment seat of God; yea, that He suffered His blessed body to be nailed to the cross that He might fasten to it the bond written in ordinances that was against us; and so has taken the curse from us upon Himself that He might fill us with His blessing; and has humbled Himself unto the very deepest reproach and anguish of hell, in body and soul, on the tree of the cross, when He cried out with a loud voice: *My God, my God, why hast thou forsaken me?* that we might be accepted of God, and nevermore be forsaken of Him; and finally has confirmed with His death and shedding of His blood the new and eternal testament, the covenant of grace and of reconciliation, when He said: *It is finished.*

And that we might firmly believe that we belong to this covenant of grace, *the Lord Jesus Christ,* in His last supper, *took bread, and when he had given thanks, he brake it, and gave to the disciples and said, Take, eat, this is my body which is given for you; this do in remembrance of me. In like manner after supper, he took the cup, and gave thanks, and gave to them, saying, Drink ye all of it; this cup is the new covenant in my blood, which is poured out for you and for many, unto remission of sins; this do, as often as ye drink it, in remembrance of me;* that is, as often as ye eat of this bread and drink of this cup, you shall thereby, as by a sure remembrance and pledge, be admonished and assured of this My hearty love and faithfulness towards you; that, whereas otherwise you should have suffered eternal death, I give My body in death on the tree of the cross and shed My blood for you, and nourish and refresh your hungry and thirsty souls with My crucified body and shed blood to everlasting life, as certainly as this bread is broken before your eyes and this cup is given to you, and you eat and drink with your mouth in remembrance of Me.

From this institution of the holy supper of our Lord Jesus Christ we see that He directs our faith and trust to His perfect sacrifice, once offered on the cross, as to the only ground and foundation of our salvation, whereby He is become to our hungry and thirsty souls the true food and drink of life eternal. For by His death He has taken away the cause of our eternal death and misery, namely sin, and obtained for us the life-giving Spirit, that we by that Spirit, who dwells in Christ as in the Head and in us as His members, should have true communion with Him and be made partakers of all His riches, of life eternal, righteousness, and glory.

Besides, by this same Spirit we are also united as members of one body in true brotherly love, as the holy apostle says: *Seeing that we, who are many, are one bread, one body: for we all partake of the one bread.* For as out of many grains one meal is ground and one bread baked, and out of many berries, pressed together, one wine flows and is mixed together, so shall we all who by true faith are incorporated in Christ be all together one body, through brotherly love, for Christ our dear Savior's sake, who before has so exceedingly loved us, and show this towards one another, not only in words but also in deeds.

May the almighty, merciful God and Father of our Lord Jesus Christ help us in this, through His Holy Spirit. AMEN.

That we may obtain all this, let us humble ourselves before God and with true faith implore Him for His grace:

Merciful God and Father, we beseech Thee that in this supper, in which we cherish the blessed memory of the bitter death of Thy dear Son Jesus Christ, Thou wilt so work in our hearts through the Holy Spirit that we with true confidence give ourselves up, more and more, unto Thy Son Jesus Christ, in order that our burdened and contrite hearts, through the power of the Holy Spirit, may be nourished and refreshed with His true body and blood, yea with Him, true God and man, the only heavenly bread; and that we may no longer live in our sins, but He in us, and we in Him, and so truly be partakers of the new and everlasting testament, the covenant of grace, that we do not doubt that Thou wilt forever be our gracious Father, nevermore imputing our sins unto us, and providing us with all things for body and soul, as Thy dear children and heirs.

Grant us also Thy grace that we may take up our cross cheerfully, deny ourselves, confess our Savior, and in all tribulation, with uplifted head, expect our Lord Jesus Christ from heaven, where He will make our mortal bodies like unto His glorified body, and take us unto Him in eternity.

Answer us, O God and merciful Father, through Jesus Christ, who taught us to pray:

Our Father who art in heaven,
Hallowed be thy name;
Thy kingdom come;
Thy will be done, as in heaven, so on earth.
Give us this day our daily bread;
And forgive us our debts, as we also have forgiven our debtors;
And bring us not into temptation, but deliver us from the evil one.
For thine is the kingdom, and the power, and the glory, for ever. AMEN.

May we by this holy supper also be strengthened in the catholic, undoubted, Christian faith, of which we make profession with heart and mouth, saying:

I believe in God the Father, Almighty, Maker of heaven and earth.
And in Jesus Christ, His only begotten Son, our Lord;
Who was conceived by the Holy Spirit, born of the virgin Mary;
Suffered under Pontius Pilate; was crucified, dead, and buried; He descended into
hell;
The third day He rose again from the dead;
He ascended into heaven, and sitteth at the right hand of God the Father Almighty;
From thence He shall come to judge the living and the dead.
I believe in the Holy Spirit.
I believe a holy catholic Church, the communion of saints;
The forgiveness of sins;
The resurrection of the body;
And the life everlasting. AMEN.

That we, then, may be nourished with Christ, the true heavenly bread, let us not cling with our hearts unto the external bread and wine but lift them up on high in heaven, where Christ Jesus is, our Advocate, at the right hand of His heavenly Father, whither also the articles of our Christian faith direct us; not doubting that we shall be nourished and refreshed in our souls, with His body and blood, through the working of the Holy Spirit, as truly as we receive the holy bread and drink in remembrance of Him.

¶ *In breaking and distributing the bread, the minister shall say:*
The bread which we break is a communion of the body of Christ. Take, eat, remember, and believe that the body of our Lord Jesus Christ was broken unto a complete remission of all our sins.

¶ *And when he gives the cup:*
The cup of blessing which we bless is a communion of the blood of Christ. Take, drink ye all of it, remember, and believe that the precious blood of our Lord Jesus Christ was shed unto a complete remission of all our sins.

¶ *During the communion a psalm shall be devoutly sung, or some chapter shall be read, in remembrance of the passion of Christ; as Isaiah 53, John 6, 13, 14, 15, 16, 17, 18, or the like.*

¶ *After the communion the minister shall say:*

Beloved in the Lord, since the Lord has now nourished our souls at His table, let us jointly praise His holy Name with thanksgiving; and let every one say in his heart:

Bless Jehovah, O my soul; and all that is within me, bless *his holy name.*

Bless Jehovah, O my soul, and forget not all his benefits:

Who forgiveth all thine iniquities; who healeth all thy diseases;

Who redeemeth thy life from destruction; who crowneth thee with lovingkindness and tender mercies.

Jehovah is merciful and gracious, slow to anger, and abundant in lovingkindness.

He will not always chide; neither will he keep his *anger for ever.*

He hath not dealt with us after our sins, nor rewarded us after our iniquities.

For as the heavens are high above the earth, so great is his lovingkindness toward them that fear him.

As far as the east is from the west, so far hath he removed our transgressions from us.

Like as a father pitieth his children, so Jehovah pitieth them that fear him (Psalm 103:1–4, 8–13).

He that spared not his own Son, but delivered him up for us all, how shall he not also with him freely give us all things? (Romans 8:32).

But God commendeth his own love toward us, in that, while we were yet sinners, Christ died for us. Much more then, being now justified by his blood, shall we be saved from the wrath of God *through him. For if, while we were enemies, we were reconciled to God through the death of his Son, much more, being reconciled, shall we be saved by his life* (Romans 5:8–10).

Therefore shall my mouth and heart show forth the praise of the Lord from this time forth for evermore. AMEN.

THANKSGIVING

O merciful God and Father, we thank Thee with all our heart that of Thy boundless mercy Thou hast given us Thine only begotten Son for a Mediator and sacrifice for our sins, and as our food and drink unto life eternal; and that Thou givest us a true faith, whereby we become partakers of these Thy benefits. Thou hast also through Thy dear Son Jesus Christ instituted and ordained the holy supper for the strengthening of that faith. We beseech Thee, O faithful God and Father, that through the operation of Thy Holy Spirit the remembrance of our Lord Jesus Christ and the proclamation of His death may tend to our daily increase in true faith and in blessed fellowship with Christ; through Him, Thy dear Son, in whose Name we conclude our prayers, saying:

Our Father who art in heaven,

Hallowed be thy name;

Thy kingdom come;

Thy will be done, as in heaven, so on earth.

Give us this day our daily bread;

And forgive us our debts, as we also have forgiven our debtors;

And bring us not into temptation, but deliver us from the evil one.

For thine is the kingdom, and the power, and the glory, for ever. AMEN.

FORM FOR EXCOMMUNICATION

Beloved in the Lord Jesus Christ:

It is known to you that we have from time to time made announcement to you concerning the great sin committed and the grievous offense given by our fellow-member, N——, to the end that, by your Christian admonitions and prayers, he might turn to God and recover himself out of the snare of the devil, who has taken him captive unto his will. But to our great sorrow we cannot conceal from you that no one has yet appeared before us who in the least has given us to understand that, by the frequent admonitions given him (as well in private as before witnesses and in the presence of many), he has come to any sorrow for his sin or has shown the least token of true repentance. Since, then, by his stubbornness he daily aggravates his transgression, which in itself is not small, and since we have made known to you the last time that in case he did not repent, after such patience shown him by the church, we should be constrained further to grieve for him and to come to the extreme remedy, we are therefore at the present time compelled to proceed to his excommunication according to the command and charge given us in God's holy Word; to the end that, if possible, he may hereby be made ashamed of his sins; and likewise, that by this corrupt and as yet incurable member we may not put the whole body of the church in danger, and that God's Name may not be blasphemed.

Therefore, we ministers and rulers of the church of God at this place, being assembled in the Name and the authority of our Lord Jesus Christ, declare before you all that for the aforesaid reasons we have excommunicated and hereby do ex-communicate N—— from the Church of the Lord; and that, so long as he persists obstinately and impenitently in his sins, he is excluded from the fellowship of Christ, of the holy sacraments, and of all the spiritual blessings and benefits which God promises to and bestows upon His Church; and that he is therefore to be accounted by you as a Gentile and a publican, according to the command of Christ, who says that what things soever His ministers shall bind on earth shall be bound in heaven.

Further we exhort you, beloved Christians, to keep no company with him, to the end that he may be ashamed; yet count him not as an enemy, but at times admonish him as you would a brother.

In the meantime let every one take warning by this and similar examples to fear the Lord and diligently to take heed unto himself, if he thinks he stands, lest he fall; but having true fellowship with the Father and His Son Christ, together with all believing Christians, to remain stedfast therein to the end, and so obtain eternal salvation. You have seen, dear brethren and sisters, in what manner this our ex-communicated brother has begun to fall and gradually has come to ruin. Learn, then, from him how subtle Satan is to bring man to destruction and to draw him away from all salutary means of salvation. Guard yourselves, then, against the least beginnings of evil, and according to the admonition of the apostle, lay aside every weight and the sin which so easily besets us, and run with patience the race that is set before us, looking unto Jesus the Author and Perfecter of our faith. Be sober, watch and pray, lest you enter into temptation. Today, if you will hear the voice of the Lord, harden not your hearts, but work out your own salvation with fear and trembling; and let every one repent of his sin, lest our God humble us again and we be obliged to mourn for some one of you; but may you, with one accord living in godliness, be our crown and joy in the Lord.

But since it is God who works in us both to will and to work, for His good pleasure, let us call upon His holy Name with confession of our sins:

O righteous God, merciful Father, before Thy high majesty we blame ourselves for our sins and acknowledge that we have justly deserved the sorrow and pain caused us by the excommunication of this our late fellow-member; yea, if Thou shouldst enter into judgment with us, we all deserve to be excluded and banished from Thy presence on account of our great transgression. But, O Lord, be gracious unto us for Christ's sake; forgive us our trespasses, for we heartily repent of them; and work in our hearts an ever increasing measure of sorrow for them, that we, fearing Thy judgments which Thou bringest upon the stiff-necked, may endeavor to please Thee. Grant that we may avoid all pollution of the world and of those who are excluded from the communion of the Church, in order that we may not make ourselves partakers of their sins, and that he who is excommunicated may become ashamed of his sins. And since Thou desirest not the death of the sinner, but that he may repent and live, and since the bosom of Thy Church is always open for those who return, kindle Thou, therefore, in our hearts a godly zeal, that we, with good Christian admonitions and example, may seek to bring back this excommunicated person, together with all those who through unbelief and recklessness of life go astray. Add Thy blessing to our admonitions, that we thereby may have reason to rejoice again in them for whom we must now mourn, and that thus Thy holy Name may be praised, through our Lord Jesus Christ, who has taught us to pray:

Our Father who art in heaven,
Hallowed be thy name;
Thy kingdom come;
Thy will be done, as in heaven, so on earth.
Give us this day our daily bread;
And forgive us our debts, as we also have forgiven our debtors;
And bring us not into temptation, but deliver us from the evil one.
For thine is the kingdom, and the power, and the glory, for ever. AMEN.

FORM FOR READMISSION

Beloved in the Lord:

It is known to you that some time ago our fellow-member N—— was excommunicated from the Church of Christ. We cannot now conceal from you that he, by this remedy and also by means of good admonitions and your Christian prayers, has come to be ashamed of his sin, and now requests us to be readmitted to the communion of the Church. Since we, then, according to the command of God are in duty bound to receive such persons with joy, and since it is also necessary that good order be used therein, we therefore hereby make known to you that the next time when by the grace of God we celebrate the supper of the Lord, we shall loose again the aforementioned excommunicated person from the bond of excommunication and receive him again into the communion of the Church, unless any one of you in the meantime should have valid reason why this ought not to be done, of which you must give us notice in due time. Meanwhile let every one thank the Lord for the favor shown this poor sinner, beseeching Him to perfect His work in him to his eternal salvation. AMEN.

¶ *Afterwards, if no hindrance occur, the minister shall proceed to the readmission of the excommunicated sinner according to the following form:*

Beloved Christians:

We have lately informed you of the conversion of our fellow-member N——, to the end that with your approbation he might be received again into the Church of Christ. Whereas no one has alleged anything why this readmission ought not to take place, we shall at the present time proceed to the same.

The Lord Christ, having confirmed in Matthew 18 the sentence of His Church in the excommunication of impenitent sinners, declares immediately thereupon that what things soever His ministers shall loose on earth shall be loosed in heaven; whereby He gives us to understand that when any person is excluded from His Church he is thereby not deprived of all hope of salvation, but can again be loosed from the bonds of condemnation. Therefore, since God declares in His Word that He takes no pleasure in the death of the wicked, but rather that he should return from his way and live, the Church always hopes for the conversion of the backslidden sinner and keeps her bosom open to receive the penitent. Accordingly the apostle Paul commanded that the Corinthian person (of whom he had declared that he ought to be excluded from the Church), after he, having been reproved of many, had come to repentance, should be received again and comforted, lest he should be swallowed up with his overmuch sorrow. Christ also teaches us in the aforementioned passage that the sentence of absolution, which is passed upon such a penitent sinner according to the Word of God, is counted binding and firm by the Lord; wherefore no one who truly repents ought to doubt in the least that he is certainly received by God in grace, as Christ says elsewhere: *Whose soever sins ye forgive, they are forgiven unto them.*

But to proceed now to the matter in hand, I ask you:

99

N——, do you declare with all your heart, here before God and His church that you are sincerely sorry for the sin and stubbornness on account of which you have been justly excluded from the Church?

Do you also truly believe that the Lord has forgiven you and does forgive your sins for Christ's sake?

And do you therefore desire to be readmitted to the Church of Christ, promising to live henceforth in all godliness according to the command of the Lord?

Answer: I do.

¶ *Then the minister shall further say:*

We, then, being here assembled in the Name and the authority of the Lord Christ, declare you, N——, to be absolved from the bonds of excommunication. We receive you again into the Church of the Lord, and declare unto you that you stand in the communion of Christ, of the holy sacraments, and of all the spiritual blessings and benefits of God which He promises to and bestows upon His Church. May the eternal God preserve you therein to the end, through His only begotten Son, Jesus Christ. AMEN.

Be therefore assured in your heart, my beloved brother, that the Lord has received you in grace. Be diligent henceforward to guard yourself against the subtlety of Satan and the wickedness of the world, to the end that you may not fall again into sin. Love Christ, for many sins are forgiven you.

And you, beloved Christians, receive this your brother with hearty affection; be glad, for he was dead and is alive again; he was lost and is found; rejoice with the angels of heaven over this sinner who repents; count him no longer as a stranger, but as a fellow-citizen with the saints and of the household of God.

But whereas we can have no good of ourselves, let us, praising and thanking the Lord Almighty, implore His mercy:

Gracious God and Father, we thank Thee through Jesus Christ that Thou hast given this our fellow-brother repentance unto life, and causest us to rejoice in his conversion. We beseech Thee, show him Thy grace, that he may become more and more assured in his mind of the remission of his sins, and may derive therefrom joy unspeakable and delight to serve Thee. And whereas heretofore he has offended many by his sin, grant that he may now edify many by his conversion. Grant also that he may stedfastly walk in Thy ways to the end. May we learn from this example that with Thee is grace that Thou mayest be feared. May we, counting him our brother and co-heir of life eternal, jointly serve Thee with filial fear and obedience all the days of our life, through Jesus Christ, our Lord, in whose Name we conclude our prayer:

Our Father who art in heaven,
Hallowed be thy name;
Thy kingdom come;
Thy will be done, as in heaven, so on earth.
Give us this day our daily bread;
And forgive us our debts, as we also have forgiven our debtors;
And bring us not into temptation, but deliver us from the evil one.
For thine is the kingdom, and the power, and the glory, for ever. AMEN.

FORM FOR THE ORDINATION (or: INSTALLATION) OF MINISTERS OF GOD'S WORD

Beloved brethren, it is known unto you that, at three different times, we have published the name of our brother N——, here present, to learn whether any person had aught to allege concerning his doctrine or life, on account of which he should not be ordained to the ministry of the Word (*or:* installed in this church). And whereas no one has appeared before us who has brought forward anything lawful against his person, we shall therefore, in the name of the Lord, now proceed to his ordination (*or:* installation).

To this end you, N——, are requested to arise and, together with all those who are here present, to attend to a short exposition from the Word of God of the institution and the office of pastors and ministers of the Word.

It should be observed, in the first place, that God our heavenly Father, having purposed to call and gather a Church out of the corrupt race of men unto life eternal, as a particular favor uses the ministry of men for this work.

Therefore Paul declares in Eph. 4 that the Lord Jesus Christ has given *some to be apostles; and some, prophets; and some, evangelists; and some, pastors and teachers: for the perfecting of the saints, unto the work of ministering, unto the building up of the body of Christ.* Here we see that the holy apostle says, among other things, that the pastoral office is an institution of Christ.

Now, what this holy office requires we can easily deduce from the very name itself. For as the work of a common shepherd is to feed, guide, protect, and rule the flock entrusted to him, the same applies to the spiritual shepherds, who are placed over the Church, which God calls unto salvation, and counts as the flock of His pasture. The pasture with which His sheep are fed is nothing else but the proclamation of the gospel, accompanied with prayer and the administration of the holy sacraments. The same Word of God is also the staff with which the flock is guided and governed.

Consequently, it is evident that the office of pastors or ministers of God's Word is:

First: That they thoroughly and sincerely present to their people the Word of the Lord, revealed by the writings of the prophets and the apostles, and apply the same, as well in general as in particular, for the benefit of the hearers; instructing, admonishing, comforting, and approving, according to every one's need; proclaiming repentance toward God, and reconciliation with Him through faith in Jesus Christ; and refuting with the Holy Scriptures all errors and heresies which conflict with this pure doctrine. It also belongs to their office to instruct the children of the church in the doctrine of salvation, to visit the members of the congregation at their homes, and to comfort the sick with the Word of God.

All this is clearly signified to us in Holy Writ; for the apostle Paul says that these *labor in the word*; and elsewhere he teaches that this must be done *according to the measure* or rule *of faith.* He writes also that a pastor must *hold fast* and *handle aright the faithful and sincere word which is according to the teaching*; likewise: *But he that prophesieth speaketh unto men edification, and exhortation, and consolation.* In another place he presents himself as an example to pastors, declaring that he, *publicly and from house to house, has taught and testified repentance toward God and faith toward our Lord Jesus Christ.* But we have a clear description of the office of a minister of the gospel especially in 2 Cor. 5:18–20, where the apostle speaks as follows: *But all things are of God, who reconciled us to himself through Christ, and gave unto us the ministry of reconciliation; to wit, that God was in Christ reconciling the world unto himself, not reckoning unto them their trespasses, and having committed unto us the word of reconciliation. We are ambassadors therefore on behalf of Christ, as though God were entreating by us: we beseech you on behalf of Christ, be ye reconciled to God.* Concerning the refutation of false doctrine, the same apostle says in Tit. 1:9 that a minister must *hold to the faithful word which is according to the teaching, that he may be able both to exhort in the sound doctrine, and to convict the gainsayers.*

Second: It is the office of the ministers publicly to call upon the Name of God in behalf of the whole congregation; for what the apostles say in Acts 6:4, *We will continue stedfastly in prayer, and in the ministry of the word,* these pastors have in common with the apostles; to which St. Paul alludes when he speaks thus to Timothy: *I exhort therefore, first of all, that supplications, prayers, intercessions, thanksgivings, be made for all men; for kings and all that are in high place; that we may lead a tranquil and quiet life in all godliness and gravity* (1 Tim. 2.1, 2).

Third: Their office is to administer the sacraments, which the Lord has instituted as seals of His grace; as appears from the command which Christ gave to His apostles at the institution of holy baptism and of the Lord's supper, which command concerns also the ministers of the Word.

Fourth: The task of the ministers of the Word is with the elders to keep the Church of God in good discipline, and to govern it in such a manner as the Lord has ordained; for Christ, having spoken of the Christian discipline, says to His apostles: *Whatsoever thou shalt bind on earth shall be bound in heaven* (Matt. 16:19). And Paul would have the ministers know how to rule their own house, since otherwise they can neither provide for nor rule the Church of God. This is the reason why in Scripture the pastors are also called stewards of God and bishops, that is, overseers and watchmen; for they have the oversight of the house of God, wherein they abide, to the end that there everything may be transacted with good order and decency; and that they may open and shut, with the keys of the kingdom of heaven committed to them, according to the charge given them by God.

From these things one can see what a glorious work the pastoral office is, because of the great things accomplished by it; yea, how indispensable it is for bringing men to salvation; which is also the reason why the Lord would have such an office always remain. For Christ, when He sent forth His apostles to fulfil their holy ministry, spoke as follows: *Lo, I am with you always, even unto the end of the world;* where we see that it is His will that this holy office—for the persons whom He addresses here could not live to the end of the world—should always be maintained on earth. And therefore Paul admonishes Timothy to commit that which he had *heard from him among many witnesses to faithful men, who should be able to teach others also* (2 Tim. 2:2); as he also, accordingly, having ordained Titus as a pastor, further commands him to *appoint elders* or bishops *in every city* (Tit. 1:5).

Forasmuch, therefore, as we also, in order to maintain this office in the Church of God, are now to ordain a new minister of the Word (*or:* to install a new minister of the Word in this church), having spoken sufficiently of the office of such persons, therefore you, N———, shall answer the questions which shall be proposed to you, to the end that every one may hear that you are minded to accept said office, as previously described.

First: Do you feel in your heart that you are lawfully called of God's Church, and therefore of God Himself, to this holy office?

Second: Do you believe the writings of the Old and the New Testament to be the only Word of God and the complete doctrine of salvation, and do you reject all doctrines conflicting therewith?

Third: Do you promise faithfully to discharge your office, as previously described, according to the same doctrine, and to adorn it with a godly life; also, to submit yourself, in case you should become delinquent either in doctrine or in life, to ecclesiastical discipline, according to the public ordinance of the churches?

Answer: I do, with all my heart.

¶ *Thereupon the minister who asked these questions of him, or another minister, if there are other ministers present, shall lay his hand upon his head*, and shall say:*

God, our heavenly Father, who has called you to this holy office, enlighten you with His Spirit, strengthen you with His hand, and so govern you in your ministry, that you may be engaged therein properly and fruitfully, to the magnification of His Name, and the extension of the kingdom of His Son Jesus Christ. AMEN.

¶ *Then the officiating minister shall exhort the ordained minister and the congregation in the following manner:*

Now, therefore, beloved brother and fellow-servant in Christ, *take heed unto thyself and to all the flock, in which the Holy Spirit hath made thee bishop, to feed the church of the Lord which he purchased with his own blood.* Love Christ and feed His sheep, *exercising the oversight not of constraint, but willingly; nor yet for filthy lucre, but of a ready mind: neither as lording it over the charge allotted to thee but making thyself an ensample to the flock. Be thou an ensample to them that believe, in word, in manner of life, in love, in faith, in purity. Give heed to reading, to exhortation, to teaching. Neglect not the gift that is in thee; be diligent in these things; give thyself wholly to them; that thy progress may be manifest unto all. Take heed to thy teaching,* and *continue in these things.* Bear patiently all suffering and oppression, *as a good soldier of Jesus Christ, for in doing this thou shalt both save thyself and them that hear thee. And when the chief Shepherd shall be manifested, thou shalt receive the crown of glory that fadeth not away.*

And you likewise, beloved Christians, receive this your minister *in the Lord with all joy; and hold such in honor.* Remember that God Himself through him speaks unto you and entreats you. Receive the Word, which he, according to the Scripture, shall preach unto you, *not as the word of men, but, as it is in truth, the word of God.* Let *the feet of them that preach* the gospel of *peace, and bring good tidings of good,* be *beautiful* and pleasant unto you. *Obey them that have the rule over you, and submit* to them; *for they watch in behalf of your souls, as they that shall give account; that they may do this with joy, and not with grief: for this* were *unprofitable for you.* If you do these things, it shall come to pass that the peace of God shall enter your houses, and that you who receive this man *in the name of a prophet, shall receive a prophet's re-*

---

* The laying on of hands shall not take place in the case of those who are already in the ministry.

ward, and through his preaching believing in Christ, shall through Christ inherit eternal life.

But since no man is of himself sufficient for any of these things, let us call upon God with thanksgiving:

Merciful Father, we thank Thee that it pleases Thee by the ministry of men to gather a Church to Thyself unto life eternal, out of the lost human race; and that Thou hast so graciously provided the church in this place with a faithful minister. We beseech Thee to qualify him more and more by the Spirit for the office for which Thou hast prepared and called him, enlightening his mind that he may understand Thy Holy Scripture, and giving him *utterance in opening his mouth to make known with boldness the mystery of the gospel.* Endow him with wisdom and valor to rule aright the people over which he is placed, and to preserve them in Christian peace, to the end that Thy church, under his ministry and by his good leadership, may increase in number and in virtues. Grant him courage to bear all troubles and difficulties which will confront him in his ministry, that he, being strengthened by the comfort of Thy Spirit, and remaining stedfast to the end, may be received with all faithful servants into the joy of his Lord. Grant also to this people, Thy church, that they may properly deport themselves toward their pastor, acknowledging him as having been sent by Thee, receiving his doctrine with all reverence, and submitting themselves to his exhortation, to the end that they, believing in Christ through his Word, may become partakers of eternal life. Hear us, O Father, through Thy beloved Son, who has taught us to pray:

Our Father who art in heaven,
Hallowed be thy name;
Thy kingdom come;
Thy will be done, as in heaven, so on earth.
Give us this day our daily bread;
And forgive us our debts, as we also have forgiven our debtors;
And bring us not into temptation, but deliver us from the evil one.
For thine is the kingdom, and the power, and the glory, for ever. AMEN.

FORM FOR THE ORDINATION OF ELDERS AND DEACONS

Beloved Christians, having previously made known unto you the names of our brethren who were chosen to the office of elders and deacons in this church, and no one having appeared to allege anything lawful against them, we shall therefore, in the Name of the Lord, proceed to their ordination.

It is well, first, to remind ourselves of what the Word of God teaches regarding these offices.

The office of elder is based on the kingship of our Lord Jesus Christ, who, when He ascended, left His Church in the world and provided it with officers who should rule in His Name. The apostle Paul, in Acts, insists upon the ordination of elders in every church, and, in his letter to Timothy, commands those who *rule well to be counted worthy of double honor, especially those who labor in the word and in teaching.* In this and other passages Paul distinguishes between the elders who labor particularly in the ministry of the Word and the sacraments, and those who have the supervision of the church together with the ministers of the Word. Therefore the Church, from the beginning, has had elders in addition to ministers and pastors.

The work of the elders is that of ruling in the Name of the ascended King, and as servants of the great Shepherd, caring for His flock. It is therefore also the duty of the elders to maintain the purity of the Word and sacraments, to uphold the good order of the church, carefully guarding the sacredness of the offices and faithfully exercising discipline. They should, moreover, with love and humility promote the faithful discharge of the office by their fellow-officers, having particular regard to the doctrine and conduct of the minister of the Word, that the church may be edified and may manifest itself as the pillar and ground of the truth.

To fill worthily so sacred an office, the elders should set an example of godliness in their personal life, in their home life, and in their relations with their fellow-men. Walking thus in all godliness, and faithfully discharging their office, *when the chief Shepherd shall be manifested, they shall receive the crown of glory that fadeth not away.*

The office of deacon is based upon the interest and love of Christ in behalf of His own. This interest is so great that He deems what is done unto one of the least of His brethren as done unto Him, thus appointing the needy to represent Himself in our expression of sympathy and benevolent service on earth. *For I was hungry, and ye gave me to eat; I was thirsty, and ye gave me drink; I was a stranger, and ye took me in; naked, and ye clothed me; I was sick, and ye visited me; I was in prison, and ye came unto me.*

According to Acts 6, the apostles themselves in the beginning ministered unto the needy; but afterwards, being overburdened with this service to the extent that some were neglected, certain men were chosen to whom they committed the special responsibility of exercising this ministry, leaving the apostles greater opportunity to continue stedfastly in prayer and in the ministry of the Word. Since that time the Church has recognized this service as a distinct office.

The work of the deacons consists in the faithful and diligent ingathering of the

105

offerings which God's people in gratitude make to their Lord, in the prevention of poverty, in the humble and cheerful distribution of gifts according to the need, and in the relief of the distressed both with kindly deeds and words of consolation and cheer from Scripture.

To fill worthily so sacred an office, the deacons, as well as the elders, should set an example of godliness in their personal life, in their home life, and in their relations with their fellow-men. Thus conducting themselves as worthy representatives of Christ's loving care, and faithfully ministering in His Name to those who are the beloved of God, they *gain to themselves a good standing and great boldness in the faith which is in Christ Jesus.*

To the end, therefore, beloved brethren, that the church may hear that you are willing to take your respective offices upon you, you are requested to answer the following questions:

First: Do you, both elders and deacons, feel in your hearts that you are lawfully called of God's church, and consequently of God Himself, to these your respective holy offices?

Second: Do you believe the Old and the New Testament to be the only Word of God, and the doctrinal standards of this church to be in harmony therewith?

Third: Do you, having heard the exposition of the meaning and requirements of these offices, promise to discharge them faithfully by the grace of God: you elders, in the government of the church, together with the ministers of the Word; and you deacons, in the ministration to the poor?

Fourth: Do you promise to walk in all godliness and submit to the government of the church in all things pertaining to your office?

N——, what is your answer?

Answer: I do (*to be given by each individually*).

¶ *Then the minister shall say:*

The Almighty God and Father replenish you all with His grace, that you may faithfully and fruitfully discharge your respective offices. AMEN.

I charge you, elders, in the Name of the Lord Jesus Christ, to be diligent in the government of the church which is committed to you jointly with the minister of the Word. Be faithful watchmen over the house of God, taking heed that purity of doctrine and godliness of life be maintained.

I charge you, deacons, in the Name of the Lord Jesus Christ, to be diligent in receiving the gifts of God's people, prudent and cheerful in the distribution of the same, sympathetic and self-denying in the ministry of Christian mercy.

I charge you, beloved Christians, to receive these brethren as the servants of God, sustaining them with your daily prayers. Render to the elders all honor, encouragement, and obedience in the Lord. Provide the deacons generously with the necessary gifts for the needy, remembering that in so much as you do it unto the least of these His children, you do it unto Him. May God give us to see in the ministry of the elders the supremacy of Christ, and in the ministry of the deacons the care and love of the Savior.

Being thus engaged in your respective callings, each one of you shall receive of the Lord the reward of righteousness.

PRAYER

O Lord God and heavenly Father, we thank Thee that it has pleased Thee, for the better edification of Thy Church, to ordain in it, besides the ministers of the Word, rulers and assistants, by whom Thy Church may be preserved in peace and prosperity, and the needy assisted; and that Thou hast at present granted us in this place men who are of good testimony and, we trust, endowed with Thy Spirit. We beseech Thee, replenish them more and more with such gifts as are necessary for them in their ministration: with the gifts of wisdom, courage, discretion, benevolence, sympathy, and self-denial, to the end that every one may, in his respective office, acquit himself as is becoming—the elders in taking diligent heed unto doctrine and life, in keeping out the wolves from the sheepfold of Thy beloved Son, and in admonishing and reproving disorderly persons; in like manner, the deacons in carefully receiving alms and liberally and prudently distributing them to the poor, and in comforting them with Thy holy Word. Give grace both to elders and deacons, that they may persevere in their faithful labor, and never become weary by reason of any trouble, pain, or persecution of the world. Grant especially Thy divine grace to this people, over whom they are placed, that they may willingly submit themselves to the good exhortations of the elders, counting them worthy of honor for their work's sake. Give unto the rich liberal hearts towards the needy, and to the needy grateful hearts towards those who help and serve them; to the end that, every one acquitting himself of his duty, Thy holy Name may thereby be magnified, and the kingdom of Thy Son Jesus Christ enlarged, in whose Name we conclude our prayers, saying:

Our Father who art in heaven,
Hallowed be thy name;
Thy kingdom come;
Thy will be done, as in heaven, so on earth.
Give us this day our daily bread;
And forgive us our debts, as we also have forgiven our debtors;
And bring us not into temptation, but deliver us from the evil one.
For thine is the kingdom, and the power, and the glory, for ever. AMEN.

FORM FOR THE INSTALLATION OF PROFESSORS OF THEOLOGY

Beloved brethren, it is known to you that our brother in the holy ministry, N——, was called by our recent synod to the important office of professor of theology at our theological seminary. To our joy he has accepted this call, and we are now assembled to install him in his office. Therefore we request you, brother N——, to arise and to hear what pertains to this office and is entrusted to you by the Lord and His Church.

Since our God, who is rich in mercy, has, in His great love, chosen a Church for Himself unto eternal life, and wills to gather this Church through His Spirit and Word unto the fellowship of His Son, in the unity of the true faith, and to cause it to increase in the knowledge of His will, it pleases Him, by His Holy Spirit to raise up men who as ministers of His Word shall preach the tidings of salvation among those who already belong to the Church and among those without, who are still wholly deprived of the true knowledge of God's ways.

The first messengers of peace in the days of the New Testament were taught directly by our Lord Jesus Christ, and were by Him personally trained and sent. After the outpouring of the Holy Spirit He gave them great diversities of extraordinary gifts and knowledge of the mysteries, unto the salvation of sinners and the upbuilding of the saints. But since those extraordinary methods lasted only as long as the Lord judged them to be necessary for the founding of His Church among the nations, the necessity was soon recognized of training youths and men for the holy ministry under the ordinary dispensation of the Spirit by the regular methods of education. And this especially in view of what Paul wrote in 2 Tim. 2:2, *And the things which thou hast heard from me among many witnesses, the same commit thou to faithful men, who shall be able to teach others also.* The apostle here points to what he himself had done and had required of his disciple Timothy.

In accordance with this apostolic precept, such training was given originally by learned and capable overseers of the Church. Afterwards the schools of Alexandria, Antioch, and other important cities, were especially engaged in this work. And when, toward the end of the middle ages, and in the sixteenth and seventeenth centuries, universities arose in many places, theology was not introduced merely as a faculty among other faculties, but usually recognized as "the queen of sciences." This was the more easily done because the Church, both Roman Catholic and Protestant, exercised control over, or busied itself with, almost the whole of life.

As long as a university is founded on the Holy Scripture, accepts the creed of a certain communion, and this communion has part control in the appointment of professors of theology, it cannot be disapproved that future ministers of the Word receive their education at such an institution.

Since, however, Paul expressly declares in Rom. 3:2 that the primary advantage of the Church of the Old Dispensation, and therefore also of the Church of the New Dispensation, was that to it were entrusted the oracles of God, it follows that the Church has a divine mission to proclaim the Word of God, to derive from that Word

108

its symbols of faith, to engage in theological study according to that Word, and further to promote whatever is directly connected with this study.

Conscious of this calling, also our Church has established a theological seminary and called the reverend brother N—— to devote his powers to this school.

In behalf of our Church we charge you, esteemed brother, with the task of instructing and confirming the students, who hope one day to serve in His Church, in the knowledge of His Word. Expound to them the mysteries of the faith; caution them against the errors and heresies of the old but especially of the new day; seek to explain to them not only how they, as teachers, are to instruct the sheep of the Lord but also how they, as pastors, are to shepherd them. Help to maintain good order and discipline among the students, that our seminary may retain the respect, the devotion, the appreciation, the love, and the prayer of the Church. Be a pattern of piety to them, that they may not only profit from your learning, but also find in you a good example of the power and practise of true godliness.

Do all this according to the measure of the gifts which God has given you, in dependence upon the Lord's help and the illumination of the Holy Spirit.

That it may now publicly appear that you, highly esteemed brother, are thus minded, you are to answer to the following questions:

First: Do you feel in your heart that you are lawfully called of God's Church, and therefore of God Himself, to the aforesaid office?

Second: Do you believe the writings of the Old and the New Testament to be the only Word of God? Do you reject all doctrines which conflict with them, and do you accept the doctrinal standards of the Christian Reformed Church as the purest interpretation of the doctrine of salvation?

Third: Do you promise faithfully to discharge your office, as previously described, according to the same doctrine, and to adorn it with a godly life?

Fourth: Do you promise to submit yourself, in case you should become delinquent either in doctrine or in life, to the admonition of the Church, and if necessary to its prescribed discipline?

Answer: I do, with all my heart.

¶ *Thereupon the minister who asked these questions of him shall say:*

God, our heavenly Father, who has called you to this holy office, enlighten you with His Spirit, strengthen you with His hand, and so govern you in your ministry, that you may be engaged therein properly and fruitfully, to the magnification of His Name, and the extension of the kingdom of His Son Jesus Christ. AMEN.

¶ *The ceremony is then concluded with appropriate prayer.*

FORM FOR THE ORDINATION (or: INSTALLATION) OF MISSIONARIES

Beloved Christians, it is known to you that our brother, N——, here present, called by .... as minister of the Word among the Gentiles (Dispersed), (and recently examined by the Classis of ....), is now to be publicly ordained as minister of the Word (installed as missionary).

We therefore request you, beloved brother, N——, to arise and to attend to a short exposition of your office and work.

Since our God, according to His infinite mercy, has chosen for Himself a Church unto eternal life, and gathers it through His blessed gospel out of all nations, tribes, and tongues, unto the fellowship of His Son, in the unity of the true faith, our risen Savior has ordained a ministry and raised up men to proclaim the message of salvation to all peoples, saying to His apostles, and in them to all lawful ministers of the Word: *Go ye into all the world, and preach the gospel to the whole creation* (Mark 16:15). *For he that ascended far above all the heavens, that he might fill all things, gave some to be apostles; and some, prophets; and some, evangelists; and some, pastors and teachers; for the perfecting of the saints, unto the work of ministering, unto the building up of the body of Christ* (Eph. 4:10–12). And the apostles, responding to this, went forth into the world, *declaring the whole counsel of God*, particularly *repentance, and remission of sins* through faith in Christ Jesus, testifying, *For God so loved the world, that he gave his only begotten Son, that whosoever believeth on him should not perish, but have eternal life* (John 3:16). *But all things are of God, who reconciled us to himself through Christ, and gave unto us the ministry of reconciliation: to wit, that God was in Christ reconciling the world unto himself, not reckoning unto them their trespasses, and having committed unto us the word of reconciliation. We are ambassadors therefore on behalf of Christ, as though God were entreating by us: we beseech you on behalf of Christ, be ye reconciled to God* (2 Cor. 5:18–20).

Without this word of reconciliation, faith in Christ and consequently salvation are and remain forever impossible; for the Holy Scripture says in Acts 4:12, *And in none other is there salvation: for neither is there any other name under heaven, that is given among men, wherein we must be saved;* and elsewhere, in Rom. 10:14, 15, 17, *How shall they believe in him whom they have not heard? and how shall they hear without a preacher? and how shall they preach, except they be sent? So belief cometh of hearing, and hearing by the word of Christ.*

Although the ministers of the Word have in common that to them is committed the preaching of the gospel, the administration of the sacraments, the government of the Church, and the maintenance of Christian discipline, yea, all that according to the Word of God pertains to the office of pastor and teacher; and although the difference of field of labor causes no difference in office, authority, or dignity, since all have the same commission, the same office, and the same authority, it is nevertheless necessary that some labor in the churches already established, while others are called and sent to preach the gospel to those who are without, in order to bring

110

them to Christ. And, *let each man abide in that calling wherein he was called* by the Church of God and consequently by God Himself, and whereto gifts were imparted to him, unless it please the Lord to lead him, in a lawful way, to a different field of labor.

That also to the Gentiles these glad tidings must be brought appears plainly from Matt. 28:19, *Go ye therefore, and make disciples of all the nations, baptizing them into the name of the Father and of the Son and of the Holy Spirit; teaching them to observe all things whatsoever I commanded you.*

The Lord signified the same thing to Peter by showing him from heaven a great sheet with all manner of beasts, thereupon commanding him to go to Cornelius the Gentile, and saying, *Arise, and get thee down, and go with them, nothing doubting: for I have sent them* (Acts 10:20). Likewise He spoke to Paul in a vision in the temple, saying, *Depart: for I will send thee forth far hence unto the Gentiles* (Acts 22:21).

This divine charge was carried out also by the church of Antioch, when, after fasting and prayer, they laid their hands upon Barnabas and Saul and sent them away to preach the gospel also unto the Gentiles (Acts 13). And when these men, on their first missionary journey, had arrived at Antioch in Pisidia, they testified to the Jews who contradicted them, *Lo, we turn to the Gentiles. For so hath the Lord commanded us,* saying, *I have set thee for a light of the Gentiles, that thou shouldest be for salvation unto the uttermost part of the earth* (Acts 13:46, 47).

And besides, it is evident that the work of missions is the task of the Church, since the Lord Jesus Himself calls His Church *the salt of the earth,* and says, *Ye are the light of the world. A city set on a hill cannot be hid. Neither do men light a lamp, and put it under the bushel, but on the stand* (Matt. 5:13–15).

That unto the Dispersed also these glad tidings must be brought is to be inferred from what God says in Ezek. 34:11–16, *For thus saith the Lord Jehovah, Behold, I myself, even I, will search for my sheep, and will seek them out. As a shepherd seeketh out his flock in the day that he is among his sheep that are scattered abroad, so will I seek out my sheep; and I will deliver them out of all places whither they have been scattered in the cloudy and dark day. And I will bring them out from the peoples, and gather them from the countries, and will bring them into their own land; and I will feed them upon the mountains of Israel, by the watercourses, and in all the inhabited places of the country. I will feed them with good pasture, and upon the mountains of the height of Israel shall their fold be: there shall they lie down in a good fold, and on fat pasture shall they feed upon the mountains of Israel. I myself will be the shepherd of my sheep, and I will cause them to lie down, saith the Lord Jehovah. I will seek that which was lost, and will bring back that which was driven away, and will bind up that which was broken, and will strengthen that which was sick. But the fat and the strong I will destroy: I will feed them in justice.*

That the Lord does this through His servants is shown clearly by the way in which God, in the same chapter, rebukes the unfaithful shepherds, *Neither have ye brought back that which was driven away.* And He voices His holy indignation because *my sheep wandered through all the mountains, and upon every high hill: yea, my sheep were scattered upon all the face of the earth; and there was none that did search or seek them* (Ezek. 34:4, 6).

The same follows also from the fact that the Lord Jesus, who Himself was *sent to the lost sheep of the house of Israel,* calls the Church *the salt of the earth;* while the example of the apostle Paul teaches us plainly that it is our high calling to bring the bread of life to our dispersed brethren after the flesh everywhere, and therefore certainly first of all to those in our own land, and to gather them, if possible, as churches of Christ.

And since you, beloved brother, were called and now are sent out to labor among the Gentiles (Dispersed), you are to consider the important duties which will devolve upon you:

First of all, you are to acquaint them, by all proper and honorable means, with the glad tidings that Jesus Christ has come into the world to save sinners. Let all you do and leave undone, your speech and your silence, yea, all your influence, re-enforce your proclamation and recommendation of the gospel of Christ. *Be free from the love of money; abhor that which is evil; cleave to that which is good,* that you may be able to say with the apostle Paul in 1 Cor. 9:19, 22b, 27, *For though I was free from all men, I brought myself under bondage to all, that I might gain the more. I am become all things to all men, that I may by all means save some. I buffet my body, and bring it into bondage: lest by any means, after that I have preached to others, I myself should be rejected.*

Again, you are bound, if it please God to make your work fruitful unto the gathering of a church or churches, to administer the sacrament of holy baptism, according to the institution of the Lord and the requirement of the covenant.

Further, you are called to ordain elders and deacons, wherever it is necessary and possible, even as Paul charged Titus, saying, *For this cause left I thee in Crete, that thou shouldest set in order the things that were wanting, and appoint elders in every city, as I gave thee charge.* But, *lay hands hastily on no man* (Titus 1:5; 1 Tim. 5:22a).

Moreover, as a minister of Christ and steward of the mysteries of God, you are charged with the administration of the Lord's supper, according to the institution of Christ. And we also commend to you the maintenance of Christian discipline in the midst of the church, by the faithful use of the keys of the kingdom of heaven, as our Lord Jesus has spoken, *And if he refuse to hear the church also, let him be unto thee as the Gentile and the publican;* and again, *Whatsoever thou shalt bind on earth shall be bound in heaven* (Matt. 18:17; 16:19).

And finally, beloved brother, be a faithful servant of Jesus Christ, and shepherd the flock with loving care. *Preach the word; be urgent in season, out of season; reprove, rebuke, exhort, with all longsuffering and teaching. Be thou an ensample to them that believe, in word, in manner of life, in love, in faith, in purity. Give heed to reading, to exhortation, to teaching. Neglect not the gift that is in thee. Be diligent in these things; give thyself wholly to them; that thy progress may be manifest unto all. Take heed to thyself, and to thy teaching. Continue in these things; for in doing this thou shalt save both thyself and them that hear thee* (2 Tim. 4:2; 1 Tim. 4:12b–16).

And now, beloved brother, that every one present may hear that you are willing and ready to accept the ministry of the Word among the Gentiles (Dispersed), you are to answer sincerely to the following questions:

First: Do you feel in your heart that you are lawfully called of God's Church, and therefore of God Himself, to this holy ministry?

Second: Do you believe the writings of the Old and the New Testament to be the only Word of God and the complete doctrine of salvation, and do you reject all doctrines conflicting with them?

Third: Do you promise faithfully to discharge your office, as previously described, according to the same doctrine, and to adorn it with a godly life?

Fourth: Do you promise to submit yourself, in case you should become delinquent either in doctrine or in life, to the admonition of the Church, and if necessary to its prescribed discipline?

Answer: I do, with all my heart.

¶ *Thereupon the minister who asked these questions of him, or another minister, if there are other ministers present, shall lay his hand upon his head*, and shall say:*

Go, then, beloved brother, and teach all nations, baptizing them into the Name of the Father and of the Son and of the Holy Spirit. God, our heavenly Father, who has called you to this holy ministry, enlighten you with His Spirit, strengthen you with His hand, and so govern you in your ministry, that you may be engaged therein properly and fruitfully, to the magnification of His Name, and the extension of the kingdom of His Son Jesus Christ. AMEN.

¶ *The ceremony is then concluded with appropriate prayer.*

---

* The laying on of hands shall not take place in the case of those who are already in the ministry.

FORM FOR THE SOLEMNIZATION OF MARRIAGE

¶ *Where the wedding takes place before the congregation (cf. Art. 70 of the Church Order), the following announcement is to be made on the previous Sunday:*

N—— and N—— have signified their desire to be united in marriage in this church on .... If there are no lawful objections, the ceremony will take place on that date.

Beloved in the Lord, we are assembled here in the presence of God for the purpose of joining in marriage N—— and N——. Since we have received no lawful objections to their proposed union, let us reverently call to mind the institution, purpose, and obligations of the marriage state.

The holy bond of marriage was instituted by God Himself at the very dawn of history. Making man in His own likeness, He endowed him with many blessings and gave him dominion over all things. Moreover, God said: *It is not good that the man should be alone; I will make him a help meet for him.* Thereupon God created woman of man's own substance and brought her unto the man. *Therefore shall a man leave his father and his mother, and shall cleave unto his wife; and they shall be one flesh.*

Our Lord Jesus honored marriage by His blessed presence at the wedding in Cana, and confirmed it as a divine ordinance, as an honorable estate, and a lasting bond when He declared: *What God hath joined together let not man put asunder.* The apostle Paul shows its exalted nature when he calls holy wedlock a symbol of the mystic union of the Savior and the Church, His redeemed bride, commending it as a state honorable among all.

The purpose of marriage is the propagation of the human race, the furtherance of the kingdom of God, and the enrichment of the lives of those entering this state. This purpose calls for loving devotion to each other, and a common responsibility for the nurture of the children the Lord may give them as His heritage and as parties to His covenant.

For the home which marriage establishes the Lord ordained that the man should be the head of the wife even as Christ is the Head of the Church, and that he should protect her and provide for her in love, a love which, if exercised in the spirit and after the example of Christ, will be conducive to mutual happiness. God also ordained that the wife should be subject to the husband in all things that are according to His Word, showing him deference even as the Church to Christ. Thus the liberty of both husband and wife is glorified by mutual loyalty to law, and a home so begun in the name of the Lord and regulated by His commandments becomes the very foundation of a Christian society and affords a foretaste of the eternal home.

Marriage, then, is a divine ordinance intended to be a source of happiness to man, an institution of the highest significance to the human race, and a symbol of the union of Christ and His Church. We may, therefore, as Christians look with

114

confidence for grace in the discharge of our mutual responsibilities and for guidance and help in our common perplexities and trials.

And now, N—— and N——, having heard from the Word of God the teaching concerning marriage, do you assent thereto, and do you desire to enter into this holy estate as ordained by God?

Each answers: I do.

[*Optional:* Who gives this woman to this man?
The father or guardian answers: I do.]

¶ *The minister shall cause the man to extend his right hand and to take the woman's right hand, and shall say:*

May the Lord God confirm the desire and purpose of your hearts, and your beginning be in the Name of Jehovah, who made heaven and earth.

To the bridegroom:

N——, do you solemnly declare that you take to yourself and acknowledge as your wife N——, here present, and do you promise that you will, with the gracious help of God, love, honor, and maintain her, live with her in the holy bonds of marriage according to God's ordinance, and never forsake her, so long as you both shall live?

The bridegroom answers: I do.

To the bride:

N——, do you solemnly declare that you take to yourself and acknowledge as your husband N——, here present, and do you promise that you will, with the gracious help of God, love, honor, and obey him in all things lawful, live with him in the holy bonds of marriage according to God's ordinance, and never forsake him so long as you both shall live?

The bride answers: I do.

[*Optional ring ceremony, either single or double.*

To the bridegroom:

N——, do you give this ring as a symbol of your constant faithfulness and abiding love?

The bridegroom answers: I do. *He shall then put the ring on the fourth finger of the bride's left hand.*

To the bride:

N——, do you receive (*or in case two rings are used:* Do you give) this ring as a symbol of your constant faithfulness and abiding love?

The bride answers: I do. *In case two rings are used, she shall then put the ring on the fourth finger of the bridegroom's left hand.*]

Thereupon the minister says:

According to the laws of the State and the ordinances of the Church of Christ, I now pronounce you, N—— and N——, husband and wife, in the Name of the

Father and of the Son and of the Holy Spirit. What therefore God has joined together let not man put asunder. Henceforth you go down life's pathway together, and may the Father of all mercies, who of His grace has called you to this holy state of marriage, bind you together in true love and faithfulness and grant you His blessing.

¶ *The bridegroom and the bride now kneel while the minister offers the following prayer:*

Most merciful and gracious God, of whom the whole family of heaven and earth is named, we beseech Thee, set the seal of Thy approval upon the marriage into which our brother and sister have entered this day. Give them Thy fatherly benediction; grant them grace and Thy Holy Spirit to fulfil with pure and constant affection the vow and covenant between them made. Guide them in the way of righteousness and peace, that, loving and serving Thee with one mind and heart all the days of their life, they may be abundantly enriched with the tokens of Thy everlasting favor in Christ Jesus our Lord. In all life's experiences lift up Thy countenance upon them, that they may be thankful in prosperity and patient in adversity. May their marriage be fruitful for this life and for the life to come. Grant them wisdom and strength to build a home which shall be to the glory of Thy Name and the coming of Thy kingdom. May they live together many years, and in the hour of death may they part in the blessed hope of celebrating forever with all the saints of God the marriage of Christ and the Church He loved. Hear our prayer in the Name of our Lord Jesus Christ, who taught us to pray, saying:

Our Father who art in heaven,
Hallowed be thy name;
Thy kingdom come;
Thy will be done, as in heaven, so on earth.
Give us this day our daily bread;
And forgive us our debts, as we also have forgiven our debtors;
And bring us not into temptation, but deliver us from the evil one.
For thine is the kingdom, and the power, and the glory, for ever. AMEN.

¶ *It is suggested that the ceremony be concluded with appropriate song.*